CORE-PLUS MATHEMATICS PROJECT

Course
Part A **4**

Contemporary Mathematics in Context
A Unified Approach

Course **4**
Part A

Contemporary Mathematics in Context
A Unified Approach

Arthur F. Coxford
James T. Fey
Christian R. Hirsch
Harold L. Schoen
Eric W. Hart
Brian A. Keller
Ann E. Watkins
with
Beth E. Ritsema
Rebecca K. Walker

EVERYDAY
LEARNING

Chicago, Illinois

Photo Acknowledgments

Cover images: Roller coaster, Richard Cummins/CORBIS; Wheat fields, Kevin Schafer/CORBIS; Satellite dish, VCG/FPG International; Hurricane, VCG/FPG International; Calculator, Courtesy Texas Instruments Incorporated
Cover design: Design Associates
Photo credits are given on page 365 and constitute a continuation of the copyright page.

Everyday Learning Development Staff

Editorial: Anna Belluomini, Mary Cooney, Eric Karnowski, Luke Zajac
Design: Fran Brown, Hector Cuadra, Jess Schaal
Production: Annette Davis, Elizabeth Gabbard

Additional Credits

Carlisle Communications (production)
Maureen Laude (editorial)
Lucy Lesiak (design)
Abby Tanenbaum (editorial)

This project was supported, in part, by the National Science Foundation.
The opinions expressed are those of the authors and not necessarily those of the Foundation.

ISBN 1-57039-885-2 (Part A)

ISBN 1-57039-886-0 (Part B)

1 2 3 4 5 6 7 8 9 WC 05 04 03 02 01

Dedication

The authors, teachers, and publication staff who have collaborated in developing *Contemporary Mathematics in Context* dedicate this fourth course in the series to the memory of our friend and professional colleague Arthur Coxford, who passed away on March 5, 2000. Professor Coxford's breadth of knowledge and experience in mathematics education, his consistent good judgment and hard work, and his good-humored leadership were instrumental in all aspects of the Core-Plus Mathematics Project. We will miss his thoughtful contributions to project activities, but he has left an invaluable legacy of creative work and a striking example of personal and professional commitment and integrity.

Core-Plus Mathematics Project

Project Director
Christian R. Hirsch
Western Michigan University

Project Co-Directors
Arthur F. Coxford
University of Michigan
James T. Fey
University of Maryland
Harold L. Schoen
University of Iowa

Senior Curriculum Developers
Eric W. Hart
Western Michigan University
Brian A. Keller
Michigan State University
Ann E. Watkins
California State University, Northridge

Professional Development Coordinator
Beth Ritsema
Western Michigan University

Evaluation Coordinator
Steven W. Ziebarth
Western Michigan University

Advisory Board
Diane Briars
Pittsburgh Public Schools

Gail Burrill
University of Wisconsin–Madison
Jeremy Kilpatrick
University of Georgia
Kenneth Ruthven
University of Cambridge
David A. Smith
Duke University
Edna Vasquez
Detroit Renaissance High School

Curriculum Development Consultants
Kenneth A. Ross
University of Oregon
Richard Scheaffer
University of Florida
Paul Zorn
St. Olaf College

Collaborating Teachers
Emma Ames
Oakland Mills High School, Maryland
Mary Jo Messenger
Howard County Public Schools, Maryland
Valerie Mills
Ann Arbor Public Schools, Michigan

Graduate Assistants
Cos Fi
University of Iowa

Sarah Field
University of Iowa
Kelly Finn
University of Iowa
Chris Rasmussen
University of Maryland
Heather Thompson
Iowa State University
Roberto Villarubi
University of Maryland
Rebecca Walker
Western Michigan University
Edward Wall
University of Michigan
Marcia Weinhold
Western Michigan University

Technical Coordinator
James Laser
Western Michigan University

Production and Support Staff
Kelly MacLean
Wendy Weaver
Kathryn Wright
Teri Ziebarth
Western Michigan University
Catherine Kern
University of Iowa

Core-Plus Mathematics Project Field-Test Sites

Special thanks are extended to these teachers and their students who participated in the testing and evaluation of Course 4.

Ann Arbor Huron High School
Ann Arbor, Michigan
  Ginger Gajar
  Brenda Garr

Ann Arbor Pioneer High School
Ann Arbor, Michigan
  Jim Brink

Arthur Hill High School
Saginaw, Michigan
  Virginia Abbott
  Cindy Bosco

Battle Creek Central High School
Battle Creek, Michigan
  Teresa Ballard
  Steven Ohs

Battle Creek Mathematics & Science Center
Battle Creek, Michigan
  Dana Johnson
  Serena Kershner
  Rose Martin
  Lily Nordmoe

Bedford High School
Temperance, Michigan
  Ellen Bacon
  David J. DeGrace

Bloomfield Hills Andover High School
Bloomfield Hills, Michigan
  Jane Briskey
  Cathy King
  Linda Robinson
  Mike Shelly

Brookwood High School
Snellville, Georgia
  Ginny Hanley

Caledonia High School
Caledonia, Michigan
  Jenny Diekevers
  Gerard Wagner

Centaurus High School
Lafayette, Colorado
  Dana Hodel
  Gail Reichert

Clio High School
Clio, Michigan
  Bruce Hanson
  Lee Sheridan
  Paul Webster

Davison High School
Davison, Michigan
  John Bale
  Tammy Heavner

Ellet High School
Akron, Ohio
  Marcia Csipke
  Jim Fillmore

Firestone High School
Akron, Ohio
  Barbara Crucs

Goodrich High School
Goodrich, Michigan
  John Doerr
  Barbara Ravas
  Bonnie Stojek

Grand Blanc High School
Grand Blanc, Michigan
  Charles Carmody
  Linda Nielsen

Grass Lake Junior/Senior High School
Grass Lake, Michigan
  Brad Coffey

Kelloggsville Public Schools
Wyoming, Michigan
  Steve Ramsey

Lakeview High School
Battle Creek, Michigan
  Larry Laughlin
  Bob O'Connor
  Donna Wells

Midland Valley High School
Langley, South Carolina
  Ron Bell
  Janice Lee

North Lamar High School
Paris, Texas
  Tommy Eads
  Barbara Eatherly

Okemos High School
Okemos, Michigan
  Lisa Magee
  Jacqueline Stewart

Portage Northern High School
Portage, Michigan
  Renee Esper
  Pete Jarrad
  Scott Moore

Prairie High School
Cedar Rapids, Iowa
  Judy Slezak

San Pasqual High School
Escondido, California
  Damon Blackman
  Ron Peet

Sitka High School
Sitka, Alaska
  Cheryl Bach Hedden
  Dan Langbauer

Sturgis High School
Sturgis, Michigan
  Craig Evans
  Kathy Parkhurst

Sweetwater High School
National City, California
  Bill Bokesch

Tecumseh High School
Tecumseh, Michigan
  Jennifer Keffer
  Elizabeth Lentz

Traverse City Central High School
Traverse City, Michigan
  Dennis Muth
  Tonya Rice

Traverse City West High School
Traverse City, Michigan
  Tamie Rosenburg
  Diana Lyon-Schumacher
  John Sivek

Ypsilanti High School
Ypsilanti, Michigan
  Steve Gregory
  Mark McClure
  Beth Welch

Overview of Course 4

Part A

Unit 1 ▶ Rates of Change

Rates of Change develops student understanding of the fundamental concepts underlying calculus and their applications.

Topics include average and instantaneous rates of change, derivative at a point and derivative functions, accumulation of continuously varying quantities by estimation, the definite integral, and intuitive development of the fundamental theorem of calculus.

Unit 2 ▶ Modeling Motion

Modeling Motion develops student understanding of two-dimensional vectors and their use in modeling linear, circular, and other nonlinear motion.

Topics include concept of vector as a mathematical object used to model situations defined by magnitude and direction; equality of vectors, scalar multiples, opposite vectors, sum and difference vectors, position vectors and coordinates; and parametric equations for motion along a line and for motion of projectiles and objects in circular and elliptical orbits.

Unit 3 ▶ Logarithmic Functions and Data Models

Logarithmic Functions and Data Models develops student understanding of logarithmic functions and their use in modeling and analyzing problem situations and data patterns.

Topics include inverses of functions; logarithmic functions and their relation to exponential functions, properties of logarithms, equation solving with logarithms; logarithmic scales and re-expression, linearizing data, and fitting models using log and log-log transformations.

Unit 4 ▶ Counting Models

Counting Models extends student ability to count systematically and solve enumeration problems, and develops understanding of, and ability to do, proof by mathematical induction.

Topics include systematic counting, the Multiplication Principle of Counting, combinations, permutations; the Binomial Theorem, Pascal's triangle, combinatorial reasoning; the General Multiplication Rule for Probability; and the Principle of Mathematical Induction.

Overview of Course 4

Part A   (continued)

Unit 5 ▶ Binomial Distributions and Statistical Inference

Binomial Distributions and Statistical Inference extends student understanding of the binomial distribution, including its exact construction and how the normal approximation to the binomial distribution is used in statistical inference to test a single proportion and to compare two treatments in an experiment.

Topics include binomial probability formula; shape, mean, and standard deviation of a binomial distribution; normal approximation to a binomial distribution; hypothesis test for a proportion; design of an experiment; randomization test; and hypothesis test for the difference of two proportions.

Part B

Unit 6 ▶ Polynomial and Rational Functions

Polynomial and Rational Functions extends student ability to use polynomial and rational functions to represent and solve problems from real-world situations while focusing on symbolic and graphic patterns.

Topics include factored and expanded symbolic forms, computational complexity, connections between symbolic and graphical representations, multiplicity of zeroes, end behavior; Factor Theorem, Remainder Theorem, complex numbers and their use in the solution of polynomial equations, Fundamental Theorem of Algebra; equivalent forms of rational expressions; horizontal, vertical, and oblique asymptotes; and optimization.

Unit 7 ▶ Functions and Symbolic Reasoning

Functions and Symbolic Reasoning extends student ability to manipulate symbolic representations of exponential, logarithmic, and trigonometric functions; to solve exponential and logarithmic equations; to prove or disprove that two trigonometric expressions are identical and to solve trigonometric equations; to reason with complex numbers and complex number operations using geometric representations and to find roots of complex numbers.

Topics include equivalent forms of exponential expressions, definition of *e* and natural logarithms, solving equations using logarithms and solving logarithmic equations; the tangent, cotangent, secant, and cosecant functions; fundamental trigonometric identities, sum and difference identities, double-angle identities; solving trigonometric equations and expression of periodic solutions; rectangular and polar representations of complex numbers, absolute value, DeMoivre's Theorem, and the roots of a complex number.

Overview of Course 4

Part B (continued)

Unit 8 ▶ Space Geometry

Space Geometry extends student ability to visualize and represent three-dimensional shapes using contours, cross-sections and reliefs and to visualize and represent surfaces and conic sections defined by algebraic equations.

Topics include using contours to represent three-dimensional surfaces and developing contour maps from data; sketching surfaces from sets of cross-sections; conics as planar sections of right circular cones and as locus of points in a plane; three-dimensional rectangular coordinate system; sketching surfaces using traces, intercepts and cross-sections derived from algebraically-defined surfaces; surfaces of revolution and cylindrical surfaces.

Unit 9 ▶ Informatics

Informatics develops student understanding of the mathematics of information processing, focusing on the basic issues of access, security, and accuracy.

Topics include set theory; modular arithmetic; symmetric-key and public-key cryptosystems; error-detecting and error-correcting codes, including bar codes and check digits.

Unit 10 ▶ Problem Solving, Algorithms, and Spreadsheets

Problem Solving, Algorithms, and Spreadsheets develops student understanding and skill in use of standard spreadsheet operations for mathematical problems while at the same time reviewing and extending many of the basic topics in Courses 1–3.

Topics include mathematics of finance, modeling population growth, apportionment of power in representative governments, fractals, sequences and series, and numerical solution of equations.

Capstone ▶ Mathematics in the Information Age

Mathematics in the Information Age enables students to review and apply important mathematical concepts and methods developed in the course.

Contents

Unit 1 ▶ Rates of Change

Unit 2 ▶ Modeling Motion

Unit 5 ▶ Binomial Distributions and Statistical Inference

Preface

The first three courses in the *Contemporary Mathematics in Context* series provided a common core of broadly useful mathematics for all students. They were developed to prepare students for success in college, in careers, and in daily life in contemporary society. Course 4 continues the preparation of students for college mathematics. Formal and symbolic reasoning strategies, the hallmarks of advanced mathematics, are developed here as complements to more intuitive arguments and numerical and graphical approaches to problems developed in Courses 1–3.

Course 4 of the *Contemporary Mathematics in Context* curriculum shares many of the mathematical and instructional features of Courses 1–3.

■ **Unified Content**   Course 4 continues to advance students' mathematical thinking along interwoven strands of algebra and functions, statistics and probability, geometry and trigonometry, and discrete mathematics. These strands are unified by fundamental themes, by common topics, and by habits of mind or ways of thinking.

■ **Mathematical Modeling**   The curriculum emphasizes mathematical modeling including the processes of data collection, representation, interpretation, prediction, and simulation. Models developed in Course 4 come from many diverse areas including physics, economics, navigation, sports, health care, finance, biology, information processing, political science, sociology, and engineering.

■ **Technology**   The numerical, graphics, and programming/link capabilities found on graphing calculators are assumed and capitalized on; thereby permitting students to use multiple representations—verbal, numerical, graphical, and symbolic—to model mathematical situations. Course 4 also introduces the use of spreadsheets as a problem-solving tool and the Internet as a source of rich applications. Computer algebra system (CAS) versions of Units 6 and 7 provide alternative technology-intensive approaches to the content of these units.

■ **Active Learning**   Instruction and assessment practices are designed to promote mathematical thinking by engaging students in exploring, analyzing, and applying important mathematical concepts and methods. Through investigations of real-life contexts and engaging mathematical problems, students develop a rich understanding of mathematics that makes sense to them, and which, in turn, enables them to make sense of new situations and problems. Students work in collaborative groups and individually as they investigate, conjecture, verify, generalize, prove, apply, evaluate, and communicate mathematical ideas.

■ **Flexibility**   The mathematical content and sequence of units in Course 4 allows considerable flexibility in tailoring a course to best prepare students for various undergraduate programs. For students intending to pursue programs in the *mathematical, physical, and biological sciences, or engineering,* the developers recommend the following sequence of units:

Unit 1 → Unit 2 → Unit 3 → Unit 6 →
Unit 7 → Unit 4 → Unit 5, 8, or 10

For students intending to pursue programs in the *social, management, and some of the health sciences or humanities,* the following sequence of units is recommended:

Unit 1 → Unit 2 (reduced) → Unit 3 →
Unit 4 (reduced) → Unit 5 → Unit 9 → Unit 10

The accompanying *Teacher's Guide* provides suggestions on how particular lessons in selected units can be omitted or streamlined without loss of continuity. Depending on time available, additional units of study can be selected based on student performance and interests.

■ **Multi-dimensional Assessment**   Comprehensive assessment of student understanding and progress through both curriculum-embedded assessment opportunities and supplementary assessment tasks supports instruction and enables monitoring and evaluation of each student's performance in terms of mathematical processes, content, and dispositions.

Unified Mathematics

Contemporary Mathematics in Context, Course 4 formalizes and extends important mathematical ideas drawn from four strands, with a focus on the mathematics needed to be successful in college mathematics and statistics courses.

The Algebra and Functions strand develops student ability to recognize, represent, and solve problems involving relations among quantitative variables. Central to the development is the use of functions as mathematical models. In Course 4, students extend their toolkits of function models to include logarithmic functions, polynomial functions, and rational functions. Function families are revisited in terms of the fundamental ideas of rates of change and accumulation. Increased attention is given to analysis of symbolic representations of functions. Students extend their skills in *symbolic manipulation*—rewriting expressions in equivalent forms, often to solve equations—and in *symbolic reasoning*—making inferences about symbolic relations and connections between symbolic representations and graphical, numerical, and contextual representations.

The primary goal of the Geometry and Trigonometry strand is to develop visual thinking and the ability to construct, reason with, interpret, and apply mathematical models of patterns in visual and physical contexts. In Course 4, concepts and methods of algebra, geometry, and trigonometry become increasingly intertwined in the development of models for describing and analyzing motion in two-dimensional space and surfaces in three-dimensional space.

The primary role of the Statistics and Probability strand is to develop student ability to analyze data intelligently, to recognize and measure variation, and to understand the patterns that underlie probabilistic situations. Graphical methods of data analysis, simulations, sampling, and experience with the collection and interpretation of real data are featured. In Course 4, ideas of probability distributions and data analysis are merged in the development of methods for testing a hypothesis. Work in the strand concludes with the design of experiments to produce data from which reliable conclusions can be drawn.

The Discrete Mathematics strand develops student ability to model and solve problems involving enumeration, sequential change, decision-making in finite settings, and relationships among a finite number of elements. Key themes are existence (Is there a solution?), optimization (What is the best solution?), and algorithmic problem-solving (Can you efficiently construct a solution?). A fourth theme introduced in Course 4 is that of proof, and in particular proof by mathematical induction. Abstract thinking required to construct proofs in discrete settings is also capitalized on in the development of combinatorial techniques that augment informal methods of systematic counting developed in prior courses. An introduction to the mathematics of information processing concludes work in this strand.

These four strands are connected within units by fundamental ideas such as symmetry, recursion, functions, re-expression, and data analysis and curve-fitting. The strands also are connected across units by mathematical habits of mind, such as visual thinking, recursive thinking, searching for and describing patterns, making and checking conjectures, reasoning with multiple representations, inventing mathematics, and providing convincing arguments. The strands are unified further by the fundamental themes of data, representation, shape, and change. Important mathematical ideas are frequently revisited through this attention to connections within and across strands, enabling students to develop a robust and connected understanding of mathematics.

Active Learning and Teaching

The manner in which mathematical ideas are developed can contribute significantly to the quality of student learning and depth of understanding. *Contemporary Mathematics in Context* Course 4 features multi-day lessons centered on big ideas. Lessons are organized around a four-phase cycle of classroom activities, described in the following paragraph. This cycle is designed to engage students in investigating and making sense of problem situations, in constructing important mathematical concepts and methods, in generalizing and proving mathematical relationships, and in communicating, both orally and in writing, their thinking and the results of their efforts. Most classroom activities are designed to be completed by students working collaboratively in groups of two to four students.

The launch phase promotes a teacher-led class discussion of a problem situation and of related questions to think about, setting the context for the student work to follow. In the second or explore phase, students investigate more focused problems and questions related to the launch situation. This investigative work is followed by a teacher-led class discussion in which students summarize mathematical ideas developed in their groups, providing an opportunity to construct a shared understanding of important concepts, methods, and approaches. Finally, students are given a task to complete on their own, assessing their initial understanding of the concepts and methods.

Each lesson also includes tasks to engage students in Modeling with, Organizing, Reflecting on, and Extending their mathematical understanding. These MORE tasks are central to the learning goals of each lesson and are intended primarily for individual work outside of class. Selection of tasks for use with a class should be based on student performance and the availability of time and technology. Students can exercise some choice of tasks to pursue, and at times they can be given the opportunity to pose their own problems and questions to investigate.

Following each MORE set, there is a Preparing for Undergraduate Mathematics Placement (PUMP) exercise set providing practice in skills and reasoning techniques commonly assessed on college mathematics placement tests.

Multiple Approaches to Assessment

Assessing what students know and are able to do is an integral part of *Contemporary Mathematics in Context*. Initially, as students pursue the investigations that make up the curriculum, the teacher is able to informally assess student understanding of mathematical processes and content and their disposition toward mathematics. At the end of each investigation, the Checkpoint and accompanying class discussion provide an opportunity for the teacher to assess the levels of understanding that the various groups of students have reached. Finally, the "On Your Own" problems, the tasks in the MORE sets, and the exercises in the PUMP sections provide further opportunities to assess the level of understanding of each individual student. Quizzes, in-class exams, take-home assessment activities, and extended projects are included in the teacher resource materials.

Acknowledgments

Development and evaluation of the student text materials, teacher materials, assessments, and calculator software for Course 4 of *Contemporary Mathematics in Context* were funded through a grant from the National Science Foundation to the Core-Plus Mathematics Project (CPMP). We express our appreciation to NSF and, in particular, to our program officer John Bradley for his continuing trust, support, and input.

We also are grateful to Texas Instruments and, in particular, Dave Santucci, for collaborating with us by providing classroom sets of graphing calculators to field-test schools.

As seen on page vii, CPMP has been a collaborative effort that has drawn on the talents and energies of teams of mathematics educators at several institutions. This diversity of experiences and ideas has been a particular strength of the project. Special thanks is owed to the exceptionally capable support staff at these institutions, particularly at Western Michigan University.

We are also grateful to our Advisory Board, Diane Briars (Pittsburgh Public Schools), Gail Burrill (University of Wisconsin–Madison), Jeremy Kilpatrick (University of Georgia), Kenneth Ruthven (University of Cambridge), David A. Smith (Duke University), and Edna Vasquez (Detroit Renaissance High School) for their ongoing guidance and advice.

The overall design and mathematical focus of Course 4 were informed by a working conference with prominent mathematicians held at the University of Maryland in September 1996. Participants included Jim Lewis (University of Nebraska–Lincoln), Steve Rodi (Austin Community College), Kenneth Ross (University of Oregon), Richard Schaeffer (University of Florida), Al Taylor (University of Michigan–Ann Arbor), Tom Tucker (Colgate University), and Paul Zorn (St. Olaf College). We greatly appreciate their insights on what students should know and be able to do upon entering college. Special thanks are owed to Kenneth Ross, Richard Schaeffer, and Paul Zorn who, in addition, reviewed and commented on units as they were being developed, tested, and revised.

Our gratitude is expressed to the teachers and students in our 32 evaluation sites listed on pages viii and ix. Their experiences using pilot- and field-test versions of *Contemporary Mathematics in Context* Course 4 provided constructive feedback and improvements. We learned a lot together about making mathematics meaningful and accessible to a wide range of college-bound students.

A very special thank you is extended to Anna Belluomini for her interest and support in publishing a fourth-year college preparatory course that breaks new ground in terms of content, instructional practices, and student assessment. Finally, we want to acknowledge Abby Tanenbaum and Luke Zajac for their thoughtful and careful editorial work and express our appreciation to Mary Cooney and the staff of Everyday Learning Corporation, who brought this textbook to fruition.

To the Student

Contemporary Mathematics in Context, Course 4 builds on the mathematical concepts, methods, and habits of mind developed in Courses 1–3 with particular attention to building a solid bridge to collegiate mathematics. A major focus of this course is the development of formal and symbolic reasoning strategies as a complement to more intuitive arguments and numerical and graphical approaches to problems you used in previous courses.

With this text, you will continue to learn mathematics by doing mathematics, not by memorizing "worked out" examples. You will investigate important mathematical ideas and ways of thinking as you try to understand and make sense of realistic situations. Because real-world situations and problems often involve data, shape, change, or chance, you will extend and formalize your understanding of fundamental concepts and methods from algebra and functions, from statistics and probability, from geometry and trigonometry, and from discrete mathematics. You also will see further connections among these strands—how they weave together to form the fabric of mathematics.

Because real-world situations and problems are often open-ended, you will find that there may be more than one correct approach and more than one correct solution. Therefore, you will frequently be asked to explain your ideas. You also will increasingly be asked to provide more formal arguments or proofs for mathematical statements. This text will provide help and practice in reasoning and communicating clearly about mathematics.

Because the solution of real-world problems often involves teamwork, you will continue to often work collaboratively with a partner or in small groups as you investigate realistic and interesting situations. As in Courses 1–3, you will find that 2 to 4 students working collaboratively on a problem can often accomplish more than any one of you would working individually. Because technology is commonly used in solving real-world problems, you will continue to use a graphing calculator or computer as a tool to help you understand and make sense of situations and problems you encounter.

Most colleges and universities administer a mathematics placement test to incoming students. The results of this test, together with grades in high school mathematics courses and intended undergraduate major, determine the first college mathematics course you will study. To perform well on these tests, there are a number of skills and reasoning techniques that need to be automatic. Developing that level of proficiency requires practice. To help you strengthen your skills in strategic areas, we have included special Preparing for Undergraduate Mathematics Placement (PUMP) exercise sets in each unit.

As in Courses 1–3, you will continue to learn a lot of useful mathematics, and it is going to make sense to you. You also will deepen your understanding of fundamental ideas that support future coursework in mathematics and statistics. You are going to strengthen your skills in working cooperatively and communicating with others as well. You are also going to strengthen your skills in using technological tools intelligently and effectively. Finally, you will continue to have plenty of opportunities to be creative and inventive. Enjoy.

Rates of Change

Unit **1**

Instantaneous Rates of Change

Lesson **1**

Radar and sonar devices are among the simplest and most useful inventions of our electronic age. They send out radio (radar) and sound (sonar) waves and detect echoes as those waves bounce off objects in the sky, on the ground, and underwater.

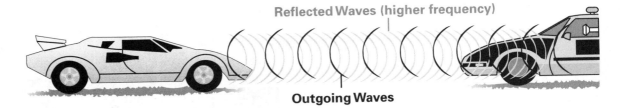

Reflected Waves (higher frequency)

Outgoing Waves

Think About This Situation

The key to both radar and sonar detection is measuring the time it takes a radio or sound wave to travel from the transmitter to a distant object and back to the receiver.

ⓐ What uses of radar and sonar devices do you know about?

ⓑ How do you think radar and sonar devices convert measures of elapsed time into estimates of distances to target objects?

ⓒ How do you think measures of time and distance can be used to detect *velocities* of the target objects if they are in motion?

ⓓ If you were using a radar device that reported only the velocity of a moving object, how could you use that information to estimate the distance traveled by the target object?

INVESTIGATION 1 ▶ Walk That Graph

Radar and sonar were first used in warfare to locate enemy airplanes and submarines. The same principles are now applied in a variety of detection and ranging devices. For example, there is a simple motion detector that connects to your graphing calculator. If you aim the detector at someone walking toward or away from you, it will produce a sequence of (*time*, *distance*) data pairs and convert them into a graph like this:

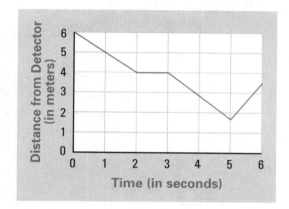

How would you walk toward or away from a motion detector to give a (time, distance) graph like that shown above?

1. After a radar or sonar device collects (*time*, *distance*) data tracking the position of some object and transforms that data into a graph, your task is to interpret the shape of that graph.

   a. How would you walk toward or away from a radar or sonar device to produce graphs with shapes like the following (*time*, *distance*) graphs? When you think you have figured out how to walk the given (*time*, *distance*) graphs, test your ideas with a motion detector connected to a graphing calculator if one is available.

i.
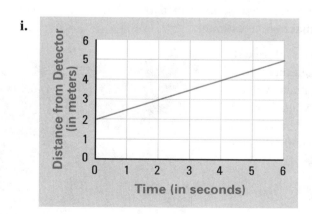

ii.
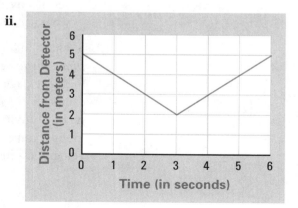

iii.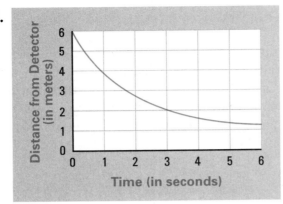

iv.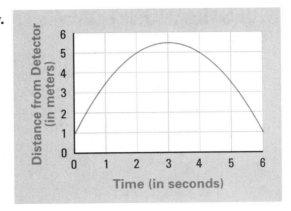

b. When radar and sonar are used to track airplanes, automobiles, submarines, or a baseball pitcher's fastball, people are often interested in *velocity* as much as distance. For walks that match the (*time, distance*) graphs in Part a, record numerical data in four tables like the one below.

Time of Walk (in seconds)	0.0	0.5	1.0	1.5	2.0	2.5	3.0	3.5	4.0	4.5	5.0	5.5	6.0
Distance from Detector (in meters)													

c. Use the data to estimate walking velocity at these points in each trip.
- when one-quarter of the walk time has elapsed
- when one-half of the walk time has elapsed
- when three-quarters of the walk time has elapsed

In each case, explain how the differences in velocity estimates are shown by the shapes of the (*time, distance*) graphs in Part a.

d. Compare your velocity estimates with those obtained by other groups and see if any differences can be explained by differences in strategies that were used for making the estimates.

2. Students in one class all used the (*time, distance*) data reported on the next page to make velocity estimates for the walk in Graph iv of Activity 1, but different groups came up with different velocity estimates.

Time of Walk (in seconds)	0.0	0.5	1.0	1.5	2.0	2.5	3.0	3.5	4.0	4.5	5.0	5.5	6.0
Distance from Detector (in meters)	1.0	2.4	3.5	4.4	5.0	5.4	5.5	5.4	5.0	4.4	3.5	2.4	1.0

a. Which of these methods of estimating velocity at a time 1.5 seconds into the walk makes most sense to you? Explain your reasoning.

- $\dfrac{4.4 - 3.5}{1.5 - 1.0} = 1.8$ m/s (meters per second)

- $\dfrac{5.0 - 4.4}{2.0 - 1.5} = 1.2$ m/s

- $\dfrac{5.0 - 3.5}{2.0 - 1.0} = 1.5$ m/s

- $\dfrac{4.4 - 1.0}{1.5 - 0} \approx 2.3$ m/s

- $\dfrac{4.4}{1.5} \approx 2.9$ m/s

b. When two groups estimated the walker's velocity at a point 4.5 seconds into the trip, one came up with 1.5 m/s and the other came up with -1.5 m/s. How do you suppose each group came up with those estimates? What does a negative velocity mean in this context?

c. What kind of information would help you make more accurate estimates for the walker's velocity at different times?

3. In addition to velocity, it is often interesting to describe *acceleration* or change in velocity. Study this (*time, distance*) graph of a walk. Make conjectures about when the walker was accelerating and when the walker was decelerating. Compare your conjectures and reasoning with those of other groups.

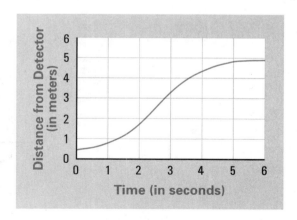

4. Velocity and acceleration are both measures of *rates of change*. That means they compare two changes.

    a. *Velocity* compares change in position to change in time. What is the appropriate unit for velocity in the situations of Activity 1?

    b. *Acceleration* compares change in velocity to change in time. What is the appropriate unit for acceleration in Activity 3?

Checkpoint

Suppose you have used a motion detector to collect data about the distance to a moving object at several points in time.

  ⓐ How can you estimate the velocity at which that object is moving?

  ⓑ How would you express velocity as a rate comparing change in position and time?

  ⓒ How can you estimate the acceleration of the moving object?

  ⓓ How would you express acceleration as a rate comparing change in velocity and time?

Be prepared to share your group's thinking with the entire class.

On Your Own

Refer to the (*time, distance*) graph of a walk below.

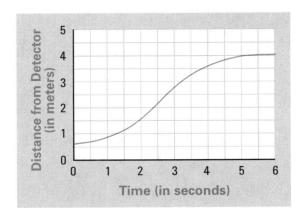

  a. Estimate the walker's velocity at 3.5 seconds into the walk.

  b. What can you say about the walker's acceleration or deceleration 3.5 seconds into the walk?

INVESTIGATION 2 Chilling Out

Pouring hot beverages at a local café.

There are electronic sensors that measure many things other than time, distance, and velocity. For example, if you pour a hot drink into a cup and set that cup on a kitchen counter, the liquid will gradually cool to room temperature. You can chart the pattern of cooling with a temperature probe that can connect to some calculators and produce a table or graph of (*time, temperature*) data.

1. When students in one science class did a cooling experiment, various groups reported quite different results. The instructor was suspicious that some groups had not been very careful in collecting data. Given at the right and below are (*time, temperature*) graphs from three groups. Describe as accurately as possible the pattern of temperature change shown in each graph.

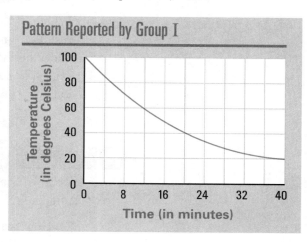

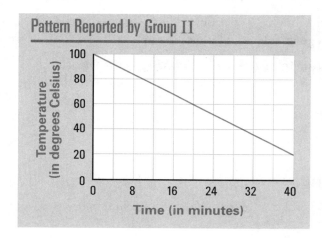

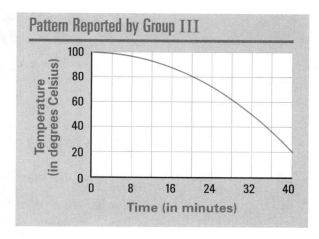

2. Look back at the graphs of different reported cooling patterns.

   a. Comparing change in temperature to change in time gives a *rate of cooling*. What is the appropriate unit for this rate of change comparison?

   b. For each model, estimate the rates of cooling at 8, 20, and 32 minutes.

   c. Explain how the different rates of cooling are shown by the shapes of the (*time, temperature*) graphs.

   d. What kind of information would help you make more accurate estimates of the cooling rates in each case?

3. Each cooling graph in Activity 1 shows a change of 80° in a period of 40 minutes.

   a. What is the *average rate of change* in temperature over that time period?

   b. How does that average rate of change compare to your estimates of the rate of change in temperature for each graph at 8, 20, and 32 minutes? The rate of change at a specific point is often referred to as the **instantaneous rate of change.**

4. Which of the reported cooling patterns do you think is most likely to match results from a careful experiment and why? If you have access to hot water and a thermometer or a calculator-based temperature probe, conduct the cooling experiment to test your ideas and to determine which of the three science class reports is most likely correct.

Checkpoint

Suppose you have used a temperature probe to collect data about the temperature of some liquid as time passes.

a How can that data be used to estimate the rate of change in temperature?

b What units would be used to report rate of change in temperature?

c How is estimating rate of change in temperature similar to estimating rate of change in velocity of a moving object?

Be prepared to share your thinking with the class.

On Your Own

Consider the cooling pattern reported by Group I in Activity 1.

a. What is the average rate of change in temperature between 16 and 32 minutes?

b. What is the instantaneous rate of change in temperature at 24 minutes?

c. Why is your answer to Part a not a good estimate of the rate of change at 24 minutes?

INVESTIGATION 3 In the Swing of Things

Things that move do not always follow straight line paths. For example, when circus trapeze flyers perform high above the ground, they swing along part of a circular arc from one side to another and back. It is not too difficult to track the motion of a trapeze flyer, giving distance along the arc from the takeoff point at any time.

1. If a trapeze swings on a 40-foot cable, then its arc from one side to the other will be about 100 ft long. Suppose that a motion detector reports *distance from the takeoff point* (*along the arc*) many times during a *complete swing* from one side to the other and back to the start. Shown below are two possible graphs of the (*time, distance*) relationship.

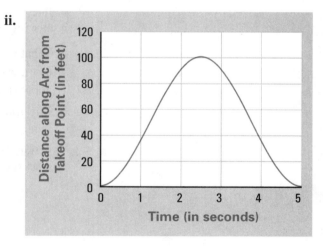

i.

ii.

a. Think about your experience with playground swings to decide which graph is the better model of what really happens to a trapeze flyer.

b. What points on the two graphs show the trapeze traveling fastest, and where will the trapeze be in its arc at those times?

c. According to the graphs, when is the trapeze accelerating? When is it decelerating?

2. Examine these two tables of (*time*, *distance*) data from the graphs in Activity 1.

Time (in seconds)	0	0.5	1.0	1.5	2.0	2.5	3.0	3.5	4.0	4.5	5.0
Distance (in feet)	0	10	35	65	90	100	90	65	35	10	0

Time (in seconds)	0	0.5	1.0	1.5	2.0	2.5	3.0	3.5	4.0	4.5	5.0
Distance (in feet)	0	6	18	40	68	100	68	40	18	6	0

   a. Which table goes with Graph i and which goes with Graph ii?

   b. Use the data table corresponding to the more accurate modeling graph to estimate the velocity of the trapeze flyer at 0.5, 1.5, 2.5, and 3.5 seconds. Compare your estimation strategies and results to those of other groups in the class.

   c. Locate the points at 0.5, 1.5, 2.5, and 3.5 seconds on the correct (*time*, *distance*) graph and explain how your velocity estimates match the pattern shown in the graph.

   d. What kind of (*time*, *distance*) information would you need to make more accurate velocity estimates at the indicated points?

3. In physics, the term *speed* is used to tell only how fast someone or something is moving, without regard to the direction.

   a. What is your best estimate of the maximum speed that a trapeze flyer reaches on each trip? When does that maximum speed occur? What is the flyer's approximate *velocity* at each of the points where that maximum speed occurs?

   b. The trapeze flier swings a total of 200 ft in one complete trip. That trip takes 5 seconds. What is the *average speed* of the flyer? How does that average speed compare to your estimates of the *instantaneous speed* at various specific times in the trip?

The activities in this lesson focused on rates of change in several different pairs of variables.

a If a table shows one variable *y* as a function of another variable *x*, how can the numbers in the table help in estimating the rate of change in *y* as *x* changes?

b How can a graph showing *y* as a function of *x* help in estimating the rate of change in *y* at various values of *x*?

c What is the difference between average rate of change and instantaneous rate of change for a variable *y* that is a function of a variable *x*?

Be prepared to explain your ideas to the entire class.

On Your Own

Most modern businesses have computer accounting systems that allow them to track income and expenses from minute to minute every day of the year. The graph at the right shows the accumulated profit of a department store in Montgomery Mall during the month of December.

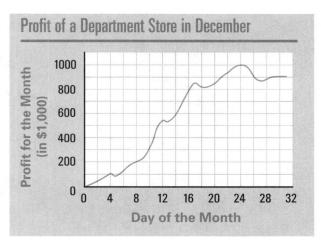

Profit of a Department Store in December

Holiday shopping

a. Use the graph to estimate the store's profit after 8 days of the month have passed and the instantaneous rate of change in profit at that time.

b. Use the graph to estimate the store's profit after 26 days of the month have passed and the rate of change in profit at that time.

c. At what time(s) in the month was the rate of change in store profit greatest? What was the approximate rate of change at that time?

d. In what ways do the patterns of increase or decrease in store profit shown by the graph seem reasonable, based on what you know about shopping trends in December?

Modeling • Organizing • Reflecting • Extending

Modeling

These tasks provide opportunities for you to use the ideas you have learned in the investigations. Each task asks you to model and solve problems in other situations.

1. When you turn on your oven, it gradually heats up from room temperature to whatever temperature you set. Suppose that you set the oven control to 450°F for baking a pizza.

a. Describe the patterns of heating illustrated by the following graphs. Decide which you believe is most likely to match the pattern in a typical oven.

i.

Oven Temperature (in degrees Fahrenheit) vs **Heating Time (in minutes)**

ii.

Oven Temperature (in degrees Fahrenheit) vs **Heating Time (in minutes)**

iii.

Oven Temperature (in degrees Fahrenheit) vs **Heating Time (in minutes)**

b. Shown below are three tables of (*time, temperature*) data that you might get by watching an oven warm up from room temperature to 450°F. Match these tables to the graphs in Part a. Explain how the different patterns of temperature change are illustrated in the matching graphs.

Data Pattern A

Heating Time (in minutes)	0	1	2	3	4	5	6	7	8	9	10	11	12	13	14	15
Temp (in °F)	70	95	120	145	170	195	220	245	270	295	320	345	370	395	420	445

Data Pattern B

Heating Time (in minutes)	0	1	2	3	4	5	6	7	8	9	10	11	12	13	14	15
Temp (in °F)	70	80	90	115	140	170	210	260	310	350	380	405	430	440	445	450

Data Pattern C

Heating Time (in minutes)	0	1	2	3	4	5	6	7	8	9	10	11	12	13	14	15
Temp (in °F)	70	125	170	210	250	280	310	335	360	380	400	415	430	440	445	450

c. Estimate the rate of heating predicted by each graph and table 5 minutes after the oven is turned on. Be sure to explain the units in which those rates of heating should be measured and reported.

2. When a museum used electronic turnstiles to count people entering and leaving, an employee created the graph on the next page showing the number of people in the museum at any time during a summer Saturday. The museum opened at 9 A.M. and closed at 9 P.M.

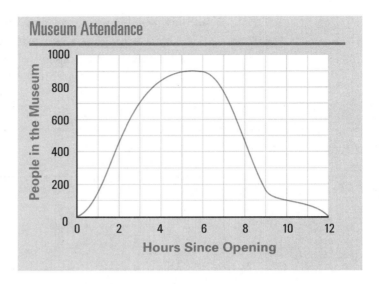

Museum Attendance

Use the graph to estimate the rate at which the number of people in the museum was changing at each of the following times.

a. 11 A.M.   **b.** 1 P.M.   **c.** 3 P.M.   **d.** 5 P.M.   **e.** 7 P.M.

3. In big-city subway systems, the trains might travel 2,000–3,000 meters between stations and cover that distance in 2-3 minutes. They do not travel at a constant speed.

   Suppose that you were able to track the progress of one subway car on its trip of 2,500 m between two stations and that the trip took a total of 3 minutes.

   a. Sketch a (*time*, *distance*) graph that you believe would match the pattern of motion of a typical subway train on such a trip.

   b. Make a table of (*time*, *distance*) data with entries for every 15 seconds in the 3-minute trip so that the pattern of that data matches the graph sketched in Part a.

   c. Describe in words the pattern of subway train speed shown in your graph and table, including times when the train was going fastest and times when the train was accelerating and decelerating.

4. If you have access to a motion detector connected to a calculator, you can test your ideas about the shape of the (*time*, *distance*) graph for a trip of a trapeze flyer as described in Investigation 3.

   a. Build a model trapeze and hang a model flyer from it.

   b. Collect (*time*, *distance*) data from several complete swings of the trapeze and make a scatterplot of the data showing the pattern of motion.

   c. How well does the pattern in the scatterplot match your thinking about the rate of change in distance as time changes?

Organizing

These tasks will help you organize the mathematics you have learned in the investigations and connect it with other mathematics.

1. Among the most familiar problems concerning distance, time, and rate of motion are those that involve balls that have been thrown, hit, or kicked. For example, if a soccer ball is kicked straight up into the air, its height will be a function of time in flight. This function might be given by a graph and table like those below.

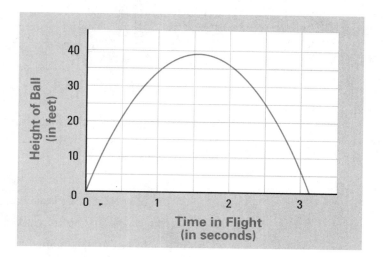

Time in Flight (in seconds)	0	0.25	0.5	0.75	1.0	1.25	1.5	1.75	2.0	2.25	2.5	2.75	3.0
Height of Ball (in feet)	0	11.5	21	28.5	34	37.5	39	38.5	36	31.5	25	16.5	6

   a. Use the table and graph to estimate both the *speed* and *velocity* of the moving ball at times 0.5 second and 2.5 seconds into its flight.

   b. Explain the difference between speed and velocity for the ball and how that difference shows up in the graph and the table of the (*time, height*) relation.

2. Sketch graphs of functions $f(x)$ that model the following patterns of change. For each function graph, describe the type of function rule that would match the pattern you sketched.

   a. As x increases, $f(x)$ increases at a constant rate.

   b. As x increases, $f(x)$ decreases at a constant rate.

   c. As x increases, $f(x)$ increases at a rate that is gradually increasing.

   d. As x increases, $f(x)$ increases at a rate that is gradually decreasing.

   e. As x increases, $f(x)$ decreases at a rate that is gradually decreasing.

3. Suppose that a traffic radar detector is aimed at a car and produces the following graph of (*time, distance*) data. What conclusions can you make about the *speed* and *velocity* of that car while it was being observed?

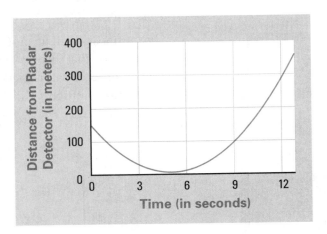

4. Suppose $d(t)$ gives the distance in meters of a walker from a motion detector as a function of time t in seconds. Write an algebraic expression that gives each of the following:

   a. the average velocity of the walker between $t = 1$ and $t = 5$

   b. the average velocity of the walker over the interval $0 \le t \le 6$

   c. the average velocity of the walker over the interval $a \le t \le b$

   d. an estimate of the instantaneous velocity of the walker at $t = 3$ seconds

   e. an estimate of the instantaneous velocity of the walker at $t = a$ seconds

Reflecting

These tasks will help you think about what the mathematics you have learned means to you. These tasks also will help you think about what you do and do not understand.

1. Measurement instruments are used to record data about many familiar quantitative variables that change as time passes or in response to changes of some other variable.

   a. Make a list of several devices that record (*time, amount*) data for different quantities.

   b. For each device, explain the units that would measure rate of change in the recorded amount and how you could estimate the rate of change in that quantity at any point in time.

2. Think about your experience on roller coaster rides or similar amusement park rides. Draw a sketch of a side view of part of a roller coaster track and explain where you think the ride would be fastest and where it would be slowest. Explain your reasoning.

3. Examine the (*time, distance*) data reported below for Carl Lewis in the 100-meter final at the World Championship in Rome in 1987. Some runners, particularly in short races, are running the fastest as they cross the finish line. Does that seem to be the case for Carl Lewis in this race? If not, during which part of the race did he attain his maximum speed?

Carl Lewis at the 1987 World Championships in Rome, Italy.

Time (in seconds)	0.00	1.94	2.96	3.91	4.78	5.64	6.50	7.36	8.22	9.07	9.93
Distance (in meters)	0	10	20	30	40	50	60	70	80	90	100

Source: "Mathematical Models of Running" by W.G. Pritchard, SIAM Review, 35, 1993. Pages 359-379.

4. After completing Lesson 1, Lynette said to her teacher, "When I estimate the instantaneous rate of change for a function, I am really just finding an average rate of change." Do you agree or disagree with Lynette? Explain your response.

Extending

Tasks in this section provide opportunities for you to explore further or more deeply the mathematics you are learning.

1. Look back at the (*time, height*) data of a kicked soccer ball in Organizing Task 1.

   a. Find a function rule that describes the relation between elapsed time and height of the ball.

   b. Determine the maximum height the ball will reach. What should the velocity of the ball be at the time the ball reaches its peak? Check your conjecture.

2. The instrument panel on every car has both an odometer (showing distance traveled) and a speedometer (showing current speed). Recall that when the speed of a moving object increases, that change is called *acceleration*.

The data in the following graph and table were recorded from the speedometer of a prototype four-cylinder sports car being tested for its acceleration.

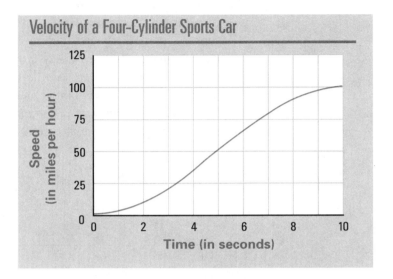

Time (in seconds)	0	1	2	3	4	5	6	7	8	9	10
Speed (in mph)	0	3	10	22	35	50	65	78	90	97	100

a. Describe the pattern of change in speed over the 10 seconds of this acceleration test.

b. At what point in the test does the car seem to be accelerating most rapidly? Explain how your answer is shown in the table and on the graph.

c. Estimate the rate at which the car is accelerating at the point that is exactly 4 seconds into the test. Explain the units in which that acceleration should be reported.

d. The graph and table give information about the speed of the accelerating car. The speed is given in miles per hour, but time is given in seconds.

■ How far (in miles) would a car travel in 10 seconds at an average speed of 50 mph?

■ How far (in feet) would a car travel in 8 seconds at an average speed of 75 mph?

e. Estimate the total distance (in miles and in feet) traveled by the sports car during its 10-second acceleration test.

3. Suppose the growth of a population over time is modeled by the recursion equation $P_t = 1.5P_{t-1}$.

a. Assuming that the initial population size was $P_0 = 10$, show that $P_t = 10(1.5^t)$.

b. How would you interpret the constant 1.5?

c. Show that the equation $P_t - P_{t-1} = 0.5P_{t-1}$ is equivalent to $P_t = 1.5P_{t-1}$.

d. The left side of the equation in Part c can be interpreted as the change in the population or as a rate of change since $P_t - P_{t-1} = \frac{P_t - P_{t-1}}{t - (t-1)}$. What intepretation can you give to the constant 0.5 in the equation $\frac{P_t - P_{t-1}}{t - (t-1)} = 0.5P_{t-1}$?

e. Produce a graph of the population size as a function of time. Describe the instantaneous rate of change in the population at various times along the curve. How does your description match the equation in Part d?

4. Imagine a ball is rolling down each of the following ramps. For each ramp, the points A and B are in the same location.

i. 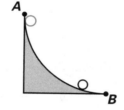   ii. 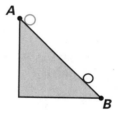   iii.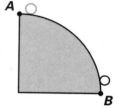

a. For which ramp, if any, does the ball travel the farthest? The shortest? Explain your reasoning.

b. For which ramp, if any, is the ball traveling the fastest one quarter of the way down the ramp? The slowest? Explain.

c. For which ramp, if any, do you think the speed of the ball at the bottom will be the greatest? The least? Explain your thinking.

d. For which ramp, if any, do you think the ball will reach the bottom first? Last?

e. For each of the ramps above, sketch what you think would be a graph of the speed of the ball as a function of the distance traveled over time.

Most colleges and universities administer a mathematics placement test to incoming students. The results of this test together with grades in high school mathematics courses and intended undergraduate major determine the first college mathematics course you will study.

To perform well on these tests, there are a number of skills and reasoning techniques that need to be automatic. Developing that level of proficiency requires practice. The exercises in this section, and in subsequent PUMP sections, will help you build skills in strategic areas. The exercises are presented in a multiple-choice format as commonly found on mathematics placement tests.

1. The price of an airline ticket was \$320, and it is now \$400. What is the percent of increase in the price of the ticket?

(a) 80%   (b) 0.25%   (c) 25%   (d) 20%   (e) 0.20%

2. Evaluate $ab + ac^2$ when $a = 2$, $b = -3$, and $c = -5$.

(a) -44 (b) -56 (c) 56 (d) 44 (e) -51

3. The slope of the line $2x + 5y = 20$ is

(a) 2 (b) -2 (c) $\frac{2}{5}$ (d) 10 (e) $-\frac{2}{5}$

4. If $f(x) = x^2$, then $f(a + 2) =$

(a) $a^2 + 4a + 4$ (b) $a^2 + 2$ (c) $a^2 + 4$

(d) $a^2 + 2a + 4$ (e) $a^2 + 2a$

5. Which of the following could be a portion of the graph of $y + 3 = 2x^2$?

(a)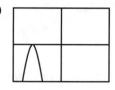

(b)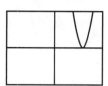

(c)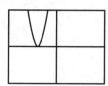

(d)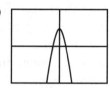

(e)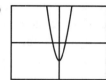

6. If $ax + b = cx + d$, then $x =$

(a) $\frac{d-b}{a-c}$ (b) $\frac{db}{ac}$ (c) $\frac{b-d}{ac}$ (d) $\frac{b-d}{a+c}$ (e) $\frac{c+d-b}{a}$

7. Which of the following is not a zero of $f(x) = 2x^4 - 6x^3 - 2x^2 + 6x$?

(a) 0 (b) 1 (c) 2 (d) −1 (e) 3

8. The distance from the point (2, 4) to the point (7, −8) is

(a) 13 (b) $\sqrt{41}$ (c) $\sqrt{13}$ (d) $\sqrt{97}$ (e) none of these

9. Simplify $\left(\frac{x^3}{3z}\right)^{-3}$.

(a) $\frac{x^6 z^3}{-27}$ (b) $\frac{-27z^3}{x^9}$ (c) $\frac{z^3}{27x^6}$ (d) $\frac{-9z^3}{x^9}$ (e) $\frac{27z^3}{x^9}$

10. If $x > 0$, then $\sqrt{36x^2 + 64x^2} =$

(a) $14x$ (b) $10x^2$ (c) $14x^2$ (d) $10x$ (e) $48x$

Lesson 2

Rates of Change for Familiar Functions

In the first three courses of the *Contemporary Mathematics in Context* program, you investigated several important families of functions—linear, power, quadratic, exponential, and trigonometric. You found that members of each family had closely-related patterns in tables, graphs, and symbolic rules. In this lesson, you will investigate patterns in the rates of change for these function families. To begin, consider the patterns of change in the height and velocity of a bungee jumper at various points in his flight.

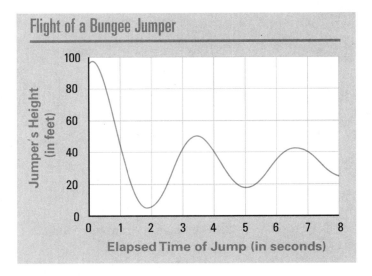

Flight of a Bungee Jumper

Jumper's Height (in feet) vs *Elapsed Time of Jump (in seconds)*

Think About This Situation

Principles of physics can be used to model the flight of a bungee jumper with a rule giving jumper height as a function of elapsed time in flight.

a What type of function model would best fit this pattern of change?

b Suppose you were given the symbolic rule for a function $h(t)$ that predicts a bungee jumper's height at any time t in his jump. How would you use that rule to estimate

- the jumper's velocity at any time?
- the times when the jumper reaches the bottom or top of a bounce?
- the times when the jumper is traveling at maximum speed?

INVESTIGATION 1 ▸ Reasoning with Rules about Rates

In Lesson 1, you estimated rates of change in relations between quantitative variables expressed in graphs and in tables of data. In this investigation, you will explore how rates of change of functions can be estimated using the algebraic rules for those functions.

Linear Functions Linear functions are the simplest relations between variables and the easiest to describe with symbolic rules. You know that any linear function can be expressed by a rule in the form $f(x) = a + bx$, and by now you should be adept at using that sort of rule to predict the shape of the graph and the patterns in a table of $(x, f(x))$ values.

1. Modern subway, train, airplane, and space travel are almost all guided by sophisticated navigational equipment. For example, the flight of an airplane trip from New York to Los Angeles usually follows a plan based on computer weather information and is monitored by on-board computer flight control technology. Suppose that in one such flight plan, the distance traveled will be a function of time in flight with rule $d(t) = 525t$ (time in hours and distance in miles).

   a. Based on this flight plan function, what is the intended average speed for the trip?

   b. How fast will the plane be traveling 1 hour, 2.5 hours, and 4.25 hours after takeoff?

   c. How are your answers to Parts a and b shown in tables and graphs of (*time, distance*) pairs for the given flight plan function?

2. When you shop for music tapes or compact discs, you probably consider the price in your decision about whether to buy. The manufacturer also considers that relationship in predicting how many copies of a tape or CD will be sold.

Suppose that the projected number of sales of a CD (in 1,000s) is related to selling price (in dollars) by the function $S(p) = 145 - 5p$.

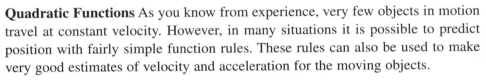

a. Based on this function rule, how does the prediction of unit sales (in thousands) change as the price is increased?

b. How is your answer to Part a shown in tables and graphs of (*price, unit sales*) pairs for the given function?

3. Suppose y is a linear function of x with rule in the form $y = a + bx$.

a. What is the rate of change of y as x changes?

b. How is the rate of change of y shown in tables, graphs, and rules of the function?

c. What rule gives the rate of change of y at any point x?

Quadratic Functions As you know from experience, very few objects in motion travel at constant velocity. However, in many situations it is possible to predict position with fairly simple function rules. These rules can also be used to make very good estimates of velocity and acceleration for the moving objects.

4. In previous courses, you have studied the motion of divers from high platforms. One of the most spectacular high-diving events is in Mexico where cliff divers drop off rocky outcroppings into ocean bays. If one of these divers drops from a spot that is 30 meters above the water, his height will be modeled well by a function with rule $h(t) = 30 - 4.9t^2$ (height in meters and time in seconds).

Use the function rule above to answer these questions as accurately as possible.

a. How long will it take the diver to reach the surface of the water?

b. What will be the diver's average velocity from takeoff to hitting the water? What will be his average speed?

c. How will the diver's speed change during his flight? How is that change shown in the shape of a $(t, h(t))$ graph?

One of the most interesting questions about the relation giving diver height as a function of time in flight is how fast the diver will be traveling when he hits the water. In Activity 4, you found that the average speed from takeoff to hitting the water (after approximately 2.47 seconds) was about 12 m/s. But common sense and the study of tables and graphs for the height function tell you that the diver's speed increases throughout his flight.

5. Devise and use a strategy for making a good estimate of the diver's speed when he hits the water. Then compare your method and results to those of other groups in your class.

6. Estimate the average speed of the diver for these time intervals in his flight.

   a. $t = 1$ to $t = 2.47$

   b. $t = 2$ to $t = 2.47$

   c. $t = 2.4$ to $t = 2.47$

   d. $t = 2.46$ to $t = 2.47$

   e. What do the answers to Parts a–d suggest about the speed of this diver when he hits the water? How does this compare with your work in Activity 5?

7. Now consider the problem of estimating the diver's speed at several other points in his dive. Try several different ways of producing what you believe are good estimates.

   a. What is his speed exactly 1 second into the dive?

   b. What is his speed exactly 2 seconds into the dive?

   c. What is his speed just as he takes off from the cliff?

8. With one exception, the questions about the cliff diver refer to *speed*, not *velocity*. Why does that make sense in this context?

Exponential Functions Exponential functions, like quadratic functions, involve nonlinear patterns of change. They are good models for the growth of human and animal populations, bacteria colonies, or money invested in bank savings accounts, as well as for the decay of radioactive chemicals. In these types of situations, it is often useful to estimate the rate at which such functions are growing or declining at various specific times.

9. Suppose that a laboratory experiment uses fruit flies that double in number every five days. If the initial population contains 100 flies, the number at any time t days into the experiment will be modeled by the function with rule $P(t) = 100(2)^{\frac{t}{5}}$ or $P(t) = 100(2^{0.2t})$.

   Dosophila (fruit flies) magnified 6 times their size.

   a. Use the rule for $P(t)$ to:

   ■ find the average growth rate of the population (flies per day) from day 0 to day 20

   ■ estimate the rates at which the fly population will be growing on day 0, on day 10, and on day 20

   b. Use the rule for $P(t)$ to:

   ■ find the average growth rate of the population (flies per day) from day 20 to day 40

   ■ estimate the rates at which the fly population will be growing on day 20, on day 30, and on day 40

10. Sketch a graph of the function $P(t) = 100(2^{0.2t})$ and explain how the shape of your graph helps to explain the growth rates calculated in Activity 9, especially the differences between average and instantaneous rates of change.

Trigonometric Functions Many interesting variable quantities such as alternating electrical current, tides in ocean harbors, hours of daylight, or sound waves from musical instruments change in repeating patterns as time passes. For example, there are places on Earth where ocean tides change the water depth in harbors by as much as 20 feet every six hours.

Low Tide

High Tide

11. Suppose that water depth in a tidal harbor is given by the trigonometric function with rule $D(t) = 9 \sin 0.5t + 15$. The depth D is measured in feet and the time t is measured in hours. Use radian measure.

   a. Based on what you know about variations of the graph of the sine function, what overall pattern of change would you expect in water depth for $0 \le t \le 24$?

   b. Use the function rule to calculate the water depth when $t = 0, 3, 6, 9,$ and 12.

   c. Use the information from Part b to calculate the average rate of change in water depth (feet per hour) in the following time intervals.

   i. $0 \le t \le 3$ **ii.** $3 \le t \le 6$

   iii. $6 \le t \le 9$ **iv.** $9 \le t \le 12$

   d. Calculate the average rate of change in water depth for $0 \le t \le 6$ and for $6 \le t \le 12$. Then sketch a graph of $D(t)$ and mark the points for $t = 0$, 6, and 12. Explain how this graph shows that the average rates of change in water depths you calculated give misleading information about the overall pattern of tidal change in the intervals from $t = 0$ to $t = 6$ and from $t = 6$ to $t = 12$.

12. Now focus on the rate at which harbor water depth is changing around $t = 10$.

   a. Calculate the average rate of change in water depth for $9 \leq t \leq 10$ and for $10 \leq t \leq 11$.

   b. Calculate the average rate of change in water depth for $9.5 \leq t \leq 10$ and for $10 \leq t \leq 10.5$.

   c. Calculate the average rate of change in water depth for $9.9 \leq t \leq 10$ and for $10 \leq t \leq 10.1$.

   d. Use the pattern in the results of Parts a, b, and c to estimate the rate at which the water depth is changing in the harbor when $t = 10$.

   e. How does the shape of the graph of $D(t)$ illustrate the pattern of change estimates in Parts a, b, and c?

13. Study the water depth graph from Activity 11 and a table of values to identify some times when you think the tide will be moving as described below. Then estimate, as accurately as possible, the rate of change in water depth at each of those times.

   a. moving in most rapidly

   b. moving out most rapidly

   c. moving in or out most slowly

Checkpoint

In this investigation, you explored the rates of change of several different quantities—distance traveled by airplanes and cliff divers, sales of compact discs, population of fruit flies, and tides in ocean harbors. Suppose you model some other situation with a function $y = f(x)$.

ⓐ How would you use the rule for $f(x)$ to discover the *overall pattern of change in $f(x)$* values over an interval of its domain $x_0 \leq x \leq x_1$?

ⓑ How would you use the rule for $f(x)$ to calculate the *average rate of change of $f(x)$* over the interval $x_0 \leq x \leq x_1$?

ⓒ How would you use the rule for $f(x)$ to estimate the *instantaneous rate of change of $f(x)$* at any specific point $(x_0, f(x_0))$?

Be prepared to explain your methods to the entire class.

On Your Own

Reproduced below is the bungee jumper graph from the beginning of this lesson. One function rule that will give a graph like this is $h(t) = 32 + \frac{80 \cos (2t - 0.7)}{t + 1}$. This rule gives height in feet as a function of time in seconds. It looks like a complicated function rule, but once you have entered it in your graphing calculator, you can explore many interesting questions about the jumper's falling and bouncing.

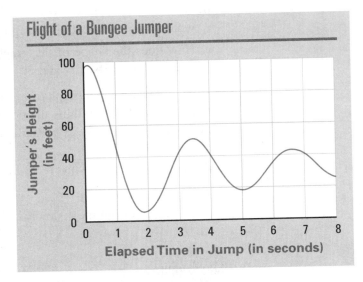

Flight of a Bungee Jumper

a. Calculate the jumper's average velocity (in feet per second) in each of these segments of his trip:
- From start to bottom of the first fall
- From bottom of first fall to top of first bounce up
- From top of first bounce to bottom of second fall
- From bottom of second fall to top of second bounce up

b. Estimate the average velocity of the jumper in each of these time intervals.
- From $t = 0$ to $t = 0.5$
- From $t = 0.5$ to $t = 1.0$
- From $t = 1.0$ to $t = 1.5$
- From $t = 1.5$ to $t = 2$

c. Estimate, as accurately as possible, the jumper's instantaneous velocity at each of these points.
- (0.5, 82.951)
- (1.0, 42.7)
- (1.5, 10.679)
- (2.0, 5.667)

d. Explain how the differences among your results in Parts b and c are illustrated by the shape of the graph of $h(t)$.

e. Find what you believe to be the time at which the bungee jumper is falling at the greatest velocity. Explain how you can determine that time by inspection of a table of values and by inspection of a graph of the height function $h(t)$.

INVESTIGATION 2 The Linear Connection

When function rules are given, it is easy to deal with rate of change questions for linear functions. It is not as easy to estimate rates of change for nonlinear functions. But there are some similarities between linear and many nonlinear functions that tie them together.

1. Here are two function graphs, one linear and one nonlinear. On each graph, three points are marked.

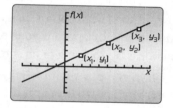 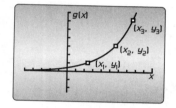

a. How could you use the coordinates of the marked points on the linear graph to find the rate of change of $f(x)$ at the point (x_2, y_2)?

b. How could you use the coordinates of the marked points on the nonlinear graph to estimate the rate of change of $g(x)$ at the point (x_2, y_2)?

c. How are the methods you used in Parts a and b similar to each other and how are they different?

2. You know that for linear functions, the rate of change of $f(x)$ appears as the slope of the graph of the function. That slope is constant, that is, the same between any two points of the graph. Use your calculator in the following explorations of graphs for nonlinear functions to find some connections with the graphs of simpler linear functions. It might help to share the work with partners and compare your findings.

a. On your calculator, graph $f(x) = x^2$ in the window $-5 \le x \le 5$ and $-5 \le y \le 25$. Draw a zoom box around the point (3, 9) and zoom in several times.

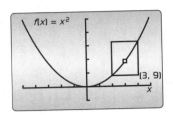

What do you notice about the shape of the graph as you look more and more closely at short segments of the graph near the point (3, 9)? Do you think the same thing will happen if you zoom in around other points on the graph? Test your ideas by zooming in on some other points.

b. On your calculator, graph $g(x) = 20(0.5^x)$ with window $0 \le x \le 5$ and $0 \le y \le 20$. Draw a zoom box around the point (3, 2.5) and zoom in several times. What do you notice about the shape of the graph as you look closer and closer at short segments of the graph near the point (3, 2.5)? Do you think the same thing will happen if you zoom in around other points on the graph? Test your ideas by zooming in on some other points of this graph.

c. Graph $h(x) = \cos x$ with window $-2\pi \le x \le 2\pi$ and $-2 \le y \le 2$. Focus on an x-intercept and zoom in on that point of the graph several times. What do you notice about the shapes of these small segments of the graph of the cosine curve? Do you think the same thing will happen if you zoom in around other points on the graph? Test your ideas by zooming in on some other points.

3. For each function in Activity 2, estimate, as accurately as you can, the rate of change of that function at the given point. Then explain how your method for making these estimates is similar to finding the slope of a linear function graph and why your work in Activity 2 makes that connection reasonable.

   a. $f(x) = x^2$ at (3, 9)

   b. $g(x) = 20(0.5^x)$ at (3, 2.5)

   c. $h(x) = \cos x$ at $\left(\frac{\pi}{2}, 0\right)$

4. Suppose that a model of a rocket under development was shot straight into the air and sent back data about its velocity (in meters per second) at various times in the flight. Use the following velocity data and the connection between rates of change and slopes of graphs to sketch a graph showing how the rocket's *altitude* (in meters) changed throughout the flight. The maximum altitude for the rocket was about 490 m.

Flight Time (in seconds)	0	1	2	3	4	5	6	7	8	9	10
Velocity (in meters per second)	0	5	10	35	65	90	110	95	55	25	0

Flight Time (in seconds)	11	12	13	14	15	16	17	18	19	20
Velocity (in meters per second)	−10	−20	−30	−40	−50	−60	−70	−80	−90	0

Checkpoint

Investigation 2 focused on finding rates of change for functions defined by symbolic rules of various kinds and relating those rates of change to the slopes of graphs.

a How is finding the rate of change for a nonlinear function $f(x)$ similar to finding the slope of the graph of that function?

b How is finding the rate of change for a nonlinear function different than for a linear function?

Be prepared to explain your group's ideas to the entire class.

Because small portions of a curve often look like straight line segments, it is usually possible to sketch the graph of a curve by plotting a sequence of points and connecting those points in order. Test this idea with the function $f(x) = x^2$.

a. Calculate $f(-5)$, $f(0)$, and $f(5)$ and plot the corresponding points on a coordinate system. Then connect those points in order with line segments.

b. Calculate $f(-3)$ and $f(3)$ and plot the corresponding points on the same diagram. Then connect all five plotted points in order (from $x = -5$ to $x = 5$) with line segments of a second color.

c. Calculate $f(-1)$ and $f(1)$ and plot the corresponding points on the same diagram. Then connect all seven plotted points in order with line segments of a third color.

d. Calculate $f(x)$ for $x = -4, -2, 2$, and 4, and plot the corresponding points on the same diagram. Connect all eleven points in order with yet a fourth color.

e. Explain how the progression of line plots illustrates the connection between finding rates of change for nonlinear functions, slopes of curved graphs, and slopes of linear functions.

f. Check your work by entering the eleven (x, x^2) pairs in your calculator data lists, making a connected plot of those data points, and graphing the function $f(x) = x^2$ over that plot.

INVESTIGATION 3 Finding Derivative Functions

In many problems, you need to find the instantaneous rate of change of a function $f(x)$ for many different values of x. A function that gives the rate of change in f for any x is called the **derivative** of f. It is common to name the derivative with the notation "$f'(x)$" which is read "f prime of x."

To find methods for calculating the rate of change of a function at any point in its domain, it makes sense to look carefully at what is involved in estimating the rate of change at one specific point for one specific function.

If $f(x) = x^2$, how would you find $f'(4)$?

From your work in Investigations 1 and 2, you know that near the point $(4, 16)$, the graph of $y = f(x)$ is very close to a straight line segment. Moreover, the rate of change for a linear function is the same as the slope of its graph. So, if you can find a good estimate for the slope of the graph of $y = f(x)$ at the point $(4, 16)$, then you have a good estimate for $f'(4)$.

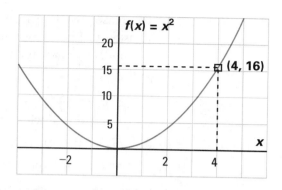

1. When students worked on the problem of making slope estimates for $f(x) = x^2$ near the point (4, 16), they came up with a variety of strategies. What strategies for estimating slope are shown in the following calculations?

   a. Group 1 used the calculation: $f'(4) \approx \frac{4.1^2 - 4^2}{4.1 - 4}$.

   b. Group 2 used the calculation: $f'(4) \approx \frac{4.1^2 - 4^2}{0.1}$.

   c. Group 3 used the calculation: $f'(4) \approx \frac{4^2 - 3.9^2}{0.1}$.

   d. Group 4 used the calculation: $f'(4) \approx \frac{4.1^2 - 3.9^2}{0.2}$.

2. What estimates are produced by each calculation in Activity 1? How could each of the estimates be made more precise?

3. The reasoning used in Activities 1 and 2 seems to give methods for estimating the derivative of $f(x) = x^2$ at the point (4, 16). It would be convenient if there were a simple rule for the derivative function f' so that you could calculate the rate of change and slope of the graph of $y = f(x)$ at any point by a simple substitution.

   a. By sharing the workload, make a table of estimates for the derivative of $f(x) = x^2$ at several different points. Plot the $(x, f'(x))$ data and see if you can find an algebraic rule for $f'(x)$.

   b. Try to adapt one of the other methods of the four groups and see if it leads to the same conclusions about the table, graph, and rule for $f'(x)$.

x	$f(x) = x^2$	$f'(x) = ?$
−5	25	
−4	16	
−3	9	
−2	4	
−1	1	
0	0	
1	1	
2	4	
...	...	

4. The reasoning used in searching for a derivative rule for $f(x) = x^2$ can be adjusted to find derivatives for other functions as well. For each derivative you find, explain why the rule makes sense.

   a. If $g(x) = 4x + 3$, what seems to be the rule for $g'(x)$?

   b. If $h(x) = -3.5x + 8$, what seems to be the rule for $h'(x)$?

   c. If $j(x) = x^2 - 4$, what seems to be the rule for $j'(x)$?

   d. If $k(x) = x^2 - 4x$, what seems to be the rule for $k'(x)$?

   e. If $m(x) = 3x^2$, what seems to be the rule for $m'(x)$?

5. One way to estimate values for a derivative function f' is to use the following rule:

   $$D(x) \approx \frac{f(x + 0.1) - f(x - 0.1)}{0.2}$$

   a. Why will $D(x)$ produce the desired derivative estimates?

   b. How could the rule for $D(x)$ be modified to make more accurate estimates?

   c. Use this derivative estimation rule to complete the following table of derivative estimates for $m(x) = 3x^2$.

x	$m(x) = 3x^2$	$D(x) \approx \dfrac{m(x + 0.1) - m(x - 0.1)}{0.2}$
−3	27	
−2	12	
−1	3	
0	0	
1	3	
2	12	

6. Use your graphing calculator and the estimation technique of Activity 5 to explore a variety of other linear and quadratic functions to see if you can find patterns that complete these statements:

   a. "For a linear function with rule $f(x) = a + bx$, the derivative function always seems to be . . ."

   b. "For a quadratic function with rule $g(x) = ax^2 + bx + c$, the derivative function always seems to be . . ."

In this investigation, you explored methods for using the rule of a given function to find the rule of its derivative function.

ⓐ How can you find the derivative of a function $f(x)$ at a specific point in its domain?

ⓑ How might you find a rule for the derivative $f'(x)$ at any point in its domain?

ⓒ What can you conclude about the derivative of a function $f(x)$ in the case that the function is

- ▪ linear with rule $f(x) = a + bx$?
- ▪ quadratic with rule $g(x) = ax^2 + bx + c$?

Be prepared to explain your group's generalizations to the class.

On Your Own

The distance, in meters, traveled in t seconds by an inline skater going down a hill can be modeled by the function $d(t) = kt^2$, where the constant k depends on the slope of the hill. Suppose that for a particular hill, the value of k is 0.5.

a. How fast will the skater be going after 10 seconds?

b. How fast will the skater be going after 20 meters?

INVESTIGATION 4 ▸ Derivatives of Other Function Types

Investigation 3 focused on finding derivatives for linear and quadratic functions. As you know, many important applications involve exponential, periodic, and power functions. Investigate derivatives for the following functions to see if you can find some general patterns relating function types to their derivatives. Share the work among group partners.

When you find patterns of interest, see if you can find some reason why that connection between function and derivative is reasonable. It will help to think about the shapes of the graphs of the functions and the way those graph shapes relate to one another and to derivatives. Compare the generalizations made by your group with those of other groups. Resolve any differences.

1. Use your calculator to explore patterns in the derivatives of the following exponential functions to see if you can find any general patterns like "The derivative of an exponential function always seems to be . . ."

   ■ $g(x) = 2^x$

   ■ $h(x) = 3^x$

   ■ $i(x) = 1.5^x$

   ■ $j(x) = 0.8^x$

   ■ $k(x) = 2^x + 10$

   ■ $m(x) = 5(2^x)$

2. Use your calculator to explore patterns in the derivatives of the following periodic functions to see if you can find any general patterns like "The derivative of a periodic function always seems to be . . ."

   ■ $f(x) = \sin x$

   ■ $g(x) = \cos x$

   ■ $h(x) = 5 + \sin x$

   ■ $i(x) = 3 \sin x$

3. Use your calculator to explore patterns in the derivatives of the following power functions to see if you can find any general patterns like "The derivative of a power function always seems to be . . ."

   ■ $j(x) = x^3$

   ■ $k(x) = x^4$

   ■ $g(x) = x^{1.5}$

   ■ $h(x) = x^{-1}$

Checkpoint

For any given function $f(x)$, if you can find the derivative $f'(x)$, what type of function will $f'(x)$ probably be if $f(x)$ is

a an exponential function?

b a periodic function?

c a power function?

Be prepared to explain your generalizations.

What types of functions do you expect as the derivatives for the following specific functions? After making predictions in each case, check your ideas with calculator tables and graphs of the original functions and the derivative estimates.

a. $f(x) = 3 + 2.5x$

b. $g(x) = 5x^2 + 4x - 3$

c. $h(x) = 1.25^x$

d. $j(x) = 4 + \cos x$

e. $k(x) = \dfrac{7}{x}$

INVESTIGATION 5 From Function Graphs to Derivative Graphs

Suppose you are interested in the derivative of a given function, but have only a graph of that function or an algebraic rule from which the derivative rule cannot be calculated easily. It is still possible to make a useful analysis of the situation. You can learn a lot about the rate at which one variable is changing in relation to the other by studying the shape of the function graph. In fact, you can usually sketch a graph of a derivative $f'(x)$ by analyzing the graph of $f(x)$.

1. The graph on the next page shows the effects of a flu epidemic on attendance at a large high school. It shows the number of students absent from school due to flu illness on different days during a two-week period. Use this graph to examine the course of the epidemic.

a. Describe the overall pattern of change in the number of absences due to flu during the two-week period shown on the graph.

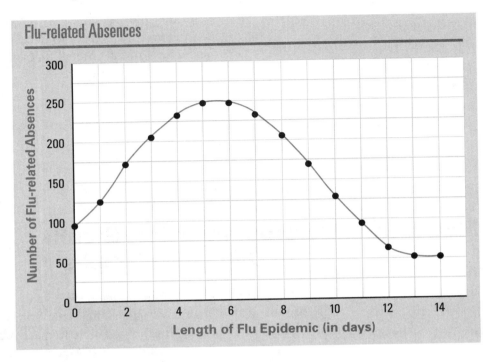

Flu-related Absences

Number of Flu-related Absences (vertical axis)

Length of Flu Epidemic (in days) (horizontal axis)

b. Suppose that the number of flu-related absences is given by the function $f(t)$. Describe where $f'(t)$ is positive, where it is zero, and where it is negative. What does each of those parts of the graph tell about the flu epidemic?

c. Sketch a graph of $f'(t)$. Explain what the shape of that graph tells about the rate at which the number of flu-related absences was changing at various times during the two-week period. In particular, identify the point(s) where the rate of increase in number of absent students was a maximum and explain how that is shown on the graph of $f(t)$.

2. Study each of the following functions and their graphs. *Without using your graphing calculator,* complete do each of the following tasks. Then check your ideas by calculating and graphing numerical estimates of the derivative function.

■ Write a description of how the derivative changes as the input variable x changes. Explain where the derivative is positive, where it is zero, and where it is negative. Also explain where the derivative is increasing and decreasing.

■ Estimate the derivative at several points by considering the slope of the graph.

■ Use your analysis to sketch a graph of the derivative function on a copy of the corresponding function graph below.

a. The graph of $a(x) = \frac{1}{2}x$ with window $-5 \leq x \leq 5$ and $-3 \leq y \leq 3$

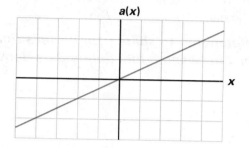

b. The graph of $f(x) = x^2 - 2$ with window $-4 \leq x \leq 4$ and $-5 \leq y \leq 10$

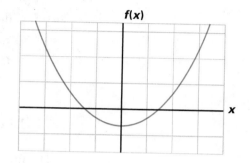

c. The graph of $g(x) = 1.5^x$ with window $-3 \leq x \leq 7$ and $-2 \leq y \leq 10$

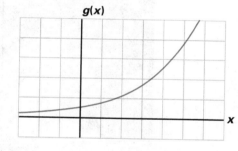

d. The graph of $h(x) = \cos x$ with window $-\pi \leq x \leq \pi$ and $-2 \leq y \leq 2$

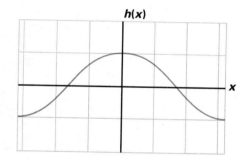

e. The graph of $j(x) = 0.5x^3 - 8x$ with window $-5 \leq x \leq 5$ and $-15 \leq y \leq 15$

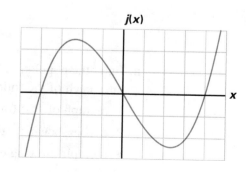

Suppose you have a function $f(x)$ for which you can find the derivative $f'(x)$.

a What does $f'(x)$ tell about:
- the graph of $f(x)$?
- the rate of change of values in a table for $f(x)$?

b How can the shape of the graph of $f(x)$ be used to describe and sketch the graph of its derivative $f'(x)$?

Be prepared to share your group's thinking about connections between a function and its derivative.

On Your Own

The function $P(t) = \dfrac{100}{1 + 20(0.5^t)}$ models growth of a fish population over time after the fish were stocked in a new lake. Time t is measured in years and the fish population is measured as a percent of the maximum capacity of the lake.

A fisherman has an easy time fishing after the lake was stocked with fish.

a. Enter the population function rule in your graphing calculator and use it to produce each of the following:
- a graph of $P(t)$ for $0 \le t \le 10$
- a table showing estimates of $P'(t)$ for $0 \le t \le 10$ in steps of 0.5
- a graph showing estimates of $P'(t)$ for $0 \le t \le 10$

b. Explain what the patterns in the table and graphs of Part a tell about the fish population.

Modeling • Organizing • Reflecting • Extending

Modeling

1. Suppose that the depth of water in an ocean harbor is a function of time in hours past midnight, but you don't know an algebraic rule for the function.

   a. If the water is 20 feet deep at 6 A.M. and the tide is rising at a rate of 1.5 ft/hr at that time, what water depth would you estimate for 7:00 A.M.? For 6:30 A.M.? For 6:15 A.M.?

   b. If the water is 17 ft deep at 12 noon and falling at a rate of 0.75 ft/hr at that time, what water depth would you estimate for 1:00 P.M.? For 12:30 P.M.? For 12:15 P.M.?

Ocean Harbor

2. Suppose the daily operating profit (in dollars) for a movie theater is a function of the number of tickets sold with rule $P(x) = 8.5x - 3,500$ for $0 \le x \le 1,000$.

   a. Find the rate at which theater profit is changing when $x = 100$, $x = 500$, and $x = 800$. Give the unit in which those rates should be expressed.

   b. How will the answers to Part a be reflected in the shape of a graph for $P(x)$?

   c. Construct a table, a graph, and an algebraic rule for $P'(x)$.

   d. What does the shape of the graph of $P'(x)$ tell about the rate of change in theater profit as the number of customers increases?

3. Suppose the height of a soccer kick (in feet) is a function of time in flight (in seconds) with rule $h(t) = -16t^2 + 50t$ for $0 \le t \le 3$.

   a. Estimate the velocity of the ball when $t = 0.5$, $t = 1.5$, and $t = 2.0$ seconds. Explain how the differences in those estimates are shown by the shape of the graph of $h(t)$.

   b. If the ball hit you on the head (instead of hitting the ground), about how fast would it be falling at that time?

   c. Sketch a graph of $h(t)$ and then $h'(t)$ on the same coordinate axes. Check your graph sense about functions and derivatives by comparing the sketches to graphs produced by a calculator.

   d. What does the graph of $h'(t)$ tell about the way the ball's velocity changes as time passes in its flight?

4. In Washington D.C., the number of minutes between sunrise and sunset varies throughout the year according to the function rule

$$S(d) = 180 \sin(0.0172d - 1.376) + 720.$$

In this rule, d represents the day of the year (with January 1 as $d = 1$).

Washington Monument

a. March 21, June 21, September 21, and December 21 are the approximate first days of spring, summer, fall, and winter. In a non-leap year, what day numbers correspond to these dates?

b. Produce a graph of $S(d)$ for $0 \leq d \leq 365$. Explain what the shape of that graph tells you about the number of minutes between sunrise and sunset throughout the year. Locate the points on the graph showing the "longest" and "shortest" days of the year. What dates are associated with these days?

c. Estimate the instantaneous rate of change in time between sunrise and sunset on the four special dates in Part a. Explain how those rates are illustrated on the graph of Part b.

d. According to your answers in Parts b and c, at what time(s) of the year are days growing "longer" or "shorter" most rapidly? Most slowly?

e. Construct a table and a graph for $S'(d)$.

f. How can you use the table and graph of $S'(d)$ to determine when the "length of days" is increasing and decreasing during the year?

5. A bus makes a regular 450-mile trip from Chicago to Minneapolis. The time (in hours) that this trip takes is a function of the *average* speed of the bus (in miles per hour) with rule $T(s) = \frac{450}{s}$ for $0 < s \leq 80$.

a. Estimate $T'(40)$ and $T'(60)$. Explain what each tells about the relationship between speed and trip time.

b. Sketch a graph of $T'(s)$. Explain how its shape and location show the effect of an increase in speed on total trip time.

6. Suppose that, under laboratory conditions, an initial population of 150 bacteria doubles every hour.

Bacteria magnified 11,000 times their size.

   a. Write a function rule giving the number of bacteria after t hours.

   b. Calculate the predicted number of bacteria after 3, 6, 9, and 12 hours.

   c. Calculate the average growth rate of the bacteria population between $t = 0$ and $t = 6$ and then between $t = 6$ and $t = 12$.

   d. Estimate the instantaneous growth rate of the bacteria population at $t = 3$, $t = 6$, $t = 9$, and $t = 12$.

   e. Compare the results from Parts c and d and explain how the differences can be seen in the shape of a graph of the growth function.

   f. What is the overall shape of the graph of the derivative of the bacteria population function? What sort of algebraic rule would you expect for that graph?

Organizing

1. The value of the derivative of a function at a point tells you how the function is changing at that point.

   a. What can you tell about the way that a function f is changing at some point x_0 if you know that:

     ■ $f'(x_0) > 0$?

     ■ $f'(x_0) < 0$?

     ■ $f'(x_0) = 0$?

   b. Explain how your conjectures about properties of $f'(x)$ will be shown in a graph of the original function $f(x)$.

2. If you have an algebraic rule for a function $f(x)$, what algebraic expressions can be used to calculate the approximate slope of the graph of that function:

   a. between two nearby points $(x_1, f(x_1))$ and $(x_2, f(x_2))$?

   b. at a particular point $(x_0, f(x_0))$ on the graph?

3. Study the pattern of change in the following graph of a function *g*. Then, on a copy of the graph, sketch the graph of $g'(x)$.

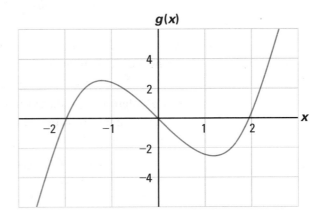

4. Sketch the graph of a quadratic function $y = f(x)$ for which $f(0) = 3$, $f'(0) = -8$, and $f'(2) = 0$.

5. Examine the following graph. Without making any specific numerical estimates of the rate of change of $g(x)$, determine the points where the rate of change is positive, where it is negative, and where it is 0. Use the results of that analysis to sketch a graph of $g'(x)$.

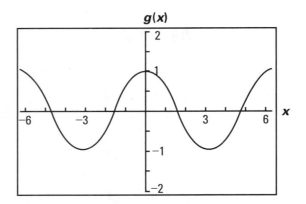

6. In Course 3, you investigated transformations of graphs of basic functions and how those transformations are reflected in symbolic function rules.

   a. How does the rate of change of $f(x) = x^2$ at $x = 1$ compare to the rate of change of $g(x) = x^2 + 5$ at $x = 1$?

   ■ Why does your finding make sense graphically?

   ■ Will your finding be the same for other values of *x*? Why or why not?

   ■ In general, what do you think is true about the rates of change at corresponding points of two functions whose graphs are related by a vertical translation? Prove your assertion using algebraic reasoning.

b. Repeat Part a for the case of vertical stretches by first comparing the rate of change of $f(x) = x^2$ at $x = 4$ and the rate of change of $h(x) = 3x^2$ at $x = 4$.

Reflecting

1. Think about the temperature, $F(t)$, in degrees Fahrenheit after t minutes, of a frozen pizza placed in a preheated oven.

   a. Is $F'(t) < 0$, $F'(t) = 0$, or $F'(t) > 0$ for the first 20 minutes the pizza is in the oven? Explain your reasoning.

   b. What is the measurement unit of $F'(15)$?

   c. What does the information that $F'(15) = 2$ tell about the pizza in the oven?

   d. Do you think $F'(t)$ is ever equal to 0? Explain.

2. What does it mean to estimate the instantaneous rate of change of some function $f(x)$ at a specific point $(x_0, f(x_0))$ versus calculating the average rate of change between two points $(x_1, f(x_1))$ to $(x_2, f(x_2))$?

3. Think about the significance of the derivative of a function in modeling applied problem situations.

   a. If $h(t)$ gives the height of a golf ball at various times in its flight, then $h'(t) = 0$ when the ball is at its maximum height. What does this result tell about the velocity of the ball at that time? Why is this result reasonable?

   b. When an earthquake strikes somewhere in the United States, news about the event spreads quickly. If $N(t)$ gives the number of people (in millions) who have heard the news t hours after the quake, what can you infer from $N(4) = 60$ and $N'(4) = 6.5$?

   c. When deep-sea divers return to the surface, they need to rise slowly to adapt to the change in pressure. Suppose that a diver has been working at a depth of 175 ft and begins returning to the surface. If the diver's depth is given by $D(t)$ at time t minutes after her ascent begins, what can you infer from $D(5) = 150$ and $D'(5) = -8$?

4. In the "On Your Own" task on page 40, you studied the pattern of growth in a fish population, from the time a few fish were stocked in a new lake to the time the fish population approached maximum capacity for the lake's food supply. The population function rule was $P(t) = \dfrac{100}{1 + 20(0.5^t)}$. Following is a graph of the derivative of this function, $P'(t)$.

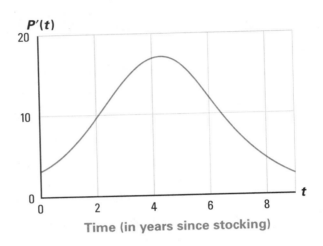

Time (in years since stocking)

   a. How should the vertical axis be labeled?
   b. According to this graph, when is the derivative a maximum?
   c. What does the answer to Part b tell about growth rate of the fish population?
   d. What would the answer to Part b tell about the graph of $P(t)$ itself?

5. Use the zoom capability of your graphing calculator to look "close-up" at the graphs of $f(x) = x^3$ and $g(x) = |x|$ near $x = 0$. What can you say about the rate of change of these functions at $x = 0$?

6. The process of finding the derivative of a function is called **differentiation.** The credit for inventing differentiation and, more generally, the main ideas of calculus is shared by Isaac Newton and Gottfried Leibniz. At roughly the same time, but in different countries and using different symbolic notation, each independently obtained similar results.

Isaac Newton

Gottfried Leibniz

Leibniz realized the importance of good notation in solving problems. For a function $y = f(x)$, Leibniz devised the notation $\frac{dy}{dx}$ to denote the "rate of change of y as x changes" or "the derivative of y with respect to x." This notation is still used today, along with the notation you have been using, $f'(x)$.

a. Have you seen or used notation similar to that devised by Leibniz in previous courses? If so, where and how was it used?

b. Sketch the graph of a function $y = f(x)$. On your sketch, show a geometric interpretation of the notation $\frac{dy}{dx}$.

c. What advantages, if any, do you see for using Leibniz's notation for the derivative?

Extending

1. In the investigations of this lesson, you found derivatives for familiar functions by estimating rates of change at specific points in the function domains and looking for patterns in those estimates. In many cases, it is also possible to deduce derivative rules by algebraic reasoning with the original function rules.

a. Give explanations for each step in the following reasoning toward a derivative rule for all linear functions $f(x) = a + bx$.

$$f'(x) \approx \frac{f(x + 0.1) - f(x)}{0.1}$$

$$= \frac{[a + b(x + 0.1)] - (a + bx)}{0.1}$$

$$= \frac{0.1b}{0.1}$$

$$= b$$

Thus, it looks as if the derivative of any linear function $f(x) = a + bx$ might be $f'(x) = b$. How does this agree with your knowledge about tables and graphs of linear functions and rates of change?

b. Give explanations for each step in the following reasoning toward a derivative rule for the quadratic function $f(x) = x^2$.

$$f'(x) \approx \frac{f(x + 0.1) - f(x)}{0.1}$$

$$= \frac{(x + 0.1)^2 - x^2}{0.1}$$

$$= \frac{x^2 + 0.2x + 0.01 - x^2}{0.1}$$

$$= \frac{0.2x + 0.01}{0.1}$$

$$= 2x + 0.1$$

If 0.1 is replaced by 0.01, 0.001, and other smaller numbers to make better derivative estimates, what happens to the estimates for $f'(x)$? What can you conclude about $f'(x)$?

2. Use reasoning like that in Extending Task 1 to deduce derivative rules for the following functions.

   a. $g(x) = ax^2$

   b. $h(x) = ax^2 + c$

   c. $j(x) = ax^2 + bx$

   d. $k(x) = ax^2 + bx + c$

3. Everyone who drives a car sometimes has to stop suddenly. The time and distance it takes to stop depends on several variables, but for a typical car on a dry asphalt road, the stopping distance (in feet) is a function of speed (in miles per hour) with a quadratic rule like $d(s) = 0.04s^2 + 0.75s$.

   This function is actually the sum of two separate functions, each related to parts of the stopping problem.

   ■ $b(s) = 0.75s$ gives the distance traveled before you manage to press the brake pedal.

   ■ $c(s) = 0.04s^2$ gives the distance traveled from the time you press the brake pedal until you stop the car.

   a. Use a calculator to make a table showing how the three functions change as the car's speed changes from 0 to 100 mph in steps of 10 mph.

Speed	$b(s)$	$c(s)$	$d(s)$
0	0	0	0
10	...	...	...
...			

   b. What do the columns of your table in Part a each tell about stopping distance for a car at various speeds?

   c. How does the rate of change in total stopping distance relate to the rate of change in braking distance and the rate of change in distance traveled after braking?

   d. Use a calculator to make another table showing approximations to the derivatives of the three functions involved in stopping a car.

Speed	$b'(s)$	$c'(s)$	$d'(s)$
0	0	0	0
10	...	...	...
...			

e. How do the columns of the table in Part d relate to each other, and how does that relationship of derivatives connect with your answer to Part c?

4. For each of the following functions, $f(x)$, find two other functions $g(x)$ and $h(x)$ so that $f(x) = g(x) + h(x)$. Then complete a table like the one below and compare $f'(x)$, $g'(x)$, and $h'(x)$.

x	$f'(x)$	$g'(x)$	$h'(x)$
−5			
−4			
...	...	...	...
4			
5			

    a. $f(x) = 5x + 3.5x$

    b. $f(x) = \sin x + \cos x$

    c. $f(x) = x^2 + 5x^2$

    d. $f(x) = \sin x + x^2$

Look back at your results for Parts a–d. What relationship do you see between $f'(x)$, $g'(x)$, and $h'(x)$ in the case that $f(x) = g(x) + h(x)$? Why is that relationship reasonable?

5. Extending Tasks 3 and 4 involve the derivative of the sum of two functions. Use algebraic reasoning like that in Extending Task 1 to justify your conjecture about the derivative of sums of functions.

1. If $\frac{x-5}{4} = -\frac{9}{5}$, then x is

(a) −2.2   (b) −12.2   (c) 2.2   (d) 12.2   (e) −5.5

2. If $a = 5$ and $b = -7$, then $\frac{b^2 - ab}{a^2 - ab} =$

(a) $\frac{49}{25}$ (b) $-\frac{7}{5}$ (c) $\frac{7}{5}$ (d) $-\frac{42}{5}$ (e) $-\frac{7}{15}$

3. For what value of b will the following system have no solution?

$$\begin{cases} y = bx - 3 \\ 3x - y = -7 \end{cases}$$

(a) −1   (b) $-\frac{1}{3}$ (c) 3   (d) 7   (e) $\frac{1}{3}$

4. The graph of $y = f(x)$ is shown.

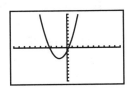

Which of the following is the graph of $y = |f(x)|$?

(a) 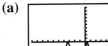   (b) 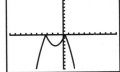   (c)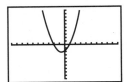

(d) 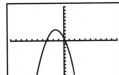   (e)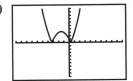

5. Which of the following is one of the solutions of the equation $2a^2 - 2a - 3 = 0$?

(a) $\dfrac{1}{2} - \dfrac{\sqrt{7}}{2}$

(b) $\dfrac{1}{2} + \dfrac{\sqrt{6}}{2}$

(c) $-\dfrac{1}{2} - \dfrac{\sqrt{7}}{2}$

(d) $-\dfrac{1}{2} - \dfrac{\sqrt{6}}{2}$

(e) $-\dfrac{1}{2} + \dfrac{\sqrt{7}}{2}$

6. If $ax + b = c$ and $a \neq 0$, then

(a) $x = a - c + b$

(b) $x = \dfrac{c - b}{a}$

(c) $x = c - b - a$

(d) $x = \dfrac{c}{b - a}$

(e) $x = \dfrac{c}{ab}$

7. Which of the following is not a zero of the polynomial, $y = x^5 + 5x^4 - 9x^3 - 45x^2$?

(a) 0

(b) −3

(c) 1

(d) −5

(e) 3

8. In the figure shown, $AB = 5$, $BE = 3$, and $AD = 10$. Which of the following best approximates CD?

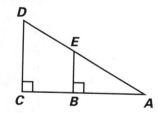

(a) 6.17

(b) 5.14

(c) 9

(d) 6

(e) 7.2

9. Simplify: $(5^2)(5^0)(5^{-3})$.

(a) $\dfrac{1}{5^6}$

(b) $\dfrac{1}{5}$

(c) 25

(d) $\dfrac{2}{3}$

(e) −150

10. Simplify: $\left(4x\sqrt{x^3}\right)^2$.

(a) $16x^6$

(b) $4x^7$

(c) $16x^5$

(d) $4x^6$

(e) $8x^5$

Lesson 3

Accumulation at Variable Rates

Some motion detectors are designed to produce tables and graphs of (*time, rate*) data rather than (*time, distance*) data. For example, police radar scanners focus on the speed of approaching cars. Baseball "radar guns" are designed to measure the speed of a pitched ball.

When automobile companies promote their new cars, one feature mentioned often is acceleration or "pickup." A standard statistic for measuring pickup is the time it takes to go from 0 to 60 mph (88 ft/sec). The following graph shows the performance of one car during an acceleration test.

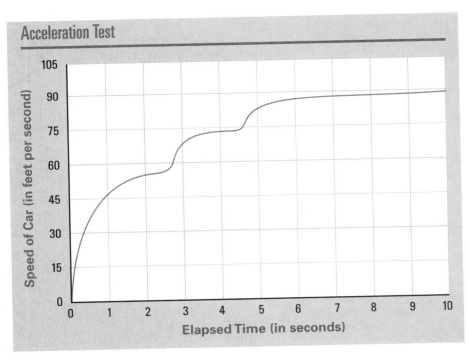

The graph shows how the speed of an accelerating car changed over the 10-second time period it took to reach 88 ft/sec.

a How would you describe the overall pattern of this graph and what it tells about the acceleration test?

b What is your best estimate of the total distance that the car traveled during the 10-second acceleration period, and how would you convince someone else that your estimate is a good one?

c At what point(s) in the 10-second trip was the car accelerating most rapidly?

INVESTIGATION 1 ▸ What's the Total?

Unlike the motions of automobiles, motorcycles, or airplanes, when people walk or run they usually reach top speed very quickly. Also, walkers can change speed and direction very quickly. The result is that tables and graphs of (*time, speed*) data for walkers are likely to be simpler than those of 0 to 60 acceleration tests.

1. Examine the several different (*time, speed*) graphs below and on the next page for students walking between classes in school. For each graph:

■ Describe (in terms of speed and acceleration) how you would walk to produce a similar graph.

■ Estimate the total distance the walker would have covered in the 10 seconds for which speeds are shown on the graph.

i.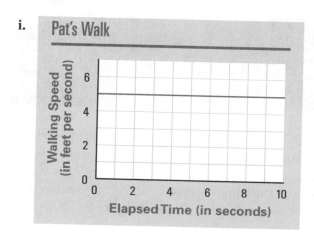

ii.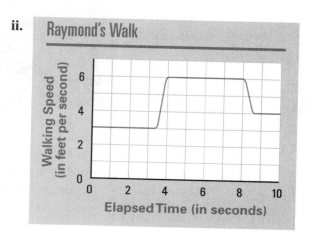

Annette's Walk

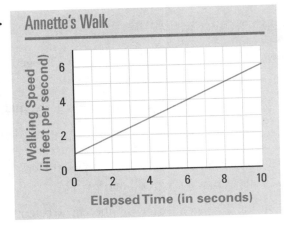

Fraser's Walk

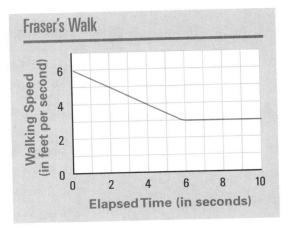

Motor vehicles, baseballs, and human walkers are not the only things in motion for which speed is commonly measured. Modern life depends on rapid flow of many different substances, from electricity and water to oil, natural gas, and heated or cooled air. These flows are very often monitored by gauges that report flow rates.

For example, farmers in many different parts of the world depend on irrigation to help their crops grow. Those irrigation systems usually depend on powerful pumps to lift water from streams or reservoirs into irrigation ditches or sprinkler systems. The pumps operate at different speeds to supply water at different rates into the fields.

2. Modern technology makes it possible to monitor the flow rates of the pumps and produce graphs like those that follow. Use the information in each graph to estimate the total amount of water pumped or sprayed onto fields in the indicated time intervals. In each case, be prepared to explain how you arrived at your estimate.

i.

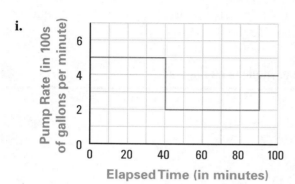

ii.

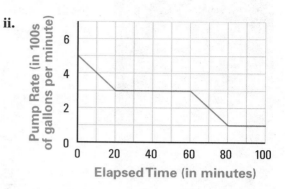

iii.

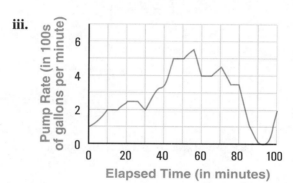

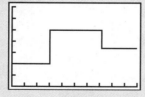 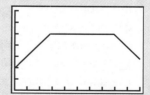 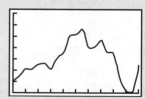

On Your Own

When an airplane touches the runway after a flight, it has to slow down fairly quickly from its landing speed of about 150 mph (about 220 ft/sec) to a taxiing speed of about 20 mph. The change in speed over time graph for such a plane might look something like the one below.

Speed of Airplane on Runway

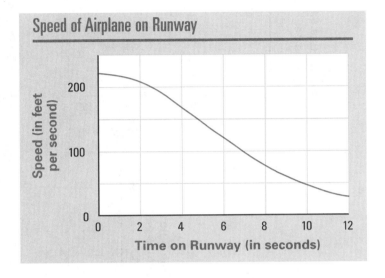

Use the graph to estimate the distance traveled by the plane during:

a. the first 6 seconds

b. the next 6 seconds

INVESTIGATION 2 ▸ Velocity and Net Change

In previous lessons, you used (*time, distance*) data from a motion detector to investigate velocity—the speed and direction of motion. Many motion detectors report (*time, velocity*) data directly in tables and graphs.

When you study such (*time, velocity*) data, it is important to be able to tell the difference between motion toward the detector and motion away from it. It is also important that you know how you can use the data to determine speed at a given moment.

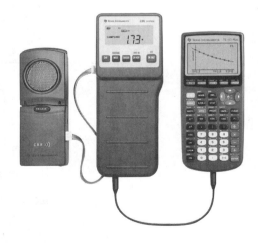

1. Here is a simplified (*time, velocity*) graph for a person who is walking toward and away from a motion detector.

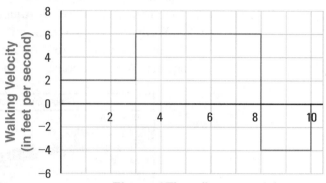

Elapsed Time (in seconds)

    a. What does it mean for this rate function to have negative values?

    b. Describe, in terms of *speed* and *direction,* how you would walk to produce such a graph.

    c. How much farther from or closer to the detector will you be at the end of the walk than at the beginning? That is, what is the **net change** in the quantity "distance to the motion detector" in the ten seconds of the walk?

2. Shown below is another sample (*time, velocity*) graph for a person who is walking toward and away from a motion detector.

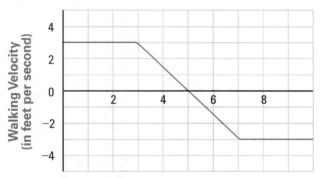

Elapsed Time (in seconds)

    a. Describe in terms of speed, acceleration, and direction how you would walk to produce such a graph.

    b. What is the net change in the walker's distance to the motion detector in the first 5 seconds of the walk?

    c. What is the net change in the walker's distance to the motion detector in the 10 seconds of the walk? What calculations support your answer?

    d. What does the graph suggest about where the walk started and where it ended?

    e. What is the total distance covered by the walker during the 10-second walk?

3. The Edwards Plateau in Texas can experience some of the highest rainfall intensities in the world, as well as severe droughts. Some regions of the Edwards Plateau did not see any rain between 1988 and 1996, while other regions experienced record rainfalls of 22 inches (about 56 cm) in less than three hours. The Edwards Aquifer is one of the largest underground reservoirs on Earth, collecting water from an area of 6,000 square miles (over 15,000 km^2). Typically, rainwater runs off into streams that disappear underground into the aquifer. Water for consumption is pumped up from wells.

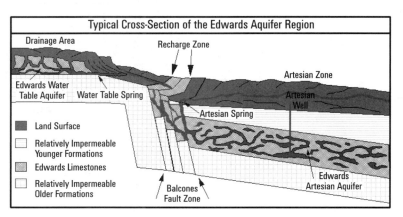

The following graph shows the rate of change in aquifer volume during 1995.

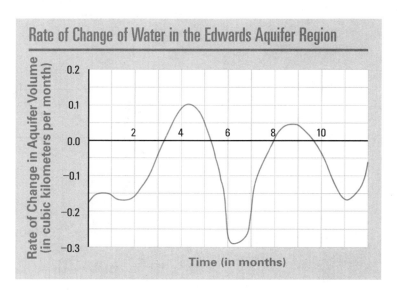

a. How would you explain, in terms of inflow and outflow, the behavior of the aquifer in 1995? Write as complete a description as you can without doing any calculations.

b. One student suggested that from the beginning of March until the end of April the volume of water in the aquifer increased at a constant rate. Do you agree?

c. How can you determine whether the aquifer gained or lost water in 1995?

d. Devise and carry out a strategy that would allow you to obtain an estimate of net change in the water volume of the aquifer during 1995. Compare your strategy and estimate to those of other groups.

Checkpoint

The activities in this investigation show again that important information about change in a quantity can be obtained from its rate-of-change graph.

ⓐ How are the rate functions in this investigation different from those in Investigation 1?

ⓑ What does it mean to have negative values for a velocity function? For a flow-rate function?

ⓒ How would you use a rate-of-change graph to estimate net change in a quantity with a rate function that is always positive? With a rate function that has both positive and negative values?

ⓓ How can you tell by looking at a rate-of-change graph if the net change is going to be positive? Negative? Approximately zero?

Be prepared to share your responses with the entire class.

▶On Your Own

The graph below shows results from a radar gun used to track the *velocity* of a bungee jumper through the first 8 seconds of a jump over a body of water. The radar gun was located on the jump tower. Motion downward, away from the detector, was recorded as negative velocity because the jumper's height above the water was decreasing. Motion upward, back toward the detector was recorded as positive velocity because the jumper's height above the water was increasing.

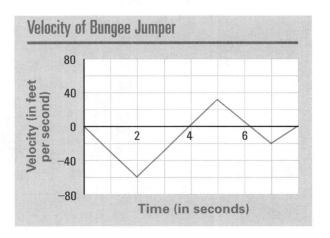

a. How does the graph show the direction and approximate speed of the jumper at various times in the flight? That is, when is the jumper falling downward, when is she bouncing back upward, when is she gaining speed in either direction, and when is she momentarily motionless?

b. If the jumper starts from a height of 125 feet, estimate her height above the water after 4 seconds, after 6 seconds, and after 8 seconds.

c. What is the total distance traveled by the jumper in the 8-second time period?

INVESTIGATION 3 Net Change, Areas, and Definite Integrals

Investigations 1 and 2 show that there is an important relationship between net change in a quantity and the areas of the regions bounded by its rate-of-change graph and the *x*-axis. When a person walks toward or away from a motion detector, a (*time, velocity*) graph shows not only speed, but also the direction of the walk.

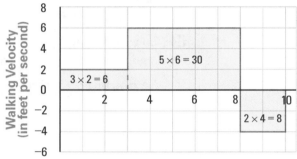

If you want to find the net change in distance from the starting point for a walker with this simple rate graph, it makes sense to calculate $(3 \times 2) + (5 \times 6) - (2 \times 4)$. On the graph, that is equivalent to finding a difference of areas.

For a less-regular rate function, it makes sense to approximate the graph by a series of line segments and estimate the net change by the difference of areas in the resulting simpler graph. For example, here is one way you might approximate the net change in volume of water in a reservoir.

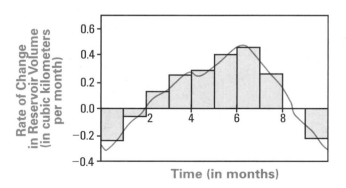

The main point is that the net change in a quantity can be calculated using the graph of its rate function to find the difference:

(*total area of regions above the x-axis*) – (*total area of regions below the x-axis*).

For a function $f(x)$ defined over an interval $a \leq x \leq b$, this difference of areas is called the **definite integral of** $f(x)$ **from** a **to** b. The definite integral is commonly indicated by the following notation:

$$\int_a^b f(x)\, dx$$

This notation for the integral is a reminder of the process by which integrals can be approximated—with a *sum* of products $f(x)\Delta x$. The symbol $\int$ is like an elongated "S" for "sum." The diagram at the right illustrates this idea. The interval from a to b is divided into smaller intervals of length Δx. In each of those sub-intervals, you choose a point x so that $f(x)$ is representative of the function on the interval. Then, when $f(x) > 0$, each product $f(x)\Delta x$ represents the area of a rectangle above the x-axis. When $f(x) < 0$, the product $f(x)\Delta x$ will be negative, but its absolute value will be the area of a rectangle below the x-axis. Thus, you can approximate the integral by adding all these products. The approximation is the difference:

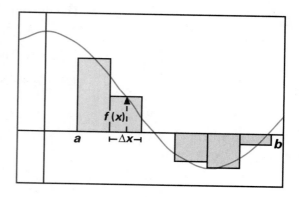

$$\int_a^b f(x)\, dx \approx \left(\begin{array}{c}area\ of\ rectangles \\ above\ the\ x\text{-}axis\end{array}\right) - \left(\begin{array}{c}area\ of\ rectangles \\ below\ the\ x\text{-}axis\end{array}\right).$$

When the graph of a function $f(x)$ is made up of familiar geometric shapes, you can use your knowledge about the areas involved to find exact values of definite integrals for $f(x)$.

1. Given at the right is a graph for a (*time, velocity*) function $v(t)$ modeling the way someone walked toward and away from a motion detector.

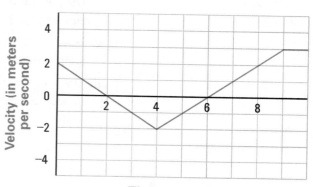

a. Evaluate each of the following definite integrals and explain what the results tell about the walker's distance from the motion detector.

i. $\int_0^5 v(t)\, dt$ **ii.** $\int_5^{10} v(t)\, dt$ **iii.** $\int_0^{10} v(t)\, dt$

b. What information about the walker's trip will be given by the total area between the graph of $v(t)$ and the t-axis?

When the rate-of-change function is defined by an algebraic rule with a curved graph, there are many useful techniques for making good estimates of the integral. There are several systematic procedures for drawing rectangles whose areas approximate the integral. These procedures can be expressed in easy-to-use calculator and computer programs.

2. The diagram below shows the part of the graph of $f(x) = -x^2 + 2x + 4$ for $0 \le x \le 3.5$. Six rectangles have been drawn to make a rough estimate of $\int_0^3 f(x)\, dx$. The total area of the six rectangles can be estimated as $4.4(0.5) + 4.9(0.5) + 4.9(0.5) + 4.4(0.5) + 3.4(0.5) + 1.9(0.5)$.

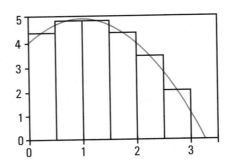

a. What do the separate terms in this sum represent, for example, $4.4(0.5)$ or $3.4(0.5)$? What does the 0.5 in each calculation represent? What do the numbers 4.4, 4.9, 4.9, 4.4, 3.4, and 1.9 represent? How are they determined by the function rule for $f(x)$?

b. The rectangles shown give an approximation of 11.95 for the integral. Do you think that approximation is larger than, smaller than, or exactly equal to the integral?

c. How could you refine the same general strategy to get a more accurate approximation for the integral?

d. Try using a calculator or computer routine for evaluating definite integrals to see how close the first estimate is to the estimate produced by standard tools.

3. Shown at the right is the graph of the function $h(x) = \frac{4}{x+1}$, for $0 \le x \le 5$. Outline a strategy for estimating the integral of $h(x)$ over that interval and then use that strategy to make a good estimate.

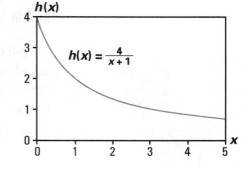

a. Write the calculations required by your strategy and the approximation that results.

b. Do you think your approximation is greater than, less than, or equal to the exact integral of $h(x)$ from 0 to 5? Why?

c. Compare your results to those of your classmates and explain any differences.

d. How would you proceed to find a better approximation?

Checkpoint

The activities of this investigation introduced the idea of a *definite integral* for a function and some of the ways that an integral can be approximated.

a What does a definite integral of a function tell about the graph of that function?

b If you are given a function describing the rate of change in some quantity, what does a definite integral of that rate function tell you about change in the quantity itself?

c If you are given the graph or rule for a function $f(x)$, what are some strategies you could use to estimate the definite integral of that function over a specific interval?

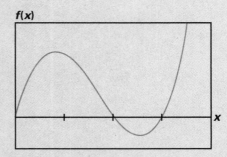

d To approximate the derivative of a function at a point, we use the fact that small portions of curved graphs look very much like straight line segments. The slope of a curve can be approximated by using the slope formula for straight lines. What similar statements would describe the process of approximating integrals?

Be prepared to explain your ideas and strategies to the class.

The following graph shows velocity of a golf ball that was thrown up into the air and allowed to bounce several times on a concrete sidewalk before it was caught again. Positive velocity indicates motion upward; negative velocity indicates motion downward.

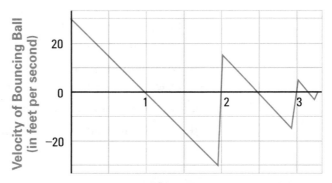

a. What does each segment of the graph tell about the motion of the ball?

b. What is the approximate net change in the ball's height above the ground after 1 second? After 2 seconds? After 2.5 seconds? After 3 seconds?

c. If the velocity function of time is indicated by $v(t)$, estimate each integral.

> **i.** $\int_0^2 v(t)\, dt$ **ii.** $\int_0^3 v(t)\, dt$ **iii.** $\int_1^3 v(t)\, dt$

Modeling • Organizing • Reflecting • Extending

Modeling

1. The following graph shows the reported speed of a cross-country skier during a 2.5-hour trip.

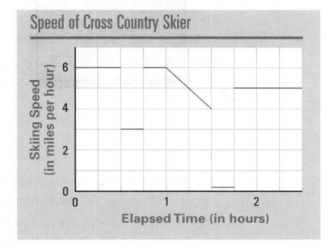

Speed of Cross Country Skier

Skiing Speed (in miles per hour)

Elapsed Time (in hours)

   a. Write a story about the ski trail and the skier's pace that would match this graph.

   b. How far did the skier go in the first hour? In the second hour?

   c. How far did the skier go in the time shown on the graph?

2. At the beginning of this lesson you studied the following acceleration test graph.

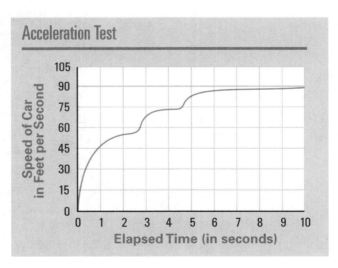

Acceleration Test

Speed of Car in Feet per Second

Elapsed Time (in seconds)

a. Estimate the total distance traveled by this car during the 10 seconds of the 0–60 acceleration test.

b. Explain a strategy that you could use to make even more accurate estimates from the same graph.

3. A church in Rockville, Maryland has four large windowed arches that look like this:

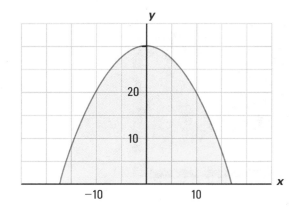

The arches can be reasonably modeled by parabolas with the equation $y = 30 - 0.1x^2$ and measurements in feet.

a. Use the window outline and grid shown to estimate the total area of glass used in each arch. Explain how you could improve the accuracy of your estimate.

b. Write an integral that could be used to calculate the total area of glass used in each arch and then use a calculator or computer integration tool to estimate that area more precisely than in Part a.

4. Below is the graph of velocity for a bouncing golf ball that you examined in the "On Your Own," page 64.

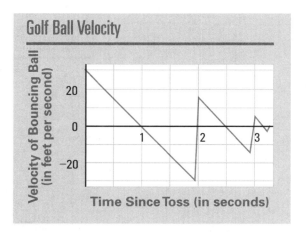

a. Sketch a graph showing the *speed* of the ball as a function of time since the toss.

b. If the speed function is indicated by $s(t)$, estimate and explain the meaning of the following integrals.

    i. $\int_0^2 s(t)\,dt$ **ii.** $\int_2^3 s(t)\,dt$ **iii.** $\int_0^3 s(t)\,dt$

c. Label in order (A, B, C, . . .) the points on the graph of $s(t)$ that indicate times when speed is 0 ft/sec and explain where the ball is in its flight at each of those times.

d. Label in order (R, S, T, . . .) the points on the graph of $s(t)$ that indicate times of maximum speed on each fall and rebound and explain where the ball is in its flight at each of those times.

Organizing

1. Consider the following graph of a function $f(x)$.

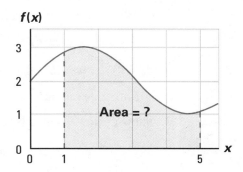

a. How would you estimate the area between the x-axis and the graph of $f(x)$ for $1 \leq x \leq 5$ using four rectangles? Copy the diagram and sketch your ideas.

b. Suppose that you were given an algebraic rule for the function $f(x)$.

    ■ Use function notation to write the calculations needed to estimate the given area by a systematic approximation procedure with four rectangles.

    ■ Explain how you could use a calculator or computer integration tool to estimate the area.

2. Shown below is a portion of a graph of the function $f(x) = 6 - x^2$.

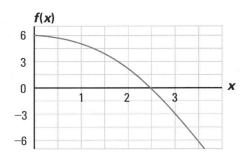

a. Write the calculations needed to estimate $\int_0^3 f(x)\,dx$ using an approximation with six rectangles. Explain your strategy for constructing the approximating rectangles.

b. Use a calculator or computer integration tool to estimate $\int_0^3 f(x)\,dx$, compare the result to the estimate in Part a and explain probable reasons for any differences.

c. Will $\int_{-2}^3 f(x)\,dx$ be larger or smaller than $\int_0^3 f(x)\,dx$? How do you know without evaluating either integral?

d. Will $\int_0^{10} f(x)\,dx$ be larger or smaller than $\int_0^3 f(x)\,dx$? How do you know without evaluating either integral?

3. Shown below is a graph of $f(x) = 6 - x^2$ over a symmetric interval around $x = 0$.

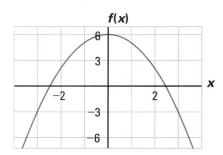

a. Write the calculations needed to evaluate the definite integral of $f(x)$ from -2 to 2 using a systematic method and four approximating rectangles. Explain the strategy you used to define the rectangles.

b. How could you refine the estimation strategy in Part a to get a better approximation?

c. What integral(s) would you need to evaluate in order to determine the total area between the graph of $f(x)$ and the x-axis from 0 to 4?

4. Find rules and sketch graphs of functions $f(x)$ with the following properties.

   a. The function $f(x)$ is linear and its definite integral from 1 to 5 is 0.

   b. The function $f(x)$ is linear and its definite integral from –5 to 5 is 0.

   c. The function $f(x)$ is periodic and its definite integral from 0 to 2π is 0.

   d. The function $f(x)$ is linear and its definite integral from 1 to 4 is 1.

Reflecting

1. One description of the derivative is that it solves problems about nonlinear functions using linear approximations. In what sense is a similar statement true of the integral?

2. The process of finding the derivative of a given function is often called *differentiation*; the process of finding the integral is called *integration*. Why do these two words seem to fit the processes that are occurring, for example, in the case of finding velocity from a distance function and vice versa?

3. You have seen that when a function $g(t)$ gives the rate of change in some quantity as time passes, the integral of $g(t)$ gives the net change in that quantity over an interval of time. How could you convince someone who has not studied calculus ideas that the rate of change-net change-integral connection makes sense?

4. Think of some measuring instruments that you encounter around the house, in cars, at school, or elsewhere where the quantity recorded is a rate of change. In each case:

   a. Give the measurement units commonly used for the rate of change.

   b. Give the measurement units that would then be used for net change.

Extending

1. In 1960, the Aral Sea in the former Soviet Union was one of the largest lakes in the world. The volume of the Aral Sea was 1,066 km³. Fed by two rivers, the Amu and the Syr, and with no outflow other than evaporation, its level was stable. In 1954, Soviet government officials decided to construct a system of canals that would divert water from the Amu and the Syr to irrigate the vast Central Asian desert and make agriculture possible there. As the irrigated area grew, less and less water reached the Aral to counteract evaporation, and it shrank dramatically.

Aral Sea

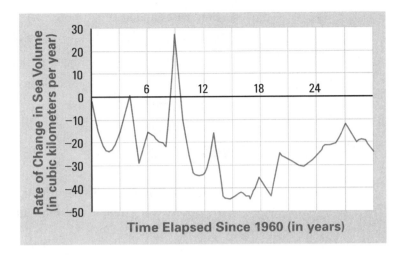

a. Explain in terms of inflow and evaporation what it means for this rate function to have negative values?

b. How would you estimate the volume of water the Aral Sea lost between 1960 and 1966?

c. What was the approximate volume of water in the Aral Sea in 1966?

d. Estimate the volume of water in the Aral Sea in 1972, 1978, 1984, and 1990.

e. Based on the pattern of your results in Part d, do you expect that the Aral Sea would have practically disappeared by the year 2000? What volume for the year 2000 do your estimates predict? What is the status of the Aral Sea today? You may want to research this topic in a library or on the Internet.

2. After work on a number of problems involving integrals, students in a class in Alaska came up with the following conjecture:

$$\int_a^b f(x)\,dx + \int_b^c f(x)\,dx = \int_a^c f(x)\,dx$$

Do you think that equation will hold true for any function $f(x)$ and any intervals $a < b < c$?

a. Use your calculator or computer integration tool to test the conjecture for a variety of different functions and intervals and summarize your findings.

b. Make sketches of graphs for a variety of different functions to help explain why the conjecture is or is not true.

c. How would you analyze this conjecture if $f(x)$ were the rate of change function of a quantity? What would each of these integrals mean in that case?

3. Examine this conjecture about integrals proposed by a class in Maryland.

$$\int_a^b [f(x) + 5]\, dx = \int_a^b f(x)\, dx + \int_a^b 5\, dx$$

a. Make sketches illustrating the conjecture and use the sketches to explain why the conjecture is or is not true.

b. Would your conclusion be the same if you substituted another number for 5 on both sides of the equation?

4. In Investigation 3, you estimated the area under a curve by approximating the area with rectangles. Another method for estimating the area under a curve is to approximate the area by trapezoids as shown in the diagram below.

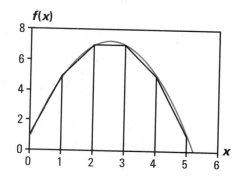

a. Calculate a trapezoidal estimate for the integral of $f(x) = -x^2 + 5x + 1$ from 0 to 5.

b. Compare the estimate in Part a to that obtained by use of a calculator or computer integration tool and to another estimate using five rectangles and comment on the relative accuracy of the various methods.

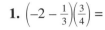

1. $\left(-2 - \frac{1}{3}\right)\left(\frac{3}{4}\right) =$

    (a) -0.5 **(b)** -1.75 **(c)** 1.25 **(d)** -1.25 **(e)** -2.25

2. Simplify: $\frac{2}{3}(x + 6) - \frac{3}{4}(x - 8)$.

    (a) $10 - \frac{x}{7}$ **(b)** $18 - \frac{x}{12}$ **(c)** $10 - \frac{x}{12}$ **(d)** $-2 - \frac{x}{7}$ **(e)** $14 - \frac{x}{12}$

3. The equation of the line through $(-2, 4)$ and $(1, -5)$ is

    (a) $-3x + y = 2$ **(b)** $x + y = 2$ **(c)** $3x + y = -2$

    (d) $-3x + y = -2$ **(e)** $x + 3y = 16$

4. If $f(x) = x^2 + x - 3$, then $f(3a) =$

    (a) $3a^2 + 3a - 3$ **(b)** $a^2 + 3a - 3$ **(c)** $3a^2 + 3a + 3$

    (d) $9a^2 + 3a - 3$ **(e)** $9a^2 - 3a + 3$

5. For what value of k will the equation $x^2 - 12x + k = 0$ have exactly one root?

    (a) 144 **(b)** 36 **(c)** 24 **(d)** 12 **(e)** 25

6. If $x \neq 5$ and $(x - 5)(x + 1) + (x - 5) = A(x - 5)$, find an expression for A.

    (a) $x + 1$ **(b)** $2(x + 1)$ **(c)** $x - 4$

    (d) $x + 2$ **(e)** $(x - 5)(x + 1)$

7. The graph of the function $y = f(x)$ is shown below.

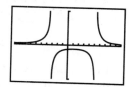

Which of the following is a possible algebraic model representing the function?

(a) $f(x) = \dfrac{2}{(x-5)(x+3)}$ **(b)** $f(x) = \dfrac{2}{(x+5)(x-3)}$

(c) $f(x) = \dfrac{-2}{(x+5)(x-3)}$ **(d)** $f(x) = \dfrac{2(x-3)}{x+5}$

(e) $f(x) = \dfrac{-2(x+3)}{x-5}$

8. In the figure shown, what is the value of x?

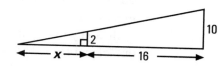

(a) 2 **(b)** 3.2 **(c)** 4 **(d)** 5 **(e)** 8

9. Simplify: $-2^x \cdot 2^{-x}$.

(a) -4^{2x} **(b)** -2 **(c)** 2 **(d)** -1 **(e)** -4^{-2x}

10. Simplify: $\sqrt{3} \cdot \sqrt{30}$.

(a) $\sqrt{33}$ **(b)** $\sqrt{10}$ **(c)** $9\sqrt{10}$ **(d)** $\sqrt[4]{90}$ **(e)** $3\sqrt{10}$

Looking Back

In this unit, you explored functions and the patterns of change in variables that they model. In particular, you investigated using derivative functions to describe instantaneous rates of change and definite integrals to describe accumulation of change. In this final lesson, you will review these key ideas and apply them in new situations.

1. In many questions about falling bodies and sport balls in flight, you have modeled the relations between time and height with quadratic functions. For motion of relatively aerodynamic bodies at relatively low speeds, those mod-

   els are good models. But when the flying objects are awkward shapes and speeds are high, the effect of air resistance makes other mathematical models more accurate.

   If a skydiver plans to jump out of a plane that is several thousand feet above ground, the expected flight could be modeled better by two functions of time like these, where t is time in seconds, d is distance in feet, and s is speed in feet/second.

   Distance Fallen: $d(t) = 120t - 540(1 - 0.8^t)$

   Speed: $s(t) = 120(1 - 0.8^t)$

   a. Use the distance function $d(t)$ to estimate $d'(t)$ at points from 0 to 10 seconds in intervals of 0.5 second, and compare those estimates to the values of $s(t)$. Explain the similarities or differences of results. Include ideas about how you could revise your procedures to improve the match between estimates and exact values.

b. Sketch graphs of $d(t)$ and $s(t)$ and explain how the pattern of change in the distance graph relates to the speed graph.

c. The diagram below shows one way to estimate the area between the t-axis and the graph of the speed function $s(t)$. Use that strategy to estimate distances fallen by the skydiver over the following time intervals:

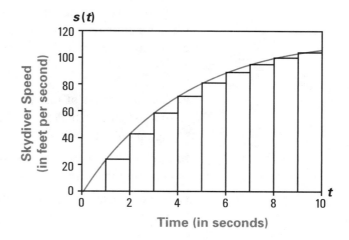

- From $t = 0$ to $t = 10$
- From $t = 1$ to $t = 5$
- From $t = 5$ to $t = 9$
- From $t = 9$ to $t = 10$

d. Use the distance function $d(t)$ to check your answers in Part c. Explain any differences that you notice. Then explain how you could modify the approach in Part c to get more accurate distance estimates.

e. Explain how each of the answers in Part c could be calculated using definite integrals. Then use a calculator or computer integra- tion tool to estimate each answer. Compare those estimates to the estimates and exact values obtained in Parts c and d.

2. For objects in motion near the surface of the moon, the relation between time and height is quite accurately modeled by a quadratic function because there is no atmosphere to provide air resistance. For example, when astronaut Alan Shepard hit a golf ball during a moon walk in 1971, the height of that ball (in feet) was a function of time in flight (in seconds) and could have been modeled by the following rule:

Alan Shepard on the moon in 1971.

$$h(t) = -2.7t^2 + 30t$$

a. Sketch a graph of this height function and use the graph to estimate the time when that ball reached its maximum height and when it returned to the moon's surface.

b. Explain how the shape of the height graph can be used to describe the changing velocity of the ball from hit to landing.

c. Use a derivative estimation method to make a table of approximations for $h'(t)$ in steps of 0.5 second from hit to landing. Explain what the pattern of values in that table tells about the ball's motion.

d. Sketch a graph of $h'(t)$ and explain how that graph (and the table of derivative estimates) can be used to find the time when the ball reached its maximum height.

e. Use the table and graph of derivative estimates to find a rule for $h'(t)$. Explain how the form of that rule matches the pattern of change found in the table and the graph of derivative estimates.

3. Compare the speed graph for the skydiver to the velocity graph of the golf ball hit on the moon. Explain how differences in those graphs tell different stories about the motion of the skydiver and the golf ball.

4. When some interesting event occurs in our country, news of the event can spread in several different ways. If the event is covered by radio, television, and newspaper reporters, the story will soon appear in those media. If the event is not reported in the news media, word might still be spread by informal contacts among individual people.

   For example, suppose that on some winter weekend there is a breakdown in a school's heating system, making it necessary to close school on Monday. Word of this school closing could spread in several ways.

a. Which of the following graphs seems most likely to model spread of the school closing news if it is reported on local radio and television? Which seems most likely if the word is spread only from person to person in the school community?

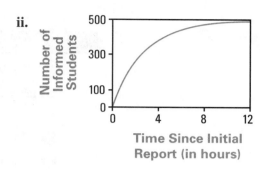

i. Number of Informed Students / Time Since Initial Report (in hours)

ii. Number of Informed Students / Time Since Initial Report (in hours)

b. What do the shapes of the graphs in Part a tell about the rate of change in the number of people who know about the school closing as time passes?

c. Two rules that match the graphs in Part a are

$$f(t) = 500(1 - 0.7^t) \qquad \text{and} \qquad g(t) = \frac{500}{1 + 500(0.4^t)}$$

Match each rule with the correct graph. How can you match them without actually producing graphs on your calculator?

d. Use estimation procedures to produce tables and graphs approximating $f'(t)$ and $g'(t)$. Then explain how the patterns of change in those derivatives match the shapes of the tables and graphs of the functions $f(t)$ and $g(t)$ and the patterns of spread of news about the school closing.

e. Explain how the graphs of $f'(t)$ and $g'(t)$ could be used to estimate the number of students who heard about the school closing between $t = 2$ and $t = 6$ and how those estimates could be checked using the rules for $f(t)$ and $g(t)$.

f. For each function, write a definite integral that could be used to find the number of students who heard about the school closing between $t = 2$ and $t = 6$.

5. Suppose a skateboarder rides the half-pipe ramp sketched at the right, moving back and forth from left to right. The side view of the ramp is a semicircle with diameter 30 feet.

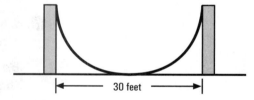

30 feet

a. What is the length of the trip from one side to the other?

b. Sketch a graph that you believe shows the probable shape of the relation between time and distance traveled from the starting point for two complete round trips.

c. Sketch a graph that you believe shows the probable shape of the relation between time and skateboarder's speed over the two round trips and explain the relation of this graph to that of Part b. Identify the point(s) on the velocity graph corresponding to maximum distance from the starting point, and identify the sections of the velocity graph corresponding to motion away from and back toward the starting point.

In this unit, you used the derivative $f'(x)$ and the definite integral $\int_a^b f(x)\,dx$ to answer questions about rates of change and accumulation of one variable as another changes.

a How can you estimate the value of $f'(x)$ for any specific input value of x?

b What does the value of $f'(a)$ tell about:
- the rate of change of $f(x)$ near $x = a$?
- the shape of the graph of $f(x)$ near $x = a$?

c How is calculating the derivative of a nonlinear function similar to finding the slope or rate of change of a linear function?

d What does $f'(x)$ tell about a situation in which $f(x)$ models
- position or distance of a moving object as a function of time?
- size of a population as a function of time?

e What does $\int_a^b f(x)\,dx$ tell about the graph of $f(x)$?

f What does $\int_a^b f(x)\,dx$ tell about a situation in which $f(x)$ models
- velocity of a moving object as a function of time?
- rate of change in a population as a function of time?

g How can you use rules for functions $f(x)$ to calculate or estimate derivatives and definite integrals?

h What strategies can be used to improve the accuracy of estimates for derivatives and definite integrals?

Be prepared to share your responses and explain your thinking to the class.

On Your Own

Write, in outline form, a summary of the important mathematical concepts and methods developed in this unit. Organize your summary so that it can be used as a quick reference in future units and courses.

Modeling Motion

Unit **2**

Modeling Linear Motion

Each day you confront motion in nearly everything you do. You tie your shoes, ride or walk to school, open and close books, and write notes. You see aircraft fly overhead and you see the sun rise in the east, move across the sky, and set in the west. You might throw, kick, or hit a ball. Not all of these motions are easily modeled mathematically. However, motion along a line and motion along a circle are easily modeled. In this unit, you will investigate an important tool for modeling motion—*vectors*. Vectors are especially useful for modeling motions because they can represent distance and direction, important descriptors of motions, simultaneously.

Planned, as well as actual, routes of boats and ships involve linear motion. Think about how you might describe or represent a planned route on a map. Think also about conditions that might affect a planned route and how you might incorporate that information in the planning process.

Think About This Situation

Suppose you wanted to map a route that involved sailing 3 km west from Bayview Harbor to Presque Island, then 6 km south to Rudy Point, and then 5 km southeast to Traverse Bay.

a How could you represent the planned route geometrically?

b How could you represent a sailing trip directly from Bayview Harbor to Traverse Bay?

c How could you estimate the length of the route in Part b? How would you describe its direction?

d How would a northwest water current affect the actual route you would sail in Part c?

Vectors and vector operations are used extensively in navigation on water and in the air. Imagine that you are navigating a boat along the small portion of the Massachusetts coast shown in the nautical chart below. Note that within the chart itself there are several aids to navigation such as mileage, scales, landmarks, and buoys. The buoys are painted red or green and may have a red or green flashing light.

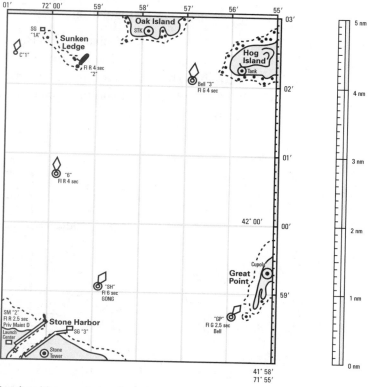

Reprinted by permission from the publisher.
© Frank J. Larkin. Basic Coastal Navigation.
Sheridan House Inc. 1998.

1. As a class, begin by examining some of the information provided by the chart.

   a. Some of the buoys are represented by two concentric circles and a diamond. Which of these have noise-making devices? What are they?

   b. Which buoys have flashing lights? What is each color? How often does the light flash?

   c. What symbol is used to represent easily recognized landmarks on the chart? What landmarks are shown?

   d. What do you think the dotted lines on the chart represent? Why is this important knowledge for navigation?

e. At the right of the chart is a *nautical mile* (nm) scale. Use this scale to find the distance from the "SH" buoy to the "GP" buoy. Measure from circle center to circle center on the chart.

f. There are other scales at the top and along the right edge of the chart. What do these scales represent?

g. What other scale on this chart can be used to measure nautical miles? What does a nautical mile represent based on this scale?

h. A nautical mile is 6,076.1033 feet. How does a nautical mile compare to a statute mile (regular mile)?

Coastal water nautical charts are designed so that the top is due north and the right side is due east. The **heading** of a boat is given in degrees clockwise from due north. Thus, due north is 0°, due east is 90°, due south is 180°, and due west is 270°. A 60° heading through a channel northwest of Anguilla Island is depicted below.

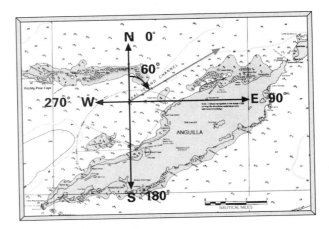

2. Use a copy of the nautical chart on page 81 to complete this activity. Measure distances to the nearest $\frac{1}{10}$ nm, using a ruler made from the nautical mile scale. Measure angles to the nearest degree using a protractor.

a. Mark and label a point *P* on the chart to represent a boat that is 3 nautical miles from the "3" bell on a heading of 200°. What buoy is nearest to *P*?

b. Draw an arrow from the "SH" buoy to the "6" buoy. What is the heading? What is the distance in nautical miles?

c. What are the heading and distance of the path from the "6" buoy to the center of the mouth of the channel at Stone Harbor?

d. A public launching ramp is located on the channel near the Launch Center. Draw an arrow showing a route from the easterly end of the ramp to the "SH" buoy. Find the heading and distance to the "SH" buoy.

e. Why are arrows particularly useful representations for nautical paths?

4. Suppose a fishing boat leaves the Stone Harbor channel on a heading of 25° at a speed of 1.5 knots (nautical miles per hour).

a. Sketch the vector representing the distance and direction traveled during the first hour of the trip. Describe the boat's location after one hour.

b. Describe how you could use the vector in Part a to determine the vector for a 3-hour trip at the same speed and heading. Sketch this vector. Describe how you could locate the fishing boat at the end of 1.5 hours, 2 hours, and 2.75 hours.

c. On a piece of plain or graph paper, draw a vector about 10 cm long. Sketch a vector that is half this vector. Now sketch another vector whose length is half that of the original vector. Are the sketched vectors equal? Must they be equal? Explain.

d. In general, how would you sketch a vector that was *n* times a given vector? How are the lengths and headings of these two vectors related?

5. Now suppose a boat begins a trip at the mouth of the channel at Stone Harbor at a heading of 20° and a speed of 2 knots.

a. Sketch the vector showing the position at the end of the first hour.

b. Suppose the boat returns to the harbor along the same route at the same velocity. Sketch the return vector and give its magnitude and heading.

c. The word "opposites" can be used to denote the vectors in Parts a and b. How is this word descriptive of the relationship?

d. Sketch a vector opposite to the vector in Part a from the "3" bell. Give its magnitude and heading. Compare your results to those in Part b.

Vectors are quantities with magnitude and direction that are represented geometrically by arrows.

a Describe how you know when two arrows represent the same vector.

b How are a vector and a multiple of the same vector similar? How are they different?

c What do you think is always true about the magnitudes and headings of any two opposite vectors?

Be prepared to explain your group's thinking to the entire class.

Vectors can be denoted in various ways. One way is to use italicized letters with arrow shapes over them, such as $\vec{a}$ or $\vec{v}$. When the **initial point** or **tail** and **terminal point** or **head** are labeled, then capitalized, italicized letters such as $\overrightarrow{AB}$ can be used. Since a vector $\vec{v}$ is determined by its magnitude r, and its heading θ, we could also represent $\vec{v}$ symbolically as $[r, \theta]$. (θ is the Greek letter "theta." Often, Greek letters are used to denote measures of angles.)

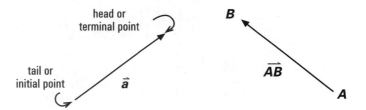

When a vector $\vec{a}$ is multiplied by a real number n, the number is called a **scalar** and the product, $n\vec{a}$, is a **scalar multiple** of $\vec{a}$. (In a similar manner, $n\overrightarrow{AB}$ is a scalar multiple of the vector $\overrightarrow{AB}$.) When $n > 0$, $n\vec{a}$ is the vector whose length is n times the length of $\vec{a}$ and has the same direction as $\vec{a}$ as pictured below. When $n < 0$, the length of $n\vec{a}$ is $|n|$ times the length of $\vec{a}$; but $n\vec{a}$ points in the opposite direction. The opposite of a vector $\vec{a}$ or $\overrightarrow{AB}$. is denoted $-\vec{a}$ or $-\overrightarrow{AB}$. If $\vec{a} = [r, \theta]$, then $n\vec{a} = [nr, \theta]$ when $n > 0$, and $[|n|r, \theta + 180°]$ when $n < 0$. Its opposite is $[r, \theta + 180°]$.

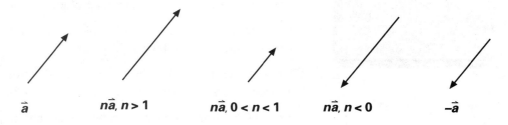

On Your Own

On a copy of this map of Lake Michigan, plot the following courses.

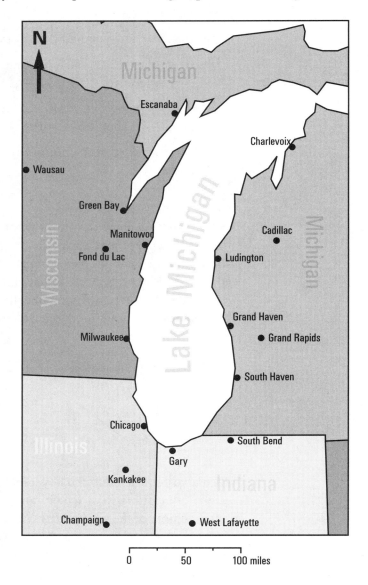

N

Michigan

Escanaba

Charlevoix

Wausau

Green Bay

Cadillac

Manitowoc

Fond du Lac

Ludington

Wisconsin

Lake Michigan

Michigan

Grand Haven

Milwaukee

Grand Rapids

South Haven

Chicago

South Bend

Illinois

Gary

Kankakee

Indiana

Champaign

West Lafayette

0   50   100 miles

a. Daily ferries shuttle people and cars between Manitowoc, Wisconsin, and Ludington, Michigan. Draw the vector for the ferry route from Manitowoc to Ludington. Label it $\vec{v}$. Find its magnitude and heading.

b. Find the magnitude and heading of $-\vec{v}$ and describe what it represents. Draw $-\vec{v}$ beginning at Charlevoix, Michigan.

c. Draw the vector for the direct course to sail from South Haven, Michigan, to Milwaukee, Wisconsin. Call it $\vec{a}$. Find the magnitude and heading of $\vec{a}$.

d. Sketch $0.5\vec{a}$ from Grand Haven, Michigan, and find its magnitude and heading.

INVESTIGATION 2 Changing Course

In the previous investigation, you used vectors to model straight-line paths. In this investigation, you will explore how vectors can be used to model routes when there is a change of course during the trip. For Activity 1, you will need a copy of the nautical chart from Investigation 1.

1. Suppose Natalie, the skipper of the fishing boat *High Hopes*, left the mouth of the Stone Harbor channel making 6 knots at 65°. She traveled for 20 minutes, then turned to a heading of 350° and traveled for 5 minutes before deciding to drop anchor and begin fishing.

   a. Using a copy of the nautical chart from Investigation 1, draw an accurate vector diagram showing the paths taken and the position of the *High Hopes* at the end of 25 minutes. (Save this chart for later use.) What units measure the lengths of these vectors? How long are these vectors?

   b. Suppose the fish are biting and Natalie wants to inform Keith, the skipper of the *Little Hope*, where she is located so that he can join her. Accurately draw a vector representing the path Keith should take from the mouth of the channel directly to the *High Hopes*. What heading should she advise him to take? How long is the trip?

   c. Suppose Natalie did not drop anchor until she traveled with a heading of 350° for 30 minutes instead of 5 minutes. In this case, what course should she advise Keith to take from the mouth of the channel?

   d. The vector representing the path that Keith should travel to the good fishing spot is called the **sum** or **resultant** of the two vectors describing the route taken by the *High Hopes*. How are the initial and terminal points of the resultant vector in Parts b and c related to the two vectors representing the trips taken by the *High Hopes?*

   e. Suppose Natalie had left the harbor at a speed of 6 knots on a heading of 350° for 30 minutes and then turned to a heading of 65° and traveled for 20 minutes. Draw an accurate vector diagram of Natalie's path and the resultant vector. Describe the resultant vector in terms of heading and magnitude. How does this resultant vector compare to the resultant vector found in Part c?

2. Consider the following vectors: $\vec{a}$ (magnitude 5 cm, heading 20°), $\vec{b}$ (magnitude 4 cm, heading 60°), $\vec{c}$ (magnitude 4 cm, heading 100°), and $\vec{d}$ (magnitude 3 cm, heading 200°). Make accurate sketches of each vector sum and measure to find the magnitude (to the nearest 0.1 cm) and heading (to the nearest 5°) for each resultant vector.

   a. $\vec{a} + \vec{b}$ **b.** $\vec{a} + \vec{d}$

   c. $\vec{a} + \vec{b} + \vec{c}$ **d.** $\vec{a} + \vec{b} + \vec{c} + \vec{d}$

3. Now investigate some general properties of vector addition. Begin by sketching any two vectors $\vec{a}$ and $\vec{b}$.

   a. Draw diagrams showing how to find $\vec{a} + \vec{b}$ and $\vec{b} + \vec{a}$. What do you notice? Compare your observations to those of another group.

   b. To which property of real number operations is this similar?

   c. Choose a point in the plane. Starting at the chosen point, draw a single diagram showing how to find $\vec{a} + \vec{b}$ and $\vec{b} + \vec{a}$. What shape is formed? Prove your conjecture.

4. On a sheet of plain or graph paper, make an accurate drawing of a vector $\vec{u}$ with magnitude 4 cm and heading 253° and a vector $\vec{v}$ with magnitude 5 cm and heading 22°.

   a. Without measuring, find the magnitude and heading of as many of the following vectors as possible. Explain your reasoning in each case.

i. $2 \cdot \vec{u}$	**ii.** $\frac{1}{2} \cdot \vec{v}$
iii. $\vec{v} + \vec{u}$	**iv.** $\vec{u} + \vec{v}$
v. $3(\vec{u} + \vec{v})$	**vi.** $3\vec{u} + 3\vec{v}$
vii. $-2\vec{v}$	**viii.** $2\vec{v} + (-2\vec{u})$
ix. $2\vec{v} + 3\vec{u}$	**x.** $-2\vec{v} + (-2\vec{u})$

   b. Find the magnitude and heading of the remaining vectors by measuring. Use as few drawings as possible. Look for possible connections between pairs of vectors that might reduce your work.

   c. What general rule is suggested by Parts v and vi? Test your conjecture.

5. Retrieve your drawing for Activity 1 Part c.

   a. Sketch three additional two-leg routes to the fishing grounds. In each case, find the resultant vector.

   b. How are the resultant vectors of Part a related to the resultant vector of Activity 1 Part c?

   c. Decide if each of the following conjectures is true or false. In each case, explain your reasoning.

   - The vector sum of any two given vectors is unique.

   - If a vector is the sum of two given vectors, it cannot be the sum of two different vectors.

6. On the chart below are drawn a vector with heading 90° and a vector with heading 0° that give one route to the good fishing area identified in Activity 1.

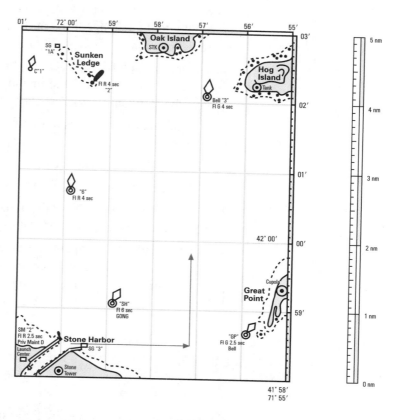

a. Measure to find the magnitudes of these two vectors. Then use those measures to *calculate* (not measure) the magnitude of the resultant.

b. Starting at the harbor, is it possible to find another pair of vectors with direction 0° and 90° that have the vector sum in Part a? Explain your reasoning.

c. Recall that for a right $\triangle ABC$:

$$\sin A = \frac{a}{c} = \frac{\text{side opposite}}{\text{hypotenuse}}$$

$$\cos A = \frac{b}{c} = \frac{\text{side adjacent}}{\text{hypotenuse}}$$

$$\tan A = \frac{a}{b} = \frac{\text{side opposite}}{\text{side adjacent}}$$

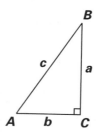

Use a pair of perpendicular vectors to compute the heading to the good fishing area. Compare your computed heading with that obtained by measuring in Activity 1 Part b.

7. Now investigate further how a vector can be thought of in terms of the sum of horizontal and vertical vectors called its **components.**

    a. Suppose a vector represents a 2-nautical mile route with a heading of 12°. Compute the lengths of the north (0°) and east (90°) legs of a route to the same location.

    b. Suppose a vector $\vec{v}$ represents a 2 nm route with a heading of 325°. Make a sketch of the vector $\vec{v}$ and include the north and west vectors that would give the resultant vector $\vec{v}$.

       ■ What are the measures of the angles of the triangle formed by these three vectors?

       ■ Compute the magnitudes of the north and west vectors.

       ■ What are the headings for the north and west vectors?

    c. Compute the magnitudes of the horizontal and vertical components of a 2 nm vector with a heading of 120°. What are the directions of the components?

    d. How would you compute the magnitudes of the horizontal and vertical components of any 2 nm vector with a heading between 180° and 270°? Any 5 nm vector with a heading between 180° and 270°? Compare your methods with those of other groups and resolve any differences.

Checkpoint

In this investigation, you explored the geometry of the addition of vectors.

  ⓐ Describe what is meant by the resultant or sum of two vectors.

  ⓑ Any nonzero vector can be represented as the sum of a horizontal vector and a vertical vector. Illustrate and explain how this can be done for a vector whose direction is given as a heading.

  ⓒ In the vector diagram below, $\overrightarrow{AC}$ and $\overrightarrow{CB}$ are the horizontal and vertical components of $\overrightarrow{AB}$ respectively.

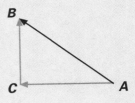

      ■ If you know the heading and magnitude of $\overrightarrow{AB}$, how would you calculate the magnitudes of $\overrightarrow{AC}$ and $\overrightarrow{CB}$?

      ■ If you know the magnitudes of $\overrightarrow{AC}$ and $\overrightarrow{CB}$, how would you calculate the magnitude and heading of $\overrightarrow{AB}$?

Be prepared to share your descriptions and illustrations with the class.

On Your Own

Refer to the nautical chart used in the investigation. Suppose Keith is fishing off Great Point due west of the cupola and due north of the "GP" buoy when he receives a report of good fishing due south of the stack and due west of the "3" buoy.

a. What heading should Keith set to get to the good fishing spot? How far will he need to travel?

b. Make an accurate drawing of the components of the route in Part a. Using scale measurements, find the length, in nautical miles, of the components.

c. Use the vector right triangle you have drawn to calculate the lengths of the components in nautical miles. Compare the calculated and measured lengths.

INVESTIGATION 3 Go with the Flow

The vector models you have been using for navigation assume that the force moving a boat is the only one acting on the craft. When this is the case, the craft moves in a straight line in the direction of the force. However, what happens when two (or more) forces act simultaneously on an object? For example, tides in the ocean are forces on boats that move the boats in the direction of the tide. Sailing ships without motors use tidal flows to help them enter and leave port. The wind, too, is a force that affects the path a boat or an airplane follows. A fundamental principle of physics is that the effect of two forces acting on a body is the sum of the forces. In this investigation, you will learn how to use this principle.

1. Suppose a boat leaves port on a heading of 30° with the automatic pilot set for 10 knots. On this particular day, there is a 5-knot current with a heading of 60°. The vector diagram at the right shows the effect of the current on the position of the boat at the end of one hour.

   a. Assuming a scale of 1 cm = 2 nm, verify the accuracy of the diagram.

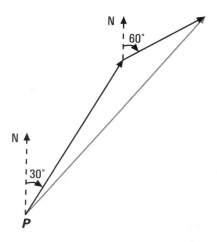

b. The sum of the course and current vectors gives the position of the boat in one hour. Determine how far the boat will actually travel in one hour:

- Using the scale diagram
- Using the Law of Cosines

c. At what speed and on what heading will the boat actually travel during the first hour? Would it continue to travel similarly during the next hour if all conditions remained the same? Explain.

2. In Activity 1, you were able to determine the actual course of the boat using either a scale drawing and measurement or using the Law of Cosines. Now examine the situation in terms of component vectors.

a. Compute the lengths of the horizontal and vertical components of the vector representing the planned course during the first hour. Sketch each vector beginning at point *P*, the initial point of the planned-course vector.

b. Compute the lengths of the horizontal and vertical components of the current vector at the end of one hour. Sketch each component vector at the terminal point of the planned-course vector.

c. Using the component vectors found in Parts a and b, find the components, magnitude, and heading of the resultant vector representing the actual route sailed. What assumption are you making about addition of vectors?

d. Compare the results of this activity with those of Activity 1.

3. Consider force vectors $\vec{v}$, with length 4 cm and heading 55°, and $\vec{u}$ with length 5 cm and heading 20°.

a. On graph paper, draw $\vec{v} + \vec{u}$.

b. Draw the horizontal and vertical components of $\vec{v}$ and of $\vec{u}$.

c. Draw the resultant of the vertical components and the resultant of the horizontal components.

d. Draw the sum of the two resultant vectors found in Part c. How is this sum related $\vec{v} + \vec{u}$? Explain.

e. Describe how the components of two vectors can be used to find the sum of the two vectors.

4. Make a sketch of a vector diagram showing the location of an airplane at the end of one hour if its heading was 60° and its speed in still air was 500 mph, but the wind was blowing at 50 mph on a heading of 120°.

a. Augment your sketch to show the horizontal and vertical components of the planned-course velocity vector. Represent the horizontal and vertical component vectors of the wind velocity vector in a manner consistent with addition of vectors in this situation.

b. Use the components of the vectors in Part a to determine the heading and distance the airplane traveled in one hour.

c. What was the effective speed of the airplane with respect to the ground? (This is called the *ground speed*.)

d. Describe another way to determine the distance traveled by the airplane in one hour.

The process illustrated in Activities 3 and 4, called **component analysis** of vectors, is a very powerful tool for analyzing linear motion problems. It reduces a complex situation to one in which only component vectors with the same direction are added.

5. Two boys have to move a doghouse on skids to a new position due east of its present location. They tie ropes to the doghouse and pull as follows: Thad pulls with a force of 100 pounds on a heading of 45°, while Jerame pulls with a force of 120 pounds on a heading of 120°.

   a. Make a sketch showing the vectors involved.

   b. Find the heading on which the doghouse should move under these conditions.

   c. If the doghouse weighs 150 lb, will it move? Explain your reasoning.

   d. How should Jerame change the heading at which he pulls so that the doghouse slides due east?

6. Mary and Kim are blockers on their respective school volleyball teams. Suppose that in a conference match, at the same time, they each hit the ball when it is directly over the net. Mary's hit has a force of 50 pounds on a 125° heading. Kim's hit has a force of 40 pounds on a 30° heading.

   a. Sketch the vectors involved if the net is on the east-west line.

   b. Assuming that the ball moves in the direction of the resultant force, on whose side of the net will the ball land? How can component vectors be used to prove this?

   c. At what angle should Mary hit the ball so that it follows the top of the net or goes into Kim's side?

7. In Activity 1, you found that a current in the water causes a boat to travel on the resultant of two forces. Recall that the boat was set to travel on a 30° heading at 10 knots and the current was flowing on a 60° heading at 5 knots. Use this information to find the vector that needs to be added to the current vector $\vec{c}$ to give the course vector $\vec{b}$. This new vector $\vec{x}$ is the path the boat needs to steer so it follows the desired course.

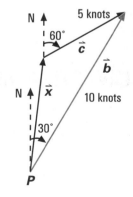

On Your Own

A commercial jet airplane cruises at 600 mph in still air. The pilot wants to fly on a heading of 20° and average 600 mph, but a 70 mph wind is blowing from the northwest (a heading of 135°).

a. Draw a vector model of the effect of the wind on the jet.

b. Draw a vector model showing the heading needed to keep the jet on course and compute the heading.

c. Compute the still air speed that the jet needs to maintain to attain the desired average of 600 mph.

INVESTIGATION 4 Coordinates and Vectors

The vectors you have used up to now have been located in a north/east coordinate system. Because the direction north can be found by sighting a star, using a compass, or by using a Global Positioning System (GPS), navigation both on water and in the air describes the direction a vector points (its *heading*) in terms of degrees clockwise from due north. Mathematicians and many scientists use a different way to describe the direction of a vector. When using a rectangular coordinate system, the **direction of a vector** is measured by the angle the vector makes with the positive *x*-axis with the angle measured counterclockwise. In this investigation, you will explore some of the advantages of representing vectors in a standard (x, y) coordinate system.

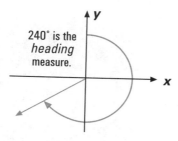 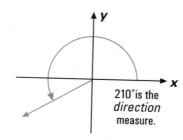

1. Sketch vectors satisfying the criteria given. Re-express headings as directions and directions as headings.

   a. $\vec{v}$ has length 4 cm and heading 80°.

   b. $\vec{p}$ has length 5 cm and direction 80°.

   c. $\vec{m}$ has length 3 cm and direction 130°.

   d. $\vec{n}$ has length 2 cm and heading 130°.

2. Describe and illustrate the differences between a vector with heading 200° and a vector with direction 200°. For what angles are the heading and direction of a vector identical?

3. A vector with magnitude 6 and direction 80° is represented on the coordinate system below.

   a. On a copy of this coordinate system, carefully draw the following additional vectors.

   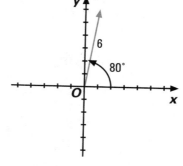

   - magnitude 4, direction 145°

   - magnitude 3, direction 240°

   - magnitude 5, direction 315°

   b. Sketch the horizontal and vertical components of each of the four "parent" vectors given above. Estimate the coordinates of the terminal point of each component vector. How are these coordinates related to the coordinates of the terminal point of the given "parent" vector?

   c. Consider the vector with magnitude 6 and direction 80°. Write equations that express the coordinates (x, y) of the terminal point of the vector in terms of its magnitude and its direction. Explain how the magnitudes of the components can be found using these equations.

   d. Using a method similar to that in Part c, compute the coordinates of the terminal points of the three vectors in Part a. Compare the coordinates with the estimates you made in Part b.

4. Suppose a coordinate system is placed on a nautical map so that the Grand Haven Marina is located at the origin and the positive *y*-axis points north. A speedboat leaves the marina at a direction of 30° and proceeds at 18 knots.

   a. Make a sketch on the coordinate system showing the path of the boat.

   b. Determine the coordinates of the boat's position on the path at $\frac{1}{2}$ hour, 1 hour, and 2 hours.

   c. Write rules giving the coordinates (*x*, *y*) of the position of the boat for any time *t* (in hours).

5. Suppose the speedboat in Activity 4 traveled at a direction of 120° rather than 30°.

   a. Sketch the path of the boat on the same coordinate system and identify its position at $\frac{1}{2}$ hour, 1 hour, and 2 hours.

   b. What are the vector components of each of the positions in Part a?

   c. Write rules giving the coordinates of the position of the boat for any time *t* (in hours).

   d. Repeat Part c if the direction is 210° and if the direction is 330°.

   e. Compare the rules you wrote for Parts c and d of this activity and for Part c of Activity 4.

6. Now consider how a standard coordinate system can be used to model straight line motion of an aircraft. Suppose a commercial jet leaves New York City and flies at a direction of 190° towards the West Coast at 600 mph.

   a. Model this situation by placing New York City at the origin of a coordinate system and sketch the aircraft's path westward.

   b. Find rules for the coordinates of the position of the aircraft *t* hours into the flight. Then find the coordinates of the aircraft's position after 0.25 hour, 1.3 hours, and 3.2 hours.

   c. Find the coordinates of the aircraft's position when it has flown 2,000 miles.

7. Two families of hikers leave a base camp on a mesa with directions of 31° and 42° respectively. Because of the ages of family members, the first family averages about 0.8 mph while the second family averages 1.1 mph.

  a. Sketch the hiking paths of the two families on a standard coordinate system. Assume the families continue to hike in the directions they started and at the indicated rates.

  b. At the end of one hour, what are the coordinates of their positions? How far apart are they?

  c. How far apart are the families after 2 hours? After 3 hours?

  d. How does the distance between the families change as a function of time?

  e. After how much time will they be about 3 miles apart?

8. Two tugboats are maneuvering a supply barge into a slip. (A slip is a docking place for a boat.) One tugboat exerts a force of 1,500 pounds with direction of –20°; another exerts a force of 2,000 pounds with direction 70°.

  a. Use a coordinate system to sketch the situation.

  b. Find the direction and magnitude of the resultant force on the barge.

Checkpoint

In this investigation, you discovered some of the advantages of representing vectors in a rectangular coordinate system.

ⓐ Suppose $\overrightarrow{OB}$ is a vector whose initial point is at the origin. If B has coordinates (5 cos 135°, 5 sin 135°), what is the length of $\overrightarrow{OB}$? What lines or segments determine the sides of the angle that has measure 135°?

ⓑ Describe the relationships among a vector, its component vectors, and the coordinates of the terminal point when the initial point of the vector is at the origin.

Be prepared to explain your responses to the entire class.

A vector with its initial point at the origin of a coordinate system is said to be in **standard position** and is called a **position vector.** The coordinates of the tip of a position vector are the coordinates of the point where the vector ends. Every vector in a given coordinate system is equal to some position vector in that system. Since the tip of every position vector has unique coordinates (x, y), the ordered pair is often called the vector. That is, if $\vec{a}$ is a position vector, then $\vec{a} = (x, y)$. Recall that $\vec{a} = [r, \theta]$, where r is the magnitude and θ is the direction. Thus, there are at least three ways to represent vectors.

On Your Own

Suppose a cruise liner is experiencing mechanical problems 4 hours out of a harbor at a direction of 110°. During these 4 hours, the ship averaged 35 knots on its 110° course. Use a standard coordinate system.

a. Assuming the origin as the launch point, how far is the ship from its launch after 4 hours?

b. Find the coordinates of the position of the cruise liner.

c. In addition to the harbor from which the ship departed, there are ports located at (–75 nm, 75 nm) and (25 nm, 125 nm). Which port is closest to the ship's position?

d. What conditions in addition to distance might the pilot consider in deciding which port to go to for repairs?

Modeling • Organizing • Reflecting • Extending

Modeling

1. Tony Hillerman is a mystery writer whose books are often based on the native American cultures of New Mexico, Utah, Colorado, and Arizona. The map below shows Hillerman country in which Navajo Tribal Police Officers Joe Leaphorn and Jim Chee solve mysteries. In Hillerman's novels, they travel by car throughout the reservations, but for this task assume they have a helicopter.

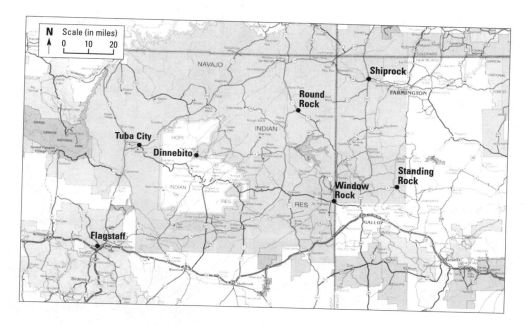

a. Suppose Jim and Joe are stationed at Shiprock. What heading should Jim chart to go to Tuba City to investigate a hit-and-run accident? What is the distance he must fly by helicopter?

b. Jim is to fly from Tuba City to Flagstaff to meet with FBI officials. What is his heading? At 100 mph, what is his flying time?

c. Plot the round trip from Shiprock to Round Rock to Window Rock to Standing Rock and back to Shiprock. Give the heading and distance of each part of the trip.

2. Refer to the nautical chart on the right of a small portion of the Massachusetts coast. The *Open C* is located just off the flashing red light at Sunken Ledge when its skipper learns that fishing action has begun near the "GP" buoy.

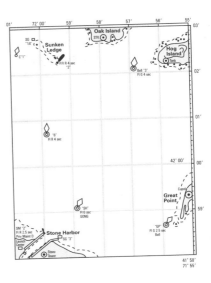

   a. What heading should the skipper set for the "GP" buoy?

   b. At 6 knots, how long would the trip take in still water?

   c. Now suppose there is a heavy wind with heading 190° that will move boats at a rate of about 2 knots. Make a vector diagram showing the effect of the wind on the course of the *Open C*.

   d. In the wind, what is the heading of the route the *Open C* actually travels?

   e. What heading should the skipper plot to account for the wind and arrive at the "GP" buoy?

3. Jim Chee, a helicopter pilot, wants to fly from Shiprock to Dinnebito in the Hopi-Navajo joint-use area. Using the map provided in Task 1, answer the following questions.

   a. What heading should he plan?

   b. If he leaves at 10:00 A.M. and travels at 100 mph, when will he arrive at Dinnebito?

   c. There is a 20-mph wind with heading 150°. Where will Jim be at his estimated time of arrival if he makes no correction for wind? How far is this from Dinnebito?

   d. What course should Jim plan that accounts for the wind and ensures ending up at Dinnebito at the arrival time calculated in Part b?

4. Two boaters leave Ludington, Michigan, at 8:00 A.M. One is heading for Manitowoc, Wisconsin, on a heading of 280°. The other heads for Milwaukee on a heading of 230°. Manitowoc is about 61 miles from Ludington; Milwaukee is about 97 mi. The radios on the boats are good for distances up to 50 mi.

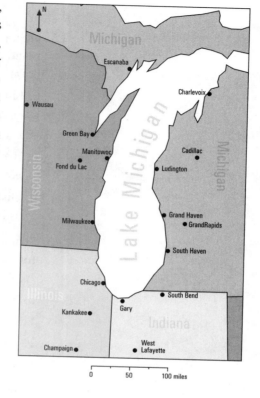

a. With Ludington as the origin, set up a coordinate system. What are the coordinates of Manitowoc and Milwaukee?

b. Sketch a vector diagram if the boat to Manitowoc travels at 8 mph and the boat to Milwaukee travels at 10 mph. How far from each other are they at 9:00 A.M.? At 11:00 A.M.?

c. At about what time will they lose radio contact?

d. How far from their destinations are the boats when they lose radio contact?

Organizing

1. Recall that for any two numbers s and t, $s - t = s + (-t)$. For example, $7.2 - 3.4 = 7.2 + (-3.4)$.

a. State in words how you would subtract one number from another using this definition.

b. By analogy to subtraction of numbers, write a symbolic description of how to subtract $\vec{b}$ from $\vec{a}$. Use your description to sketch $\vec{a}$, $\vec{b}$, and $\vec{a} - \vec{b}$.

c. Make a sketch showing $\vec{a}$, $-\vec{b}$, and $\vec{a} - \vec{b}$ and another showing $\vec{a}$, $\vec{b}$, and $\vec{a} - \vec{b}$. What would you expect to get if you added $\vec{b}$ to $\vec{a} - \vec{b}$? Do your drawings support your conjecture?

d. Use the three vectors in each of your sketches to make closed figures. Explain how each figure makes sense in terms of addition of vectors.

e. Complete the statement: $\vec{a} - \vec{b} = $ _____.

2. On a piece of paper, mark a point O in the center. Using O as the beginning point, accurately draw a 1-inch vector, $\vec{a}$, pointing to the right and accurately draw a 1.5-inch vector, $\vec{b}$, pointing straight upward.

a. Find the angle between these vectors.

b. Choose a point P so that the length of $\overrightarrow{OP}$ is 4 inches. Find scalars m and n so that $\overrightarrow{OB} = m\vec{a} + n\vec{b}$.

c. If Q is any other point, can you always find scalars m and n such that $m\vec{a} + n\vec{b} = \overrightarrow{OQ}$? Explain your reasoning.

d. Discuss your answers in Part c for cases where $\overrightarrow{OQ}$ has the same direction as $\vec{a}$ or $\vec{b}$, or where point Q coincides with point O?

3. Scalar multiplication is used to multiply a vector by a number. Which of the following statements about scalars, vectors, and their products are true? Explain your choices.

a. $m(n\vec{a}) = (mn)\vec{a}$

b. $(m + n)\vec{a} = m\vec{a} + n\vec{a}$

c. $m(\vec{a} + \vec{b}) = m\vec{a} + m\vec{b}$

d. The length of $(m + n)\vec{a}$ equals the length of $m\vec{a}$ plus the length of $n\vec{a}$.

4. Suppose $\overrightarrow{OA}$ and $\overrightarrow{OB}$ are position vectors. The length of $\overrightarrow{OA}$ is r and its direction is θ; that is, $\overrightarrow{OA} = [r, \theta]$. $\overrightarrow{OB}$ has length b and direction ϕ (Greek letter "phi") or $\overrightarrow{OB} = [b, \phi]$.

a. What are the components of $\overrightarrow{OA}$ and $\overrightarrow{OB}$?

b. What are the coordinates of A and B?

c. Find the components of $\overrightarrow{OA} + \overrightarrow{OB}$.

d. What are the components of $-\overrightarrow{OA}$?

e. How could you define $\overrightarrow{OB} - \overrightarrow{OA}$?

5. Suppose you are given position vectors $\vec{u} = (2, 3)$ and $\vec{v} = (-1, 4)$.

a. Find the lengths and directions of $\vec{u}$ and $\vec{v}$.

b. Explain how you can find $\vec{u} + \vec{v}$ using the coordinate representations of $\vec{u}$ and $\vec{v}$.

c. Suppose $\vec{u} = (x_1, y_1)$ and $\vec{v} = (x_2, y_2)$.
   - What would be the coordinate representation $\vec{u} + \vec{v}$? Explain your reasoning.
   - Explain why the definition of scalar multiplication $m\vec{u} = (mx_1, my_1)$ makes sense.

d. Using general coordinate representations $\vec{u} = (x_1, y_1)$ and $\vec{v} = (x_2, y_2)$:
   - Prove $\vec{v} + \vec{u} = \vec{u} + \vec{v}$.
   - Prove $m(\vec{v} + \vec{u}) = m\vec{u} + m\vec{v}$.

Reflecting

1. For two vectors to be equal, two conditions must be met: their lengths must be equal and their directions must be equal.

   a. Sketch vectors to illustrate the necessity of both conditions:
   - Show that two vectors with the same length may not be equal.
   - Show that two vectors with the same direction may not be equal.

   b. If two vectors are equal and begin at the same point, how are their geometric representations (arrows) related?

   c. If two vectors are equal and begin at different points, how are their geometric representations related?

2. In each of the diagrams below, a figure *F* and its image *G* under a translation are shown.

   a. How could you use vectors to describe these translations?

   b. Can every translation be described by a vector? Explain your reasoning.

3. Suppose the coordinates of the terminal point of a position vector are (a, b).

   a. How could these numbers be used to calculate the length of the vector?

   b. How do the signs (+ or −) on each coordinate help you sketch the vector? For example, if a and b are both negative, in which quadrant would you draw the vector?

   c. How can the coordinates (a, b) be used to determine the direction of the vector? When you calculate the direction of a vector, does the calculator always give you correct directions for all combinations of signs (+, −) for a and b? Experiment to discover patterns. How can you determine the correct direction?

4. Draw a vector $\overrightarrow{AB}$ with length 5. Construct a circle with center at the midpoint of the vector and passing through the initial point and terminal point of the vector.

   a. Choose a point C on the circle and connect it to the initial point and terminal point of $\overrightarrow{AB}$. What is the measure of $\angle C$?

   b. What is $\overrightarrow{AC} + \overrightarrow{CB}$?

   c. Describe the axes of a coordinate system for which $\overrightarrow{AC}$ and $\overrightarrow{CB}$ are components of $\overrightarrow{AB}$? Explain your reasoning.

    d. Choose another point C on the circle and respond to Parts a–c.

    e. Do the results of Parts a–d contradict the assertion that the horizontal and vertical components of a vector are unique? Explain.

5. Make a table of the heading and the direction of a vector as it rotates through headings from 0° to 360° in steps of 20°. Make a scatterplot of the (*heading, direction*) data. Describe patterns you see in the scatterplot. Can these patterns be described algebraically?

Extending

1. In Organizing Task 5, you may have discovered the conventional method for addition of vectors expressed in coordinate form: $(x_1, y_1) + (x_2, y_2) = (x_1 + x_2, y_1 + y_2)$. Investigate and compare properties of addition of vectors expressed in coordinate form with properties of addition of 2×2 matrices. Write a summary of your findings.

2. In Course 3, Unit 4, "Shapes and Geometric Reasoning," you may have used properties of similar triangles to prove the Midpoint Connector Theorem: If a line segment joins the midpoints of two sides of a triangle, then it is parallel to the third side and its length is one-half the length of the third side.

    a. Doris claims that this theorem could also be proved using vectors as shown. Explain why her proof is or is not valid.

    Doris's proof:

    If X and Y are the midpoints of $\overline{AC}$ and $\overline{BC}$ respectively,

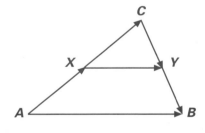

        then $\overrightarrow{AX} = \overrightarrow{XC} = \frac{1}{2}\overrightarrow{AC}$

        and $\overrightarrow{CY} = \overrightarrow{YB} = \frac{1}{2}\overrightarrow{CB}$.

        Also, $\overrightarrow{AC} + \overrightarrow{CB} = \overrightarrow{AB}$

        and $\overrightarrow{XC} + \overrightarrow{CY} = \overrightarrow{XY}$.

        So, $\frac{1}{2}\overrightarrow{AC} + \frac{1}{2}\overrightarrow{CB} = \overrightarrow{XC} + \overrightarrow{CY}$ or

        $\frac{1}{2}(\overrightarrow{AC} + \overrightarrow{CB}) = \overrightarrow{XY}$.

        Therefore, $\frac{1}{2}\overrightarrow{AB} = \overrightarrow{XY}$.

    It follows that $XY = \frac{1}{2}AB$ and $\overline{XY} \parallel \overline{AB}$.

    b. Would the above argument need to be modified if $\triangle ABC$ was an obtuse triangle? Explain your reasoning.

3. Refer to the nautical chart of the Stone Harbor, Massachusetts region on the next page. Suppose the *Angler* and the *Free Spirit* leave the mouth of the channel at Stone Harbor together. Their headings are 35° and 20° respectively. The *Angler* travels at 4 knots and after 30 minutes sights the *Free Spirit* to the north and west. The line of sight makes an angle of 110° with the path of the *Angler* from the harbor.

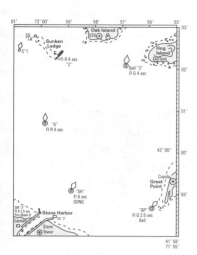

a. Draw the situation to scale.

b. Estimate the distance between the boats using the scale drawing.

c. Can vector component analysis be used to determine the distance? Explain your reasoning.

d. Use the Law of Sines to determine the distance between the two boats. Compare this distance to your estimate in Part b. At what speed is the *Free Spirit* traveling?

4. In landscaping an industrial park, a large boulder was to be moved by attaching chains to two tractors that would pull at an angle of 75° between the chains. If one tractor can pull with 1.5 times the force of the other, and the boulder requires a force of 10,000 newtons to be moved, what force is required from each tractor?

5. Every plane vector is equal to a position vector, so every two distinct vectors $\vec{a}$ and $\vec{b}$ determine an angle as shown below. Let $\vec{a} = (x_1, y_1)$ and $\vec{b} = (x_2, y_2)$.

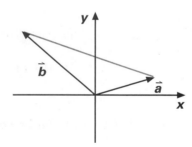

a. Write a formula for finding the angle between $\vec{a}$ and $\vec{b}$.

b. The numerator, $x_1x_2 + y_1y_2$, of the expression for the cosine of the angle determined by $\vec{a}$ and $\vec{b}$ is called the **inner product** or **dot product** of the vectors (x_1, y_1) *and* (x_2, y_2). When the angle between two vectors is 90°, what is the value of the inner product? Explain.

c. Find the angle between each pair of vectors.

- (2, 3) and (4, –3)
- (–2, 1) and (3, –5)
- (–1, –5) and (–3, –2)
- (1, 2) and (3, 4)

You are allowed to use your calculator whenever you complete exercises in the PUMP sets. However, in some cases the use of a calculator might actually slow you down. Critically examine each exercise before you complete it to determine the best strategy to use. Use your calculator wisely.

1. If 2 out of 3 registered voters will cast a ballot in an election and there are 450,000 registered voters, how many people will cast a ballot?

   (a) 225,000   (b) 660,000   (c) 675,000   (d) 900,000   (e) 300,000

2. Simplify $\left|3-5\right| - \left|7-10\right|$.

   (a) −1   (b) 5   (c) 1   (d) −6   (e) −5

3. Solve simultaneously for x and y: $-2x + 4y = -6$, $x + 3y = -12$.

   (a) (−1, 7)   (b) (3, 3)   (c) (−3, 3)   (d) $\left(18, \frac{18}{7}\right)$ (e) (−3, −3)

4. Which of the following could be a portion of the graph of a function $y = f(x)$?

   (a)    (b) 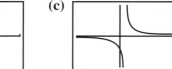   (c)

   (d) 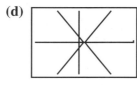   (e)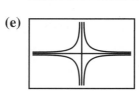

5. If $x^2 - x = 12$, then the smaller solution is

    (a) -4 (b) 1   (c) -3 (d) -2 (e) 3

6. If $11 - 5x > 7$, then

    (a) $x < 3.6$ (b) $x < -0.8$ (c) $x > 3.6$ (d) $x < 0.8$ (e) $x > 0.8$

7. The graph of a function $y = f(x)$ is shown. Which of the following is true?

    (a) $f(0) > 0$ (b) $f(1) > f(-4)$

    (c) $f(-1) < f(-2)$ (d) $f(-3) > f(0.5)$

    (e) $f(-5) < f(0)$

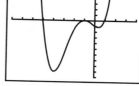

Xscl=1, Yscl=1

8. In the figure shown below, the perimeter of the square is 8. What is the area of the inscribed circle?

    (a) 16π (b) $\sqrt{8}\pi$

    (c) 4π (d) π

    (e) $4 - \pi$

9. Simplify $3x^{-3}(x^2 + x^3)$.

    (a) $-3x$ (b) $-\dfrac{3}{x} + 3$ (c) $\dfrac{3}{x} + 3$ (d) $\dfrac{3}{x} + 3x$ (e) $\dfrac{3}{x^6} + \dfrac{3}{x^9}$

10. Rewrite using radical notation: $3x^{\frac{1}{5}}y^{\frac{2}{5}}$.

    (a) $3\sqrt[5]{x}\sqrt{y}$ (b) $\sqrt[5]{3x^5y^5}$ (c) $3y\sqrt[5]{x}$ (d) $3\sqrt[5]{xy^2}$ (e) $\sqrt[5]{3xy^2}$

Lesson 2

Simulating Linear and Nonlinear Motion

In Lesson 1, you modeled linear motions of boats and airplanes. There are many other kinds of motions that are nonlinear. The wheels of an automobile or bicycle rotate around their centers. Satellites orbit Earth. A catcher for a softball or baseball team with a weak arm throws a "rainbow" to second base. A tennis player serves a ball so it just clears the net and lands in the service court. A golfer drives a ball over 300 yards to the middle of the fairway. You and a group of friends may play volleyball or compete in a friendly game of darts. In each of these contexts, direction and distance are important elements.

Think About This Situation

Carnivals and county fairs often include games in which you throw a baseball at a pyramid of bottles or at a target. Imagine that a target is 10 meters away. Your goal is to hit it with a ball.

a What are important variables that may affect the outcome of your throw?

b If you can throw hard, where should you aim?

c Where should you aim next if your first throw just barely makes it to the target?

d What are some factors that affect the path of the ball?

In this lesson, you will learn methods for simulating linear and nonlinear motions. By building graphing calculator or computer-based simulation models, you will be able to see the paths traveled by moving objects. You will even be able to simulate races and Ferris wheel rides. You will begin by simulating motion along a line.

INVESTIGATION 1 Parametric Models for Linear Motion

In Lesson 1, you learned how the coordinates of the terminal point of a vector can be determined by finding the components of the vector. In modeling the motion of a boat, the terminal point of a vector identifies the location of the boat. Motion involves change in location over time. A boat, for example, is at different places 15 minutes and 20 minutes into a trip. In Activities 1–3, you will investigate how to write rules giving the location of a moving object in terms of the time it has been moving, its *elapsed time*.

1. Suppose the *Wayfarer* begins at the origin of a coordinate system and follows a course with direction (not heading) 60° and a speed of 8 knots.

   a. Sketch this situation on a coordinate system.

   b. Write rules for the horizontal and the vertical components of a point on the ship's path in terms of elapsed time in hours (t).

   c. A partial table of values for elapsed time and the corresponding horizontal and vertical components is shown at the right. Use your rules to complete a copy of the table for values of t up to 2.0 hours.

   d. Describe how t changes; how x changes; and how y changes. What are the units of measure for x and y?

Elapsed Time t (hours)	Horizontal Component x	Vertical Component y
0.0	0	0.00
0.1	0.4	0.69282
0.2	0.8	1.3856
0.3	1.2	2.0785
0.4	1.6	2.7713
•	•	•
•	•	•
•	•	•
1.3		
1.4		
1.5		
1.6		
1.7		
1.8		
1.9		
2.0		

   e. Make a scatterplot of the (*horizontal component, vertical component*) data. Describe the pattern in the plot. Explain why this pattern makes sense.

2. Most graphing calculators and computer graphing software have a *parametric function* capability that enables you to quickly construct a table like the one above. Set your calculator or software to accept angle measures in degrees and parametric equations and, to display multiple graphs simultaneously in dot (not connected) format. The MODE screen to the left of one popular graphing calculator shows the correct settings. You may need to set graph styles differently on your calculator or software.

```
Normal Sci Eng
Float 0123456789
Radian Degree
Func Par Pol Seq
Connected Dot
Sequential Simul
Real a+bι re^θι
Full Horiz G-T
```

Now choose the ⌐ Y = ⌐ menu. Notice that the equations are paired. For the first pair, enter your rules for the *x* and *y* components from Activity 1 Part b. Your display should be similar to one of the two screens below.

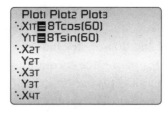

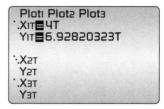

a. Why do both of these displays represent how *x* and *y* change with respect to time *t*?

b. Now use the table-building capability of your calculator or computer software to generate a table for T, X_{1T}, and Y_{1T} beginning at 0 with 0.1 increments in T. Compare this new table with the one you completed in Part c of Activity 1. Do the patterns you noted in Part d of that activity continue in this more extensive table?

Once you have the rules for X_{1T} and Y_{1T} entered in your calculator or software, you can display a graph of the model for the path of the ship. As with other graphical displays, you need to first set the viewing window. The settings shown below do the following:

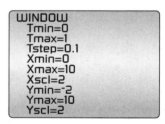

- ▪ Since the independent variable here is T, Tmin = 0 sets the calculator to begin evaluating X_{1T} and Y_{1T} at T = 0.

- ▪ Tstep = 0.1 increments T by 0.1 at each step until T is larger than Tmax.

- ▪ The X and Y settings establish the lower and upper bounds of the viewing screen.

3. Set your calculator or software to conform to the above conditions and then plot the (*x, y*) pairs from Activity 2.

a. Compare your display with the one shown at the right. If they differ, check each menu and your graph style settings.

b. Experiment with various ranges and step sizes for *t*. Try to answer questions such as the following. How many points are displayed? Why? What settings will show 21 points? Does the graph need to begin at the origin? How can you make it begin at a different point? How can you make sure all the points are displayed on the screen?

c. Explore your display by tracing along it. Compare the values of *t, x,* and *y* shown on the screen with those in your table.

The rules you used to generate the coordinates for the terminal point of the vector locating the *Wayfarer* at any time *t* are called **parametric equations** and the variable *t* is called a **parameter.** In this case, your parametric equations were

$$x = 8t \cos 60° \qquad \qquad x = 4t$$
$$\text{or}$$
$$y = 8t \sin 60° \qquad \qquad y = 6.92820323t$$

In the next several activities, you will explore ways to use parametric equations to model linear motion in different situations.

4. Suppose a commercial jet leaves Los Angeles International Airport on a course with direction 15°. The aircraft is set to travel at a speed of 600 mph in still air.

   a. Develop a parametric equation model for the location of the plane after *t* hours if the airport is placed at the origin of the coordinate system.

   b. How far east has the plane traveled in 2.5 hours? How far north?

   c. Simulate the motion of the aircraft on the calculator screen by showing its position every half hour until it reaches the East Coast, about 3,100 miles east of Los Angeles. Describe your viewing window settings.

   d. How would you modify your simulation to show the location of the plane every 12 minutes?

5. Now consider how parametric equations could be used to simultaneously model the motion of two boats. Begin by turning off the axes on your graphics screen.

   a. Suppose the *Charlotte Rose* leaves its anchorage at noon going due east at 8 knots. Write parametric equations for this motion.

   b. Find the time needed to travel 50 nm. Display the 50 nm path on your graphics screen. Trace your graph.

   c. The *Lady Anna* begins at 1:00 P.M. from a harbor 0.4 nm north of *Charlotte Rose's* starting location, traveling due east at 10 knots. Write parametric equations for this motion. Display the path.

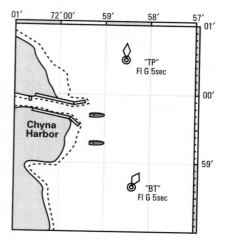

   d. Devise a way to display the paths of both the *Charlotte Rose* and the *Lady Anna* so that you can see the boats moving simultaneously, with the *Charlotte Rose* departing first.

   e. Use your display to decide which boat travels 50 nm first. Where is the other boat when the first boat has gone 50 nm? At what time will they have traveled the same distance?

f. How would you change your equations if each boat were traveling due west of the original starting point for 50 nm? Make and test the changes.

6. In previous courses, you developed the ability to predict the shape of the graph of various functions by examining their symbolic rules. This activity will help you extend your symbol sense to parametric equations. For each pair of parametric equations:

■ Predict what the graph will look like.

■ Check your prediction using your calculator or graphing software.

■ Make a sketch of the displayed graph and label it with the corresponding pair of equations.

For each case, use $\mathsf{Tmin = 0}$, $\mathsf{Tmax = 4}$, and $\mathsf{Tstep = 0.1}$. The viewing window should be $\mathsf{-40 \le X \le 40}$ and $\mathsf{-40 \le Y \le 40}$, with $\mathsf{Xscl = 10}$, $\mathsf{Yscl = 10}$.

a. $x = 5t$
$y = 8$

b. $x = -5t$
$y = 8$

c. $x = 6(t - 2)$
$y = -20$

d. $x = -7(t + 1)$
$y = 10$

e. $x = 10$
$y = 5t$

f. $x = 10$
$y = -5t$

g. $x = -20$
$y = 6(t + 2)$

h. $x = 8$
$y = -4(t - 5)$

7. Look back at the parametric equations and graphs you produced in Activity 6.

a. What general patterns do you see relating the shape and placement of a graph to the symbolic form of the equations?

b. Write a pair of parametric equations different from those in Activity 6, but with the same shape graph. Trade equations with a partner. Predict what the graph of your equations will look like and then test your prediction. If either your prediction or that of your partner is incorrect, identify the possible cause of the error and then repeat for a different pair of equations.

c. Explain why the following parametric equations have the same graph as the parametric equations in Part a of Activity 6.

$$x = 5t \cos 0°$$
$$y = 5t \sin 0° + 8$$

d. Explain why the following parametric equations have the same graph as the parametric equations in Part e of Activity 6.

$$x = 5t \cos 90° + 10$$
$$y = 5t \sin 90°$$

e. Determine which of the remaining pairs of parametric equations in Activity 6 can be represented in the form below. Explain your reasoning.

$$x = At \cos \theta + B$$
$$y = At \sin \theta + D$$

8. Test your understanding of modeling with parametric equations in the following situation: Suppose the cabin cruiser *Sawatdee* begins at noon heading due east at 8 knots. The *Delhi Dhaba* begins at noon at a location 60 nm due east of the *Sawatdee* and heads due west at 10 knots.

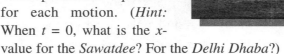

a. Represent this situation on a coordinate system.

b. Write parametric equations for each motion. (*Hint:* When $t = 0$, what is the x-value for the *Sawatdee*? For the *Delhi Dhaba*?)

c. At what location and time will they meet?

You may recall from your work with quadratic models in previous courses that when an object is dropped from a height above the surface of Earth, the velocity and distance traveled are functions of gravity and time. Neglecting air resistance, the average velocity after t seconds is $-4.9t$ meters per second or $-16t$ feet per second. Thus, the directed distance an object falls in t seconds due to gravity is $(-4.9t$ meters/second$)$ $(t$ seconds$) = -4.9t^2$ meters. In feet, the directed distance traveled is $-16t^2$ feet.

9. Suppose an object is released from a weather balloon 200 meters above the surface of Earth.

a. Explain why the height, in meters, of the object above the surface of Earth after T seconds can be represented by these parametric equations:

$$X_\mathsf{T} = 1$$
$$Y_\mathsf{T} = -4.9\mathsf{T}^2 + 200$$

b. Select appropriate values for T and a viewing window to display the motion of the object. Use dot mode. Sketch the display.

c. For a specific value of T (such as 1.34 seconds), what does the corresponding value of Y_T tell you about the object?

d. Describe how the distance the object falls per second changes with increasing time. How can this be observed in the graph? In a table?

e. How many seconds after the drop does the object strike the Earth? How did you determine the time?

f. In this example $X_\mathsf{T} = 1$. Is it important that X_T be 1, or could it be another number? Explain your reasoning.

g. Write a pair of parametric equations that describes the height, in feet, of an object that is dropped from a point 200 feet above the Earth's surface.

Preparing to launch a manned weather balloon.

In this investigation, you explored how parametric equations can be used to model linear motion.

ⓐ How do parametric equations differ from other algebraic equations you have studied?

ⓑ How are parametric equations of a point moving along a line related to vectors?

ⓒ Describe how you would write parametric equations of:

- A horizontal linear path at a constant velocity
- A vertical linear path at a constant velocity
- An oblique linear path through the origin at a constant velocity

Be prepared to share your ideas and descriptions with the class.

The general parametric equations for linear motion with a constant velocity are

$$x = At \cos \theta + B$$
$$y = At \sin \theta + D$$

When $\theta = 0°$, these simplify to $x = At + B$ and $y = D$.
When $\theta = 90°$, these simplify to $x = B$ and $y = At + D$.

On Your Own

Average velocity, after t seconds, of a falling object differs among celestial bodies.

Earth	The Moon	Jupiter

$-4.9t$ m/s	$-0.83t$ m/s	$-11.44t$ m/s

a. Suppose an object is dropped from 100-meter tall structures on Earth, on the Moon, and on Jupiter. Write parametric representations of each motion.

b. Display the motion of the objects in the same viewing window. Describe differences and similarities in the patterns of change.

c. Find the time it takes for the object to strike the surface of each body.

d. Draw the vector that shows the position of the object falling on the Moon at $t = 4.5$. What is the y-component of this vector? What does it tell you?

INVESTIGATION 2 Parametric Models for Nonlinear Motion

You have seen that linear motion can be described in terms of two components, a horizontal component and a vertical component. Most objects such as boats, trains, or airplanes continue to move along a straight line because energy is applied to maintain the speed. Without this energy, other forces such as friction or gravity would cause the object to slow down and finally stop.

In the game of slow-pitch softball, the pitcher throws the ball underhanded so that it goes high in the air and crosses the plate as it comes down. The batter tries to hit it as it comes down.

1. Consider a pitcher on a slow-pitch softball team who throws the ball toward home plate at a speed of 12 meters per second at an angle of 55° with the horizontal. Remember that the pitcher tries to get the ball to drop nearly vertically across the plate.

   a. For the moment, assume that the speed of the ball is constant at 12 m/s. Represent this situation on a coordinate system. Then sketch the vector showing the position of the ball after 1 second. Sketch the components.

   b. Write parametric equations describing the position with respect to time of a ball pitched at an angle of 55° to the ground with a constant velocity of 12 m/s and without the effect of gravity. What are the units of the parameter t in the equation?

   c. Display the graph using your graphing calculator or computer software.

   d. What are some limitations of this model?

2. Recall that the effect of gravity on the position of a falling object is represented by a vector $4.9t^2$ meters long and pointing straight down ($4.9t \times t \sin 270°$ or $4.9t \times t \sin (-90°)$). In this activity, you will refine your model in Activity 1 to take into account the effect of gravity on the softball pitch.

   a. Modify your parametric equations for the softball pitch to include the gravitational component.

   b. Sketch the vector that shows the position of the ball at each elapsed time.

   ■ 1 second

   ■ 1.7 seconds

   ■ 3.3 seconds

c. Now use your graphing calculator or software to simulate the motion of the pitched ball and investigate more closely the motion of the ball.

■ How long is the ball in the air?

■ What is its maximum height and when does it occur?

d. In slow-pitch softball, the pitcher stands on a pitching rubber 13.7 m from home plate. Will the pitched ball make it to the plate?

e. What are some limitations of this refined model?

3. Conduct the following experiments to help refine your model of the motion of the pitched ball in Activity 2.

a. Experiment 1: Physically simulate tossing a slow-pitch softball. Estimate the height above the ground at which you would release the ball. Use your result to modify the model of the slow-pitch toss.

b. Experiment 2: Use chalk or a piece of tape to simulate the front edge of the pitching rubber. Standing with both feet on the pitching rubber, step forward and simulate pitching a softball. Estimate the distance in front of the pitching rubber that you release the ball. Use your result to further modify the model to account for the distance in front of the pitching rubber that the ball is released.

c. Use your modified parametric model to estimate the height of the pitch when it passes over home plate. Should it be called a strike?

d. For a player of average height, the strike zone is between 0.5 m and 1.5 m above the ground. Modify the initial velocity of the ball until the pitch crosses the plate inside this strike zone. (Maintain the release angle at 55°.)

e. Now modify the angle of release to get the pitch across the plate inside the same strike zone when thrown with an initial velocity of 13 m/s.

f. Explain why it is difficult to consistently pitch a ball with great accuracy.

Activities 4–6 provide other contexts that can be modeled using parametric equations. Your group should scan the three activities and then, in consultation with your teacher, select one to complete and report on to the entire class.

4. World-class horseshoe pitchers are very accurate. For example, Walter Ray Williams, a national champion, averages about 90% ringers. The horseshoe pitching court has metal stakes 40 feet apart. The stakes stand 18 inches out of the ground.

a. Walter Ray pitches a horseshoe at 45 feet per second, at a 14° angle to the ground. He releases the horseshoe at about 3 feet above the ground and 2 feet in front of the stake at one end.. Write parametric equations modeling a typical throw.

b. How long is the thrown horseshoe in the air?

c. How close to 40 ft is the horizontal component when the horseshoe hits the ground?

d. If Walter Ray releases a horseshoe at 13° or 15° instead of 14°, what happens to the length of his pitch?

5. Frank Thomas, a baseball player with the Chicago White Sox, was the Most Valuable Player for the 1994 season. When he hits the ball well, it leaves the bat at about a 29° angle, 1 meter above ground, with a velocity of 40 meters per second (ignoring wind).

Frank Thomas

a. If the outfield wall is 6 m high and 125 m from home plate, how high will Frank's hit be when the ball reaches the plane of the wall? Is it a home run?

b. How long is the ball in the air?

c. How far does the ball travel?

d. What is the maximum height the ball attains?

e. How far would the ball travel if it left the bat at a 31° angle?

6. Meg Mallon, a professional golfer, can swing her driver at about 132 feet per second. A driver with 10° loft will propel a ball at about 150 ft/sec at an angle of about 30° (since the ball is met on the upswing and its compression adds to its velocity).

a. Write modeling equations that describe the position of the ball for any time t.

b. How long is the ball in the air?

c. If the ball runs 30 to 50 yards after it hits the ground, what is the total drive length in yards?

d. If a golfer wanted to lengthen her drive, should she learn to hit the ball higher by 5° or swing the club faster by 5 ft/sec? Explain your answer.

Meg Mallon

An object thrown or hit in the air may begin on a linear path, but when additional energy is not available, other forces affect the path and it becomes curved. Look back at your work on Activities 1–3 and for the activity you chose from Activities 4–6.

a Name several factors that affect the path of a moving object. Which component (horizontal or vertical) does each factor affect?

b Explain how the horizontal and vertical components of a motion may be used to model a motion and display it graphically. What units are used for each variable?

c Explain how your graphing calculator or computer software must be set up to graphically display motion as a function of time.

Be prepared to report on your chosen activity and share your group's thinking with the entire class.

In general, if there are several forces acting on a body, the resultant motion is the sum of the corresponding horizontal and vertical components. The parametric equations

$$x = At \cos \theta + Bt \cos \phi + C$$
$$y = At \sin \theta + Bt \sin \phi + D$$

model the location (x, y) of an object under forces acting at angles θ and ϕ in a plane with initial velocities A and B, respectively. The values of C and D are the initial horizontal and vertical distances of the object from the x–axis and y–axis respectively. When the second force is gravity, which has direction 270°, these equations become

$$x = At \cos \theta + \tfrac{g}{2}t^2 \cos 270° + C$$
$$y = At \sin \theta + \tfrac{g}{2}t^2 \sin 270° + D$$

where g is the gravitational constant, or equivalently

$$x = At \cos \theta + C$$
$$y = At \sin \theta - 4.9t^2 + D \text{ (distance in meters) or}$$
$$y = At \sin \theta - 16t^2 + D \text{ (distance in feet)}$$

since $\cos 270° = 0$ and $\sin 270° = -1$.

▶ On Your Own

Suppose Luisa begins her 10-meter platform dive with a velocity of about 2.3 meters per second. The angle at which Luisa leaves the platform is about 85°.

a. Write parametric equations modeling Luisa's position during the dive.

b. About how long is she in the air?

c. How high above the platform is she before she starts moving toward the water?

d. How far does she move horizontally before hitting the water?

e. Divers that push off nearly vertically could hit the platform on the way down. How many meters is Luisa from the platform when she passes it during the dive?

f. If the push-off angle were changed to 80°, how close to the platform would she come?

INVESTIGATION 3 ▶ Representing Circles and Arcs Parametrically

One of the most common *nonlinear* motions you see about you is that of objects turning around a point, that is, **circular motion.** The wheels on cars and bicycles, disks for computers, CDs of your favorite music, drive-shafts for lawn mowers, VCR tapes, carnival rides such as Ferris wheels, and many other toys, tools, and machines use circular motion in some way.

The computer information industry uses circular motion in many of its data storage devices. On a computer disk, data is stored on tracks in sectors, as illustrated in the diagram below.

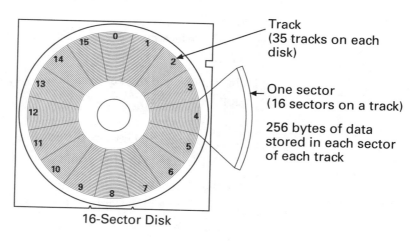

Track
(35 tracks on each disk)

One sector
(16 sectors on a track)

256 bytes of data stored in each sector of each track

16-Sector Disk

One important reason that circular disks are better than magnetic tape for recording information electronically is that the entire recording surface is accessible to the reading head almost instantaneously, simply by rotating the disk. The engineering challenge is to design a way for the reading head to identify its location on the spinning disk and, after that, where it should read information from a specific track and sector.

In the following activities, you will explore how to represent circles with parametric equations and then how to model circular motion.

1. Suppose the circle shown below has radius 6 cm. Point P is on the circle and $\overrightarrow{OP}$ makes an angle of θ with the positive x-axis as point P moves around the circle.

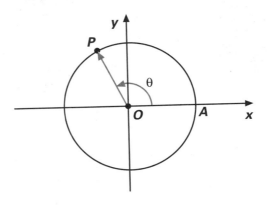

   a. How long is $\overrightarrow{OP}$?
   b. What is the direction of $\overrightarrow{OP}$?
   c. What are the components of $\overrightarrow{OP}$?
   d. Write parametric equations describing the coordinates of point P.
   e. Use your parametric equations and a graphing calculator or computer software to produce a graph of the circle. Is the graph what you expected? Explain. If necessary, change your window settings to display a graph of a circle.
   f. What does the parameter T represent? If Tmin = 0, what is the smallest Tmax value needed to produce a complete circle? Explain.

2. Investigate and then explain how you could set your calculator or computer software so that it displays only the part of the circle described in each case below.
   a. Quarter-circle between the positive x- and y-axes
   b. Half-circle to the left of the y-axis
   c. Half-circle below the x-axis
   d. Half-circle to the right of the y-axis
   e. Quarter-circle above the lines $y = x$ and $y = -x$
   f. An *arc* of a circle that a classmate describes to you

Recall that radians as well as degrees can be used to measure angles. While a degree is the measure of an angle determined by an arc that is $\frac{1}{360}$ of a complete circle, a radian is determined by an arc that is $\frac{1}{2\pi}$ of a complete circle. Since the circumference of a circle is $2\pi r$, the length of the arc corresponding to an angle of one radian is $\frac{1}{2\pi} \cdot 2\pi r = r$ linear units. The diagrams below illustrate these ideas.

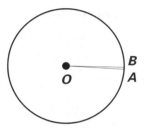

Measure of ∠AOB is 1 degree.

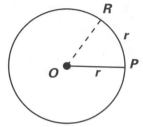

Measure of ∠POR is 1 radian.

3. In the following two diagrams, each ray corresponds to the terminal side of an angle whose initial side is the positive *x*-axis. Associated with each ray is the degree or radian measure of the angle. Using a copy of each diagram and the fact that 2π radians $= 360°$, determine the missing angle measures. Write radian measures with fractions involving π when appropriate.

a.

b.

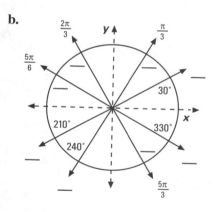

c. For each angle measure in Parts a and b, indicate the corresponding measure in revolutions. For example, $150° = \frac{5}{12}$ revolution.

Remember that, when calculating or graphing trigonometric functions, it is *very important* to always check the mode. Before proceeding with the next activity, set your calculator or graphing software to **Parametric** and **Radian** modes.

4. Consider again a circle with center at the origin and radius 6 cm as in Activity 1.

a. Explore how to produce the graph of this circle when θ is measured in radians. Write the parametric equations you would use.

b. What T settings for the viewing window enable you to produce a circle with the appropriate shape? Record your T settings.

c. Display a quarter-circle above the *x*-axis and to the right of the *y*-axis.

d. Display a half-circle below the *x*-axis.

e. Display a half-circle to the left of the *y*-axis.

f. Display a quarter-circle below the *x*-axis and to the left of the *y*-axis.

g. Display a quarter-circle above the line $y = x$ and above the line $y = -x$.

h. In what direction, clockwise or counterclockwise, were the graphs in Parts c–g drawn? Investigate how to draw them in the opposite direction.

Checkpoint

Consider these pairs of parametric equations:

$$x = 3t \cos 42° \qquad x = 3 \cos t$$
$$y = 3t \sin 42° \qquad y = 3 \sin t$$

a Which pair of equations produces a line? A circle? Explain how you can tell by looking at the symbolic form of the rules.

b What does "3" represent in each case?

c What does "*t*" represent in each case?

Be prepared to share your group's thinking with the entire class.

On Your Own

Write parametric equations for the circle with radius 8 and center at the origin.

a. With your calculator or computer graphing software set in **Degree** and **Dot** modes and axes turned off, adjust the viewing window so that it shows 42 dots on the circle in one revolution. Record your settings.

b. With your calculator or computer software in **Radian** and **Dot** modes, adjust the viewing window so that it shows 25 dots on the circle in one revolution. Record your settings.

INVESTIGATION 4 Simulating Orbits

You now know how to write parametric equations for a circle and to use a graphing calculator or computer software to display the circle. In order to simulate rotating objects such as CDs, you need to draw on the idea of *angular velocity.* Recall that the angular velocity of a rotating object is described in terms of the degrees (or radians) through which the object turns in a unit of time. For example, 3,600 degrees per second or 20π radians per second each describe the angular velocity of an object making 10 complete revolutions per second. Thus, for a particular time, t, the measure of the angle through which an object has turned is

$$\theta = 3,600°t \quad \text{or} \quad \theta = 20\pi t \text{ radians.}$$

Because the value of the parameter t determines the size of the angle θ, θ is a function of the time t.

1. Suppose a 2.25-inch radius CD is making 8 counterclockwise revolutions per second. To track the position of a point P on the CD as a function of time in a coordinate model, assume the disk revolves about the origin O and that at $t = 0$, point P is at (2.25, 0).

   a. Describe the angular velocity in degrees per second and in radians per second.

   b. Through how many degrees and how many radians has point P turned when $t = \frac{1}{100}$ sec? When $t = \frac{1}{50}$ sec? When $t = \frac{1}{10}$ sec?

   c. Write parametric equations that give the location of point P for any time t. Give both the degree and radian forms of the equations.

   d. How is t used to determine the size of the angle of rotation?

   e. Set your graphing calculator or graphing software window appropriately: Set Tmin = 0, Tmax = 1, and Tstep = 0.013, with Xmin = -5, Xmax = 5, Ymin = -3, and Ymax = 3. Set the mode to Dot and Radian. Using the radian form of the parametric equations, display the graph. How many times does the point rotate around the circle? Why does your answer make sense in terms of your window setting?

   f. Suppose you wanted to simulate the rotation of point P around the circle exactly once. How would you change the T values? How could you simulate point P moving around the circle two times? Three times?

   g. Repeat Part e but with the mode setting Connected. Describe your observations.

2. Sometimes when you expect to see a circle produced by a pair of parametric equations, you see something else. Enter the following parametric equations in your calculator or graphing software:

$$X_T = 4\cos 20\pi T \qquad Y_T = 4\sin 20\pi T$$

Set your calculator or software to **Connected** mode. Set **Tmin = 0** and **Tmax = 1**. Use $\boxed{\text{TRACE}}$ to investigate each graph for differing values of **Tstep**. Summarize your findings.

  a. Set **Tstep** $= \frac{1}{30}$. Describe the graph displayed.

  b. Set **Tstep** $= \frac{1}{60}$. Describe the graph you see.

  c. Set **Tstep** $= \frac{1}{16}$. Describe the graph displayed.

  d. Set **Tstep** $= \frac{7}{120}$. Describe the graph you see.

  e. Choose another value for **Tstep** and predict the resulting graph. Check your prediction.

3. A pulley rotates counterclockwise at 5π radians per second. Represent the center of the pulley by the origin O of a coordinate system and let P be a point on the circumference of the pulley. The parametric equations for the terminal point of a rotation vector $\overrightarrow{OP}$ are

$$x = 7 \cos \left(5\pi t + \frac{2\pi}{3}\right)$$
$$y = 7 \sin \left(5\pi t + \frac{2\pi}{3}\right)$$

  a. Describe the location of point P at $t = 0$ by giving the components of $\overrightarrow{OP}$. What are the direction and length of $\overrightarrow{OP}$?

  b. Describe the location of point P at $t = 0.1$, $t = 0.2$, $t = 0.3$, and $t = 0.4$ seconds.

  c. Use your graphing calculator or graphing software to simulate the motion of point P. Set **Tstep = 0.02**.

  d. How should you change the window setting so that point P makes only one revolution?

  e. How do these parametric equations differ from those in Activities 1 and 2? How are they similar?

4. A Ferris wheel with a 20-foot radius and center 24 ft above the ground is turning at one revolution per minute. Suppose that on a coordinate system, the ground surface is represented by the x-axis and the center of the wheel is on the y-axis.

  a. Explain why a point on the rotating Ferris wheel can be modeled by the following pair of parametric equations:

$$x = 20 \cos 2\pi t$$
$$y = 20 \sin 2\pi t + 24$$

Pulley system

b. Set your graphing calculator or graphing software so that it will display the motion of a rotating point for one revolution of the wheel. Record the viewing window settings you used. Explain why each setting was selected.

c. At what position on the Ferris wheel is the point located when $t = 0$?

d. How far above the ground is the seat that started at the 3 o'clock position when $t = 0.1$ minute? When $t = 0.5$ minute? When $t = 0.75$ minute?

e. How are the parametric equations modeling the position of a point on the rotating Ferris wheel different from those modeling a point on the rotating CD in Activity 1 and the pulley in Activity 3? How are they similar?

5. Once fully launched, a satellite or space station does not move in a circular orbit, but in an *elliptical orbit*. Ellipses will be studied more completely in Unit 8, "Space Geometry." For now, investigate how you can modify parametric equations for a circular path to produce an elliptical path.

a. What parametric equations will stretch the circular path defined by

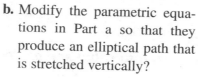

$$x = 8 \cos 2\pi t$$

$$y = 8 \sin 2\pi t$$

so that it has an elliptical shape similar to that in the diagram at the right? Compare your parametric equations with those of other groups.

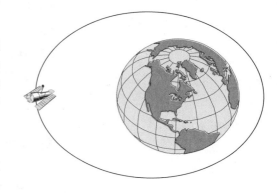

b. Modify the parametric equations in Part a so that they produce an elliptical path that is stretched vertically?

c. Write parametric equations for an elliptical path that crosses the *x*-axis at ±10 and the *y*-axis at ±5.

d. How would you modify the equations in Part c so that the "orbit" starts at (−10, 0)?

6. In completing Activities 4 and 5, you probably drew on your understanding of transformations of function graphs by translating and stretching. As you saw in Course 3, those kinds of transformations are closely connected to the symbolic form of function rules. You can extend the idea of customizing function graphs to graphs of parametric equations. Consider the path modeled by the following parametric equations:

$$x = 4 \cos t \text{ and } y = 4 \sin t, \text{ where } 0 \le t < 2\pi.$$

a. Describe the path.

b. Modify the equations so that the path is centered at (2, 1).

c. Modify the original equations so that the path is traced in a clockwise direction.

d. Modify the original equations so that the path starts at (0, 4).

e. Modify the original equations so that the path is an ellipse crossing the
  x-axis at ±8 and the y-axis at ±2.

f. Modify your equations in Part e so that the path is traced out clockwise
  starting from (–8, 0).

Checkpoint

In this investigation, you examined how the motion of a point following a
counterclockwise circular path can be modeled with parametric equations.
The fundamental equations are

$$x = A \cos Bt$$
$$y = A \sin Bt,$$

where B is the angular velocity of the moving point

a Describe the center and radius of this circular path.

b What is the location of the point following this path when $t = 0$?

c How would you modify the equations so that the path is traced in a
  clockwise direction?

d How would you modify the equations so the center of the circular
  motion is at the point with coordinates (p, q)? Explain.

e How would you modify the equations to produce an elliptical path with
  center at the origin?

Be prepared to share and explain your responses.

On Your Own

A circular disk with center at $P(0, 2)$ has a radius of 3. The disk rotates counterclockwise at 6π radians per second. Point Q on the disk has coordinates $(3, 2)$
when $t = 0$.

a. Sketch this situation.

b. Write parametric equations modeling the motion of point Q for any time t.
  Locate point Q when $t = 0.1$ and $t = 0.5$.

c. What setting of Tmax will ensure that point Q makes exactly one revolution?
  Explain.

d. Describe the settings for the parameter t that provide you with a good visual
  model of the path of point Q.

Modeling • Organizing • Reflecting • Extending

Modeling

1. In archery, as in other target shooting, the archer sets his sights so that when an arrow is shot at a particular distance, the arrow should hit the bull's-eye.

   a. Suppose an arrow leaves a bow at about 150 feet per second. Taking into consideration the effect of gravity, estimate an angle at which you think the archer should shoot so that the arrow hits the bull's-eye located 100 feet away. (Assume the center of the bull's-eye is at the same height as the release point of the arrow.)

   b. Find equations for the x- and y-components of the shot at any time t using your estimated angle.

   c. Check the adequacy of your model. How long does it take the arrow to reach the target? Does it hit the correct spot?

   d. If your model is not very accurate, modify the angle of aim until it gives better results. What angle seems to be the best?

2. Many people enjoy the game of darts. There are even national darts tournaments. To play darts, you stand 8 feet from a dart board and throw three darts per round, seeking to score points totaling 500.

   a. Suppose you are most accurate when you throw a dart at a 20° angle to the horizontal. If the bull's-eye is at the same height as your release point, about what initial velocity must you impart to the dart to hit the bull's-eye?

   b. How long is the thrown dart in the air?

   c. Suppose your dart-throwing opponent is most accurate when she throws at an initial velocity of 30 feet per second. At what angle should she throw her dart to hit the bull's-eye?

   d. About how long is her dart in the air?

3. Baseball pitchers, such as Roger Clemens of the New York Yankees, can throw a fastball pitch at nearly 100 mph. Roger Clemens is about 6 ft, 4 in. tall and releases the ball about 5 ft above the ground. The pitcher's mound is about 12 in. higher than the surrounding playing field. The pitching rubber itself is about 59 ft from the front of home plate.

   a. Make a sketch of the situation in which Roger Clemens releases the ball 4 ft in front of the pitching rubber. Is his point of release 5 or 6 ft above the field?

   b. At what angle to the horizontal should Clemens throw the ball for it to cross the front of the plate 2 ft above the ground if gravity is the only other force acting on the ball?

   c. Suppose that, due to the upward spin Clemens puts on the ball, the effects of gravity are negated over the distance to the plate. Write parametric equations that describe the position of the ball t seconds after release, if the ball is thrown so that it will cross the front of home plate about 2 ft above the ground.

      ■ At what angle to the horizontal does Clemens release the ball?

      ■ About how long does it take the pitch to get to the plate?

4. Joan Embery has spent much of her life researching the behavior of gorillas. Before examining injured gorillas, she must use a tranquilizer dart gun to sedate them. Her tranquilizer dart gun shoots darts at about 650 feet per second. Suppose Joan shot a dart (aimed horizontally at 5 ft above the ground) at a large injured gorilla 400 ft away.

   a. Would the dart reach the gorilla? Explain.

   b. How should Joan's aim be adjusted so that she will hit the gorilla at a point somewhere between 2 and 5 ft above the ground? Test your best model with a graphing calculator or graphing software and sketch the result.

   c. How much leeway does Joan have in choosing the angle at which to shoot?

5. In the diagram below, a pulley with 5 cm radius is centered at $O(0, 0)$. A second pulley with 2 cm radius is centered at $B(10, 0)$. The pulley at O is rotating counterclockwise at 2 revolutions per second.

   a. Find the angular velocity of the pulley with center at point B.

   b. Write parametric equations that model the position of point A as the pulley rotates around its center O starting at $(5, 0)$.

   c. Model the position of point C with parametric equations, if its starting position is $(12, 0)$.

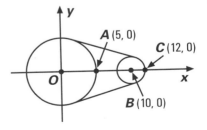

d. Set your graphing calculator or computer graphing software on Simul (simultaneous), enter the algebraic descriptions of both circles, and display the graphs.

e. Set Tmin and Tmax so that one revolution around the circle with center O is graphed. What happens to the graph of the related motion around the circle with center B? Explain.

f. Set Tmin and Tmax so that one revolution around the circle with center B is graphed. What happens to the graph of the related motion around the circle with center O? Explain.

Organizing

1. The graph of $y = 3x + 2$ is a line.

a. If $x = t$ is one of the parametric equations for this line, write the equation that expresses y as a function of t.

b. Display the graph of the parametric equations. Is the graph a line?

c. Do the equation $y = 3x + 2$ and the set of parametric equations give the same line when graphed? If not, what would you change to make them look the same in the viewing window $-10 \leq x \leq 10$ and $-10 \leq y \leq 10$?

2. Consider these two sets of parametric equations:

$$\begin{array}{ll} x = t & x = 2t + 2 \\ y = 2t - 3 & y = 4t + 1 \end{array}$$

a. Draw the graph of each pair of parametric equations on its own coordinate system. How are the two graphs related?

b. Find the x- and y-values for both sets of parametric equations when $t = 1$. Compare the results.

c. For each pair of equations, find a value of t that gives the point $(0, -3)$.

3. Consider the following two sets of parametric equations:

$$\begin{array}{ll} x = t & x = 3t \\ y = 2t & y = 6t \end{array}$$

a. Compare the graphs of these pairs of equations.

b. For each pair of equations, describe the rates at which x and y change with respect to t.

c. For each pair of equations, describe the rate at which t changes with respect to x and with respect to y.

d. How could you use the information in Parts b and c to determine the rate of change of y with respect to x?

e. Compare the rates at which a point moves along the graphs of the two pairs of parametric equations.

4. The graph of each pair of parametric equations below is a line.

    i. $x = 2t$ **ii.** $x = -3t$
        $y = 3t$ $y = 2t$

   iii. $x = 2t + 1$ **iv.** $x = at$
        $y = -t - 2$ $y = bt$

    a. For each pair of parametric equations, determine the slope of the line.

    b. For each pair of parametric equations, combine the two equations into a single equation that expresses y as a function of x.

5. In the figure at the right, there are four circles with the same center, O. The circles have radii of 1, 2, 3.5, and 5 units. Arc AB has length 1 unit.

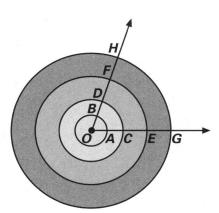

    a. What is the radian measure of $\angle O$?

    b. A size transformation with center O will transform arc AB to each other arc. Find the magnitude of each such transformation.

    c. Find the lengths of arcs CD, EF, and GH.

    d. How do similar circles and their arcs help make the definition of a radian more reasonable?

Reflecting

1. If you were an athlete who wished to throw, kick, or hit a ball as far as possible, would you rather do it on the Moon, Earth, or Jupiter? Explain your reasoning.

2. The study of parametric equations is enhanced by the use of the graphing and table-building capabilities of graphing calculators and computer graphing software. Identify the capability you find most helpful for each of the following tasks when modeling projectile motion such as that of a kicked soccer ball and explain your choice.

    a. Visualize the path.

    b. Determine the maximum height.

    c. Determine the horizontal distance traveled.

    d. Determine a point at which the vertical velocity is 0.

3. Linear motion through the origin can be modeled with parametric equations of the form

$$x = At \cos \theta$$
$$y = At \sin \theta$$

where A and θ are constants.

   a. What does A represent? What does θ represent?

   b. How would these equations be modified if $(x, y) = (4, 0)$ when $t = 0$?

   c. How would these equations be modified if $(x, y) = (0, -3)$ when $t = 0$?

4. Why is approximately the same motion defined by each pair of parametric equations?

$$x = 3t \cos 42° \qquad x = 2.2294t$$
$$y = 3t \sin 42° \qquad y = 2.0074t$$

5. According to Morris Kline, a former Professor of Mathematics at New York University, "The advantage of radians over degrees is simply that it is a more convenient unit. . . . The point involved here is no different from measuring a mile in yards instead of inches." Why do you think Kline believes the radian is a "more convenient unit"? (Morris Kline, *Mathematics for Liberal Arts*, Addison Wesley, 1967. p. 423)

Extending

1. Parametric equations can be used to represent most familiar functions. Use a graphing calculator or computer graphing software to display the graph of each function and then make a sketch of the graph on your paper. Describe the shape of the graph. Then combine the equations into a single equation relating x and y.

   a. $x = t + 1$, $y = t + 2$
   b. $x = 2 - 3t$, $y = t + 5$
   c. $x = t$, $y = \frac{3}{t}$
   d. $x = 4 \cos t$, $y = 4 \sin t$
   e. $x = 4t - 2$, $y = 8t^2$

2. Suppose John Daly drives a golf ball about 285 yards, which includes 50 yards of roll after it hits the ground. His drive leaves the club at about a 27° angle.

   a. What is the initial velocity of the ball when it leaves the club?

   b. What is the maximum height that the ball reaches?

   c. How long is the ball in the air?

3. Northwest Airlines has hubs at Detroit, Memphis, and Minneapolis. Flights from Memphis to Seattle and Detroit to Los Angeles leave at the same time and cruise at 32,000 feet. On a particular day, a 70 mph upper level northwest wind is blowing. The heading of the flight out of Memphis is 307° and the heading of the flight out of Detroit is 260°. The still air speed of each airliner is 600 mph.

a. Memphis is 400 miles west and 500 miles south of Detroit. Write parametric equations for the paths each plane will follow if they head directly toward their destinations.

b. On what heading should each plane steer to counteract the effects of the wind?

c. What is the wind-affected speed of each plane?

d. Do the paths of these two aircraft intersect? If so, what are the coordinates of the point of intersection? Is there danger of a mid-air collision? Explain your reasoning.

e. Seattle is about 1,800 mi from Memphis and Los Angeles is about 2,000 miles from Detroit. About how long will it take each plane to reach its destination at its wind-affected speed?

4. Two freighters leave port at the same time. On a coordinate system, one port is located at $A(20, 0)$ and the other at $B(-15, -4)$. The freighter *Mystic Star* leaves port A steaming west at 8 knots on a heading of 280°; the *Queensland* steams east from Port B on a heading of 70° at 10 knots.

a. Write parametric equations for each of these routes.

b. Represent the path of each of these freighters on your graphing calculator or computer graphing software. Sketch the paths on your paper.

c. Do the paths of the freighters cross? Is there a danger that the freighters will collide? Explain.

d. What is the location of the *Mystic Star* when the *Queensland* crosses its path? What is the location of the *Queensland* when the *Mystic Star* crosses its path?

5. In Investigation 4, you saw that in a coordinate system, a circular orbit with center at the origin can be described by parametric equations of the form:

$$x = r \cos At \qquad \text{and} \qquad y = r \sin At.$$

Similarly, an elliptical orbit with center at the origin can be described by parametric equations of the form:

$$x = a \cos At \qquad \text{and} \qquad y = b \sin At, \text{ where } a \neq b.$$

In the case of a satellite or space station orbiting Earth, the path is an elliptical orbit, but its center is not the center of Earth. Earth's center is one of two foci of the orbit, as indicated in the diagram below. The *apogee* is the point on the orbit farthest from Earth. The *perigee* is the point on the orbit closest to Earth.

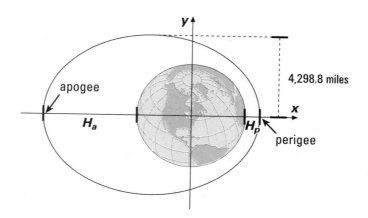

a. In the case of a space station, NASA expects the altitude of apogee H_a to be 400 miles and the altitude of perigee H_p to be 200 miles. Using the diagram above (not drawn to scale) and assuming the radius of Earth is about 4,000 mi, develop parametric models of Earth and of the orbit of a space station around Earth.

b. Simulate the motion of the space station in orbit around Earth and verify the coordinates of the apogee and perigee.

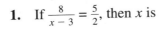

1. If $\frac{8}{x-3} = \frac{5}{2}$, then x is

   (a) 14   (b) 0.2   (c) 19   (d) 6.2   (e) 6.1

2. $\frac{3}{x} - \frac{4}{y} =$

   (a) $\frac{3y - 4x}{xy}$ (b) $\frac{3x - 4y}{xy}$ (c) $\frac{-1}{x - y}$ (d) $\frac{-1}{x + y}$ (e) $\frac{-1}{xy}$

3. Find the value of b, if the slope of the line $12x - by = 15$ is -36.

   (a) $\frac{5}{4}$ (b) -3 (c) 3 (d) $\frac{1}{3}$ (e) $-\frac{1}{3}$

4. If $f(x) = x^2 + 2x - 3$, then $f(a - 1)$ is

   (a) $a^2 + 4a + 4$ (b) $a^2 - 5$ (c) $a^2 + 5$

   (d) $a^2 - 4$ (e) $a^2 + 2a - 4$

5. Solve $6m^2 - 11m = 35$ for m.

   (a) $m = \frac{5}{3}$, or $m = -\frac{7}{2}$ (b) $m = -\frac{5}{3}$, or $m = \frac{7}{2}$ (c) $m = -\frac{3}{5}$, or $m = \frac{2}{7}$

   (d) $m = \frac{3}{5}$, or $m = -\frac{2}{7}$ (e) no real solution

6. The solutions to $2\left|x-5\right|-3=15$ are $x=$

    (a) -14 and 14 (b) -4 and 4 (c) 14 (d) -4 (e) -4 and 14

7. If $(x+4)^3=50$, then which of the following best approximates x?

    (a) 3.58 (b) 0.92 (c) -0.32 (d) 3.78 (e) 2.32

8. $\sin(-x)=$

    (a) $\cos(-x)$ (b) $-\sin x$ (c) $\sin x$ (d) $\cos x$ (e) $\frac{1}{\sin x}$

9. If $3^x=54$, then which of the following best approximates x?

    (a) 3.631 (b) 18 (c) 162 (d) 0.056 (e) 3.780

10. Solve $\sqrt[3]{2x+6}=6$.

    (a) 105 (b) 2 (c) -2.32 (d) 216 (e) none of these

Looking Back

In this unit, you investigated how vectors can be used to model navigation routes. In that setting, the idea of the sum or resultant vector was found to be useful in determining courses of ships and airplanes that were moving with a constant velocity. You also examined how vectors, their components, and the parametric equations derived from the components can be used to analyze linear and projectile motion. These ideas are also useful in representing circular motion of a point on a disc rotating at a constant velocity. Using ideas of transformations of graphs, you were able to develop models for elliptical orbits. In this final lesson, you will have the opportunity to review and apply these important ideas in new contexts.

1. The Gulf Stream is a warm ocean current flowing from the Gulf of Mexico along the east coast of the United States. It is about 50 nautical miles wide.

   a. Off New York City, the Gulf Stream flows at about 3 knots on a heading of about 35°. Sketch a vector representing the Gulf Stream current.

   b. Suppose the freighter *Morocco* out of New York City is steaming at 12 knots on a heading of 100° when it meets the Gulf Stream. Represent the *Morocco*'s course with a vector.

   c. Make a vector model showing the effect of the Gulf Stream on the *Morocco* as it moves across the Gulf Stream.

   d. What course should the *Morocco* steer to cross the Gulf Stream and remain on its planned course?

   e. How long will it take the *Morocco* to cross the Gulf Stream?

2. Preliminary testing of robocarriers (as pictured) used in paper mills involves parallel tracks 85 meters long. Suppose a robocarrier programmed to travel 20 meters per minute (m/min) is placed on one track and a robocarrier programmed to travel at 30 m/min is placed on the second track.

   a. Model the motion of the two robocarriers under the conditions that the testing of the second robocarrier begins 30 seconds after the first.

Robotic Paper Movers

b. Which robocarrier reaches the end of the test track first? How close to the end of its track is the other robocarrier when this happens?

c. Does the second robocarrier overtake the first? If so, at what time?

d. How could the rates of the robocarriers be adjusted so that both robocarriers arrive at the end of their tracks at about the same time?

3. Helen Alfredsson is a Swedish golfer. She and Robert Gamez lost a playoff in the 1994 J.C. Penney Classic to Marta Figueras-Dotti and Brad Bryant. Alfredsson typically can hit her drives 230 yards, including about 30 yards of roll. Suppose her drives leave the tee at about a 25° angle.

Helen Alfredsson

   a. Sketch a vector model for the position of the ball of a typical Alfredsson drive at time *t* seconds.

   b. Write rules for the components. Use variables for any unknown quantities.

   c. What initial velocity must her club head impart to the ball for it to stay in the air for 200 yards?

   d. How long is the ball in the air?

   e. How far will Alfredsson hit her drive if she is hitting with a 5 mph wind?

   f. How far will Alfredsson hit her drive if she hits from a tee region that is elevated 30 feet and there is no wind?

4. Laserdiscs in the constant angular velocity (CAV) format rotate at 1,800 revolutions per minute. Such a disc is shown at the right. Each side of a 12-inch CAV disc has 54,000 tracks; each track contains one frame of a motion picture.

Laserdisc factory

   a. Motion pictures are recorded at 30 frames per second. How many CAV laserdiscs are needed to record a 1-hour, 59-minute motion picture?

   b. Express the angular velocity of a CAV laserdisc in radians per second and in degrees per second.

   c. Write parametric equations to describe the location of a point, *P*, on a track 4.5 inches from the center *O*, if $\overrightarrow{OP}$ points along the *x*-axis when *t* = 0.

5. Write parametric equations describing each of the following paths of an object moving at a constant velocity.

   a. A vertical line through the point (5, –2)

   b. A line through the points (2, 4) and (6, –2)

   c. A circle of radius 5 centered at the origin, traced counterclockwise, starting at the point (0, 5) when $t = 0$

   d. An ellipse centered at the origin, traced counterclockwise, crossing the x-axis at ±8 and the y-axis at ±12

   e. How would you modify the parametric equations in Parts c and d if the paths were to be traced out clockwise?

6. The following problem was posed by Neal Koblitz in the March 1988 issue of the *American Mathematical Monthly*. The problem is one of several applied problems given to his calculus classes at the University of Washington. Solve the problem using methods developed in this unit.

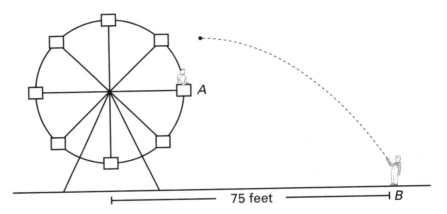

   You are standing on the ground at point B (see diagram), a distance of 75 ft from the bottom of a Ferris wheel with radius 20 ft. Your arm is at the same level as the bottom of the Ferris wheel. Your friend is on the Ferris wheel, which makes one revolution (counterclockwise) every 12 seconds. At the instant when she is at point A, you throw a ball to her at 60 ft/sec at an angle of 60° above the horizontal. Take $g = -32$ ft/sec^2, and neglect air resistance. Find the closest distance the ball gets to your friend. (Source: *American Mathematical Monthly*, March 1988, page 256.)

Checkpoint

Vectors and parametric equations are very useful for modeling and analyzing motion: linear, nonlinear, and circular.

ⓐ What is a vector? What characteristics distinguish a vector from a number? From a segment? How are vectors added? Subtracted?

ⓑ How many variables are involved in modeling motion with parametric equations? What is the significance of each variable?

ⓒ Describe parametrically and graphically the following paths of a point P.

- P is moving in the direction of θ at a constant velocity of 7 m/s.

- P is propelled at an angle θ with an initial velocity of 100 m/s and then flies freely in the air.

- P is on a circle with radius 2 m making 15 counterclockwise revolutions per minute.

ⓓ How are parametric equations for circular motion similar to, and different from, those for elliptical motion? For linear motion? For projectile trajectories?

Be prepared to explain your responses and thinking to the entire class.

On Your Own

Write, in outline form, a summary of the important mathematical concepts and methods developed in this unit. Organize your summary so that it can be used as a quick reference in future units and courses.

Logarithmic Functions and Data Models

Inverses of Functions

A fundamental idea in mathematics is that of an *inverse*. For example, in your previous work you solved equations like $12x - 5 = 31$ or $10x^2 + 8 = 648$ by reasoning with inverse operations. You were able to solve some matrix equations of the form $AX = C$ by multiplying by an inverse matrix. In Unit 2, you used the inverse tangent function on your calculator to calculate direction angles for vectors. In this lesson, you will investigate inverses of functions more generally.

One of the events in hot-air balloon competitions is hitting a target on the ground while the balloon is in flight. Suppose a "drop bag" is dropped from a balloon at an altitude of 500 feet. The two tables below give velocity and total-distance-fallen data as functions of time.

Time (in seconds)	Velocity (in feet/second)
0	0
1	32
2	64
3	96
4	128
5	160

Time (in seconds)	Distance (in feet)
0	0
1	16
2	64
3	144
4	256
5	400

Examine the tables of (*time, velocity*) and (*time, distance*) data on page 142.

ⓐ Explain why velocity is a function of time and write a rule that expresses this relationship.

ⓑ Imagine interchanging the columns of the first table. Is time a function of velocity? Can you write a rule that expresses this relationship?

ⓒ Explain why distance is a function of time and write a rule that expresses this relationship.

ⓓ Imagine interchanging the columns of the second table. Is time a function of distance?

ⓔ Do you think interchanging the input and output variables of a given function will always produce a new function? Explain your reasoning.

INVESTIGATION 1 When Does a Function Have an Inverse?

Look back at your responses to the "Think About This Situation." To express the fact that the velocity v of the bag tossed from the hot-air balloon is a function of time t, you may have written $v = f(t) = 32t$. Since for each value of v in the table there is exactly one value of t, it is also the case that t is a function of v. This fact can be expressed by writing the equation $t = f^{-1}(v)$, which is read "t equals f-inverse of v."

Similarly, you may have used the equation $d = g(t) = 16t^2$ to express the fact that the distance d the bag falls is also a function of time t. Since, for each value of d in the second table there is a unique value of t, you can express this fact by the equation $t = g^{-1}(d)$.

1. Using the tables on page 142 and the notation $v = f(t)$ and $d = g(t)$, evaluate each expression and interpret your work in terms of the context.

   a. $f(3)$

   b. $f^{-1}(160)$

   c. $g(4)$

   d. $g^{-1}(64)$

2. The velocity function $f(t) = 32t$ and the distance-fallen function $g(t) = 16t^2$ have restricted domains because of their applied context. Now consider the functions $f(x) = 32x$ and $g(x) = 16x^2$ over the domain of all real numbers.

   a. What is the range of $f(x)$ in this case? If a is any number in the range of $f(x)$, is there exactly one value for x such that $f(x) = a$? Explain.

b. What is the range of $g(x)$ in this case? If b is any number in the range of $g(x)$, is there exactly one value for x such that $g(x) = b$? Explain.

3. Examine each of the following graphs of a function defined by an equation $y = f(x)$. For which functions is it the case that if r is any value in the range of $y = f(x)$, there is a unique x such that $f(x) = r$? Such functions are called **one-to-one functions**.

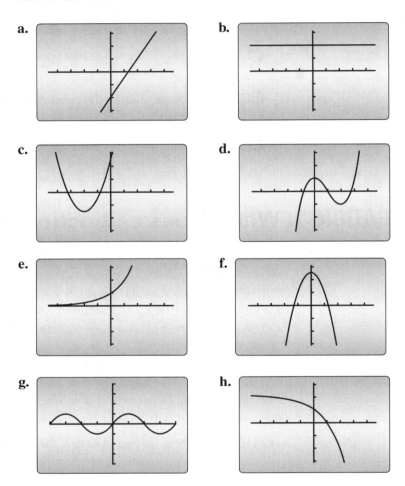

A function $y = f(x)$ has an inverse if and only if it is one-to-one. The **inverse function** is denoted f^{-1} and is read "the inverse of f" or "f-inverse."

$$f^{-1}(r) = q \text{ means that } f(q) = r.$$

4. Look back at your answers to Activity 3. How do graphs of functions that have inverses differ from those that do not? Does the function $y = |x|$ have an inverse? Explain.

5. Reconsider the functions $f(x) = 32x$ and $g(x) = 16x^2$ in Activity 2. Which of these functions have inverses? Explain your reasoning.

6. The table below gives values for a function $y = g(x)$ with domain $\{-4, -3, \ldots, 3, 4\}$.

x	-4	-3	-2	-1	0	1	2	3	4
g(x)	-11	-9	-7	-5	-3	-1	1	3	5

    a. Explain why the function $y = g(x)$ has an inverse.

    b. Evaluate the following:

       ■ $g^{-1}(-3)$ ■ $g^{-1}(5)$ ■ $g^{-1}(-9)$ ■ $g^{-1}(1)$

    c. Construct a table for a function that does not have an inverse. Exchange tables with other groups and discuss why the functions represented do not have inverses.

7. Charter buses regularly make the 450-mile trip from Las Vegas to Reno. The time T (in hours) the trip takes is a function of *average speed* of the bus x (in miles per hour). The rule for this function is $T(x) = \frac{450}{x}$ for $0 < x \le 80$.

    a. Explain why this function has an inverse.

    b. Evaluate and interpret each of the following expressions:

       ■ $T^{-1}(7.5)$ ■ $T(50)$

       ■ $T^{-1}(9.375)$ ■ $T^{-1}(7.03125)$

Composing a function and its inverse has similarities to multiplying a nonzero number and its multiplicative inverse. Examine the diagram below. For a function $f(x)$, an inverse function f^{-1} is a function that will, when applied to an element in the range of f, undo the effects of f. That is, if you begin with x, you will end with x after applying f and then f^{-1}. Symbolically, this is denoted $f^{-1}(f(x)) = x$ and read "f-inverse of f of x equals x."

Since functions f and f^{-1} are inverse functions if $f^{-1}(f(x)) = x$ for every x in the domain of f and $f(f^{-1}(x)) = x$ for every x in the domain of f^{-1}, you can use this property to verify that two functions are inverses.

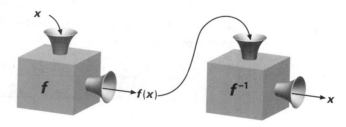

8. Refer back to the function $y = g(x)$ defined by the table in Activity 6.

    a. Verify that $g^{-1}(g(0)) = 0$.

    b. Evaluate the following:

       ■ $g^{-1}(g(3))$ ■ $g^{-1}(g(-4))$

9. Think about the definition of an inverse function and the information conveyed by the compact notation $f^{-1}(f(x)) = x$.

   a. How are the domain of f^{-1} and the range of f related?

   b. If (p, q) is on the graph of f, why is (q, p) on the graph of f^{-1}?

   c. Explain why if $f(x) = 2x + 6$, then $f^{-1}(x) = \frac{1}{2}x - 3$.

Checkpoint

In this investigation, you saw that not all functions have inverses.

a What characteristic of a graph of a function ensures the function has an inverse?

b What characteristic of a table of ordered pairs defining a function ensures that the function has an inverse?

c For which of the following families of functions does each member of the family have an inverse?

- Non-constant linear functions
- Exponential functions
- Power functions
- Quadratic functions
- Trigonometric functions

d Suppose a function $y = h(x)$ has an inverse and that $h(-2) = 8$, $h(0) = 0$, and $h(8) = 21$. Evaluate $h^{-1}(8)$, $h^{-1}(0)$, and $h^{-1}(h(8))$.

Be prepared to share your group's responses and reasoning with the class.

On Your Own

For each function $y = f(x)$ defined below, determine whether the function has an inverse. If the function has an inverse, find $f^{-1}(2)$. If the function does not have an inverse, explain why not.

a.

x	−3	−2	−1	0	1	2
y	−14	−10	−6	−2	2	6

b.

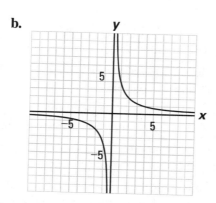

c.

x	-3	-2	-1	0	1	2	3
y	9	4	1	0	1	4	9

d. $y = 2.25x^2 + 4$, with domain all real numbers

INVESTIGATION 2 Function Inverses and Their Graphs

In the previous investigation, you learned that not all functions have inverses. However, every one-to-one function will have an inverse. In this investigation, you will explore how the graph of a function and that of its inverse are related and, in particular, how the graph of $y = f(x)$ can be used to find the graph of $y = f^{-1}(x)$. You will also explore how the equation for $y = f(x)$ can be used to derive an equation for the inverse function.

1. Begin by considering the linear function $f(x) = 2x - 4$ and its inverse.

   a. Examine the table and scatterplot of sample $(x, f(x))$ values given below. On a copy of the grid, make a scatterplot of the corresponding $(f(x), x)$ values for f^{-1} using ☐ markers.

x	f(x)
0	-4
1	-2
2	0
3	2
4	4
5	6
6	8
7	10
8	12
9	14
10	16

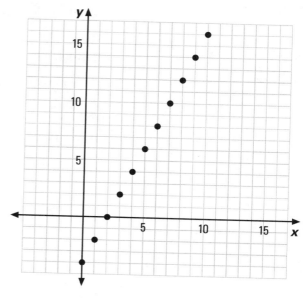

b. Write a "$y = \ldots$" rule for f^{-1} that fits the numerical and graphical patterns of the $(f(x), x)$ values.

c. Using different colored pens or pencils, draw graphs of the functions $y = f(x)$ and $y = f^{-1}(x)$ on your grid.

d. Using a third color, add the graph of $y = x$ to your grid. How do the graphs of $y = f(x)$ and $y = f^{-1}(x)$ appear to be related? Provide evidence that supports your observation.

e. Each member of your group should test if your observation in Part d is true in other cases. Repeat Parts a–c for a different linear function and its inverse. Based on your findings, how are the graphs of a linear function and its inverse related?

f. If you want to sketch the graph of the inverse of $f(x) = 3x + 1$, what procedure is suggested by Part e? Why does this procedure make sense in terms of the coordinate description of a reflection across the line $y = x$?

2. Now consider three linear functions:

   i. $f(x) = -2x + 1$ **ii.** $g(x) = 1.5x - 5$ **iii.** $h(x) = -0.7x + 2$.

   a. For each function sketch its graph and that of its inverse on the same coordinate axes.

   b. Find a rule for the inverse of each function.

   c. Explain why the inverse of any linear function $f(x) = ax + b$, $a \neq 0$, will be a linear function.

In Activity 2, you found the equation for the inverse of a linear function by reasoning graphically. You reflected the graph of $y = f(x)$ across the line $y = x$ and then wrote an equation for the image line. Recall that a reflection across the line $y = x$ is defined by the mapping $(x, y) \to (y, x)$. You can use this fact to find the equation of the inverse of the function by reasoning symbolically: simply apply the transformation $(x, y) \to (y, x)$ to the equation of the linear function.

For example, suppose that: $y = f(x) = 3x - 9$

The reflection of $y = f(x)$
across the line $y = x$ is given by: $x = 3y - 9$

Rewrite with y as a function of x: $y = \frac{1}{3}x + 3$

So, $f^{-1}(x) = \frac{1}{3}x + 3$

To verify, compute $f^{-1}(f(x))$: $f^{-1}(f(x)) = \frac{1}{3}(3x - 9) + 3$

$$= \frac{1}{3} \cdot 3x - \frac{1}{3} \cdot 9 + 3$$

$$= x$$

Thus, $f^{-1}(f(x)) = x$, so $f^{-1}(x) = \frac{1}{3}x + 3$ is the inverse of $f(x) = 3x - 9$.

3. Use symbolic reasoning to find a rule for the inverse of each of the following functions. For each rule, verify that it represents the inverse function.

   a. $f(x) = \frac{1}{2}x - 2$

   b. $g(x) = -2x + 1$

   c. $h(x) = x - 7$

4. The property $f^{-1}(f(x)) = x$ can be interpreted as saying that f^{-1} "undoes" the effect of f on each input x.

   a. To evaluate $f(x) = 3x - 9$, what operations are performed on an input x, and in what order?

   b. How would you undo these operations to return to the input x? Use these ideas to write a rule for $f^{-1}(x)$. Compare your rule to that in the example on page 148.

   c. Use this method of "undoing" to write rules for the inverses of each of the functions in Activity 3. Compare your results to those you obtained in Activity 3.

5. Consider the power function $f(x) = x^3$.

   a. Explain why this function has an inverse.

   b. Sketch the graph of this function and its inverse on the same coordinate axes.

   c. Find a rule for $f^{-1}(x)$. What is $f^{-1}(125)$? What is $f^{-1}(-64)$?

   d. Under what conditions will a power function of the form $g(x) = x^n$, n a positive integer, have an inverse? What kind of function will the inverse be?

Checkpoint

A function and its inverse have important geometric and algebraic relationships.

ⓐ Describe how the graphs of $y = f(x)$ and $y = f^{-1}(x)$ are related.

ⓑ Describe how you can find the equation for $f^{-1}(x)$ from the equation for $f(x)$.

ⓒ What is the simplest symbolic form for $y = f^{-1}(f(x))$? Describe its graph and table.

Be prepared to explain your descriptions to the entire class.

On Your Own

The basic unit of Mexican currency is the peso. On February 1, 2000, the Mexican peso was worth 0.1058 U.S. dollar. Use this exchange rate for the following questions.

a. How many U.S. dollars should you get for 100 pesos?

b. Write a rule for the function, *f*, for converting money from Mexican to U.S. currency.

c. Find a formula for the inverse of *f*.

d. What does the inverse function tell you in practical terms?

MORE

Modeling • Organizing • Reflecting • Extending

Modeling

1. If you live in or have visited a community in the northern United States, you may have noticed that weather reports during late fall and winter give both an actual temperature and the temperature you feel as a result of the *wind chill factor*. The wind chill factor measures how much colder it feels due to the wind. For example, if the

Chicago during a winter snowstorm.

thermometer reads 20°F, but the wind chill temperature is 10°F, you will feel as cold as if the actual temperature were 10°F with no wind. The function $f(T) = -52 + 1.6T$, where T is the actual temperature measured in degrees Fahrenheit, can be used to estimate a wind chill temperature for a wind speed of 40 mph.

a. What is $f(32)$, and what does it mean in this context?

b. Does the function $f(T)$ have an inverse? Explain your reasoning.

c. Using only the function rule $f(T) = -52 + 1.6T$ and your calculator or computer software, find $f^{-1}(20)$ and describe what it means in this context. What is $f^{-1}(-12)$ and what does it mean?

d. Find a rule for $f^{-1}(T)$.

e. Using your rule from Part d, find $f^{-1}(20)$ and $f^{-1}(-12)$ and compare with your answers in Part c.

2. Suppose daily operating profit, in dollars, for a movie theater is a function of the number of tickets sold with rule $P(x) = 8.5x - 2,500$, for $0 \le x \le 1,000$.

   a. What is $P(625)$ and what does it mean?

   b. Explain why the profit function has an inverse.

   c. $P(400) = 900$. Rewrite this equation in terms of P^{-1}.

   d. Verify that $P^{-1}(4,470) = 820$ and describe what this equation means in this context.

   e. Find a rule for $P^{-1}(x)$ and then verify that $P^{-1}(P(450)) = 450$.

3. The formulas for the area of a circle and the volume of a sphere can be thought of as functions of the radii of the shapes.

   a. Write a rule expressing the area of a circle as a function of its radius. What is the domain of this function? Sketch a graph.

   b. Does this function have an inverse? If so, write a rule for the inverse.

   c. Explain why it makes sense that the radius of a circle should be a function of its area. In what contexts would this function be useful?

   d. Does the function $f(x) = \pi x^2$, where x is any real number, have an inverse? Compare your answer to that in Part b. Explain any differences.

   e. Now write a rule expressing the volume of a sphere as a function of its radius. What is the domain of this function? Sketch its graph.

   f. Does this function have an inverse function? If so, write a rule for the inverse function.

   g. Explain why it makes sense that the radius of a sphere should be a function of its volume. In what contexts would this function be useful?

   h. Does the function $g(x) = \frac{4}{3}\pi x^3$, where x is any real number, have an inverse? Compare your answer to that in Part f. Explain any differences.

4. In previous courses, you have seen that many irregular shapes in the natural world can be modeled by fractals. The number of new branches at each stage of the fractal tree shown below can be represented by the function $B(n) = 2^n$.

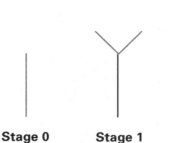

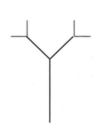

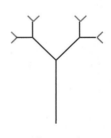

Stage 0   Stage 1   Stage 2   Stage 3

a. Explain why $B(n) = 2^n$ has an inverse.

b. What does the expression $B(16)$ represent? What does the expression $B^{-1}(16)$ represent?

c. $B(9) = 512$. Rewrite this expression in terms of B^{-1}.

d. Evaluate: $B^{-1}(128)$ and $B^{-1}(32{,}768)$.

e. Sketch the graph of $y = B(n)$ and $y = B^{-1}(n)$ on the same coordinate axes.

f. Does the function $y = B^{-1}(n)$ belong to one of the basic function families you have previously studied? Explain.

Organizing

1. As you have seen in the case of the function $g(x) = x^2$, not every function has an inverse. Note that the horizontal line $y = 9$ intersects the graph of $g(x) = x^2$ in two points.

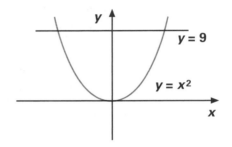

a. Why does this fact imply that the function g does not have an inverse?

b. Use a *horizontal line test* to determine which of the following functions have inverses.

  i. $f(x) = 3(0.5^x)$ **ii.** $g(x) = x^4$ **iii.** $h(x) = x^5 + 2$

  iv. $v(x) = |x|$ **v.** $c(x) = \cos x$ **vi.** $s(x) = \sin x$

c. How can you use a *vertical line test* to determine whether a given graph is that of a function?

2. For each function below, sketch the graph of the function and its inverse on the same coordinate system. Then find a rule for the inverse of the function. Verify your work by writing an equation for $f^{-1}(f(x))$.

  a. $f(x) = 3x - 2$ **b.** $f(x) = -2x + 3$

  c. $f(x) = 4x$ **d.** $f(x) = x$

3. Suppose $f(x) = ax, a \neq 0$.

  a. Describe the graph of $y = f(x)$.

  b. Explain why the graph of $y = f^{-1}(x)$ contains the origin.

  c. Find an equation for $f^{-1}(x)$.

4. Suppose $f(x) = ax + b$, $a \neq 0$, and $b \neq 0$.

  a. Describe the graph of $y = f(x)$.

  b. Find an equation for $f^{-1}(x)$ and verify that your equation gives the inverse of $f(x)$.

  c. For what conditions on a and b do the graphs of $y = f^{-1}(x)$ and $y = f(x)$ have a single point in common?

  d. Find the coordinates of the common point under the conditions stated in Part c.

5. The application of one function followed by the application of a second function to the result of the first as in $f^{-1}(f(x))$ is called **composition of functions**. The two functions need not be inverses of each other. In the diagram below, the output of one function $f(x)$ is used as the input for a second function $g(x)$. In this case, the *composite* is denoted $g(f(x))$ which is read "g composed with f of x" or "g of f of x."

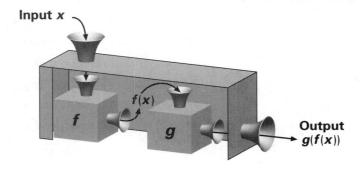

  a. Suppose f and g are functions defined by the following table:

x	−3	−2	−1	0	1	2	3
f(x)	10	8	7	−3	−4	−7	−8
g(x)	3	1	0	2	−3	−1	−2

  i. Make a table of values for $f(g(x))$ with $x = -3, -2, -1, 0, 1, 2, 3$. Remember to always start with the innermost set of parentheses.

  ii. Make a table of values for $g(g(x))$ with $x = -3, -2, -1, 0, 1, 2, 3$.

  iii. Explain why you cannot find the composite function $g(f(x))$.

  b. Consider the two functions $f(x) = -x^2 + 7$ and $g(x) = 3x + 4$. Using input values of −1, 2, 0.5, and 8 for x:

  i. Calculate $f(g(x))$ for each input value.

  ii. Calculate $g(f(x))$ for each input value.

  c. If f and g are two functions, what must be true about the domains and ranges of f and g in order for $f(g(x))$ to make sense? What must be true for $g(f(x))$ to make sense?

Reflecting

1. Sometimes operations that you might think are inverses really aren't.

   a. A gasoline company raised its prices by $0.06 for the Memorial Day holiday. After the holiday, it lowered its prices by $0.06. Are these two actions inverses? Explain.

   b. A gasoline company raised its prices at the pump by 6% for sales during Memorial Day week. Following the holiday, the company lowered its prices by 6%. Are these two actions inverses? Explain.

2. In your previous studies, you learned that geometric transformations of a plane such as rotations, translations, and size transformations are functions whose domains and ranges are all points in the plane. Describe the inverse of each of the following transformations and explain how you know you have found each inverse.

   a. Counterclockwise rotation of 60° about the origin

   b. Translation with components 3 and −4

   c. Size transformation with magnitude 4 and center at the origin

   d. Counterclockwise rotation of 80° about the origin followed by a size transformation with center at the origin and magnitude $\frac{1}{2}$

   e. Reflection across the line $y = 5$

3. Suppose g is a function that is always increasing. Explain why g has an inverse. What can you say about the behavior of g^{-1}?

4. Look back at your work for Organizing Task 5.

   a. If it is possible to form the composite of two functions, will the composite itself be a function? Explain your reasoning.

   b. Consider the functions: $f(x) = -x^2 + 7$ and $g(x) = 3x + 4$.

   - How would you find a rule for the composite $f(g(x))$?
   - How would you find a rule for the composite $g(f(x))$?

   c. In the case of the functions in Part b, is $g(f(x)) = f(g(x))$?

Extending

1. Recall that functions may be defined in terms of a parameter t. For example, the equations $x = t - 1$ and $y = 2t + 3$ give a parametric representation for $y = 2x + 5$.

   a. Derive the equation $y = 2x + 5$ from the parametric representation given above.

b. Graph $x = t - 1$, $y = 2t + 3$ using the parametric graphing capability of your calculator or computer graphing software.

c. Graph $x = 2t + 3$, $y = t - 1$.

d. How are the graphs in Parts b and c related? How are the functions related?

e. Justify your response to Part d by giving a logical argument.

2. Consider the following *piecewise-defined function*.

$$g(x) = \begin{cases} x - 2 \text{ if } x \le 2 \\ 2x - 4 \text{ if } x \ge 2 \end{cases}$$

Find an algebraic representation of the inverse of g and sketch a graph of $y = g^{-1}(x)$.

3. Recall that one way to estimate the instantaneous rate of change (derivative) of a function $f(x)$ is to calculate the difference quotient: $\frac{f(x + 0.1) - f(x)}{0.1}$.

a. What is the instantaneous rate of change of $f(x) = ax + b$ at $x = x_0$?

b. Find the inverse of $f(x) = ax + b$.

c. Find the instantaneous rate of change of $f^{-1}(x)$ at $x = x_0$.

d. Compare the instantaneous rates of change at $x = x_0$ for $f(x)$ and $f^{-1}(x)$.

4. In Organizing Task 1, you found that $s(x) = \sin x$ and $c(x) = \cos x$ do not have inverses because they fail the horizontal line test. However, many calculators have $\sin^{-1}$ and $\cos^{-1}$ keys. These are inverse sine and inverse cosine functions.

a. Produce the graph of $y = \sin^{-1} x$ in the standard ZTrig viewing window. (If your calculator does not have the ZTrig option, which is found on the ZOOM menu on TI calculators, use the following window settings: Xmin = -2π, Xmax = 2π, Xscl = $\frac{\pi}{2}$, Ymin = -4, Ymax = 4, Yscl = 1. The results will be almost the same.)

- Is the graph produced a graph of a function? Why?

- On the same set of axes, produce the graph of $y = \sin x$.

- What restriction is placed on the domain of $y = \sin x$ so that an inverse function exists?

- Are there other ways to restrict the domain of $y = \sin x$ so that an inverse function exists?

b. Now produce the graph of $y = \cos x$ and $y = \cos^{-1} x$ on the same set of axes using the standard ZTrig viewing window.

- What restriction is placed on the domain of $y = \cos x$ so that an inverse function exists?

- Are there other ways to restrict the domain of $y = \cos x$ so that an inverse function exists?

The number of items on college mathematics placement tests varies, but most are *timed* tests. For example, 20 minutes is usually allowed to complete a 20-item placement test. As you complete the PUMP sections in this unit and units to follow, you should work toward the goal of accurately completing the 10 items in 10 minutes.

1. The ages and genders of the students in a certain school are given in the following table. What percent of the students are males age 17 or older?

Age	Male	Female
16	250	270
17	325	325
18	125	205

   (a) $16\frac{2}{3}\%$ (b) 64.3%   (c) 30%   (d) $8\frac{1}{3}\%$ (e) 48.5%

2. If $a = -5$ and $b = -1$, then $2a^2 - 3b^3 =$

   (a) 23   (b) 53   (c) -47   (d) 47   (e) 17

3. How many solutions does this system have?

$$\begin{cases} 3x + 2y = 4 \\ -x + 3y = -5 \end{cases}$$

   (a) none   (b) an infinite number   (c) two   (d) one   (e) three

4. Let $f(x) = x^2 - 2x$. Find $\frac{f(1 + h) - f(1)}{h}$.

   (a) $h^2 - 1$ (b) $h^2 - 2h + 2$ (c) h (d) $h^2 + 2h + 2$ (e) $h - 2$

5. Solve for a: $a + 3\sqrt{a} - 4 = 0$.

(a) $a = 1$ or $a = -4$ (b) $a = 1$ or $a = -2$ (c) $a = 2$

(d) no real solutions   (e) $a = 1$

6. If $(x + 3)(x - 1) > 0$, then

(a) $-3 < x < 1$ (b) $x < -1$ or $x > 3$ (c) $-3 < x < -1$

(d) $x < -3$ or $x > 1$ (e) $-1 < x < 3$

7. The solutions to $\frac{(2x - 14)(x + 3)}{x - 2} = 0$ are $x =$

(a) 7, 3, and 2   (b) -7 and 2   (c) 7, -3, and 2

(d) 7 and -3 (e) 7, -3, and -2

8. A given rectangle has length L and width W. Its area is 80 square inches, and its length is 10 inches greater than its width. Which pair of equations describes these conditions?

(a) $\begin{aligned} LW &= 80 \\ L + 10 &= W \end{aligned}$ (b) $\begin{aligned} LW &= 80 \\ W + 10 &< L \end{aligned}$ (c) $\begin{aligned} LW &= 80 \\ W + 10 &= L \end{aligned}$

(d) $\begin{aligned} 2L + 2W &= 80 \\ L + 10 &= W \end{aligned}$ (e) $\begin{aligned} 2L + 2W &= 80 \\ W + 10 &< L \end{aligned}$

9. If $5^{3x - 1} = 1$, then $x =$

(a) $\frac{1}{5}$ (b) $\frac{1}{3}$ (c) $\frac{2}{3}$ (d) $-\frac{4}{3}$ (e) no real solutions

10. Simplify $\frac{a}{\sqrt[3]{4}}$.

(a) $\frac{a\sqrt[3]{2}}{2}$ (b) $\frac{a\sqrt[3]{4}}{4}$ (c) $\frac{2a^3}{4}$ (d) $\frac{a}{2}$ (e) $\frac{a\sqrt[3]{4}}{16}$

Lesson 2

Logarithmic Functions

Newspapers and news programs on television report several economic indices which, taken together, provide a measure of the "health" of the U.S. economy. One of the indices is the Dow Jones Industrial Average (DJIA). The DJIA is a weighted average of the stock prices for 30 major American corporations. It provides a benchmark to help determine the overall trend of the stock market. The table and plot below display the DJIA at 5-year intervals beginning in 1922.

Year	DJIA
1922	93.2
1927	175.8
1932	64.6
1937	166.4
1942	107.2
1947	177.6
1952	270.8
1957	475.7
1962	639.8
1967	879.1
1972	949.1
1977	894.6
1982	884.4
1987	2,264
1992	3,282
1997	7,448

Source: *Value Line Publishing Inc.,* 1998.

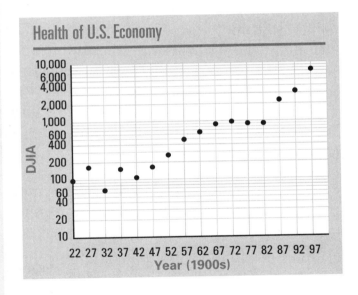

Think About This Situation

Examine the plot of (*year, DJIA*) data on the previous page.

a How would you describe the pattern of change in the DJIA over the period 1922–1997?

b The scale on the horizontal axis is a *linear scale*. It shows 75 years in about 6.8 cm. Why do you think the scale is called linear?

c How does the vertical scale differ from the horizontal scale?

d What would be some drawbacks of using a linear scale on the vertical axis?

The scale on the vertical axis of the plot on the previous page is called a *logarithmic scale*. Here equal distances correspond to powers of 10. This method of scaling is based on a new function. This function is the focus of Investigation 1.

INVESTIGATION 1 Common Logarithms

In Lesson 1, you discovered a relationship between the graph of a function and the graph of its inverse. You also examined conditions under which a function had an inverse. You saw that a function has an inverse if and only if it is one-to-one. This means that all strictly increasing or decreasing functions such as linear functions $y = ax + b$, with $a \neq 0$, have inverses. In this investigation, you will explore possible inverses for exponential functions.

Consider repeatedly folding a sheet of paper in half as shown below.

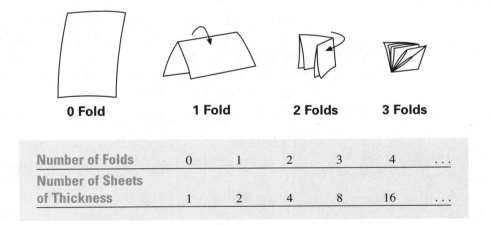

| **0 Fold** | **1 Fold** | **2 Folds** | **3 Folds** |

Number of Folds	0	1	2	3	4	. . .
Number of Sheets of Thickness	1	2	4	8	16	. . .

1. The pattern in the table on the previous page relating number of folds x and number of sheets of thickness y can be modeled by the rule $y = 2^x$.

   a. What is the thickness if the paper is folded 7 times?

   b. How many folds would be needed to get the number of sheets in a 500-page novel, assuming that one could actually fold a piece of paper that many times?

   c. Sketch the graph of $y = 2^x$. Explain why the function $y = 2^x$ has an inverse. Sketch the graph of its inverse on the same coordinate axes.

   d. If the domain of $y = 2^x$ is all real numbers, what is the range? What are the domain and range of its inverse?

   e. Is $x = 2^y$ the equation of the inverse of $y = 2^x$? Explain your reasoning. Can you rewrite $x = 2^y$ with y expressed as a function of x?

As you saw in Activity 1, an exponential function has an inverse. To write the equation for the inverse of $y = 2^x$, $x = 2^y$, in the familiar "$y = \ldots$" form, a special notation is used.

If $2^y = x$, then $y = \log_2 x$ (which is read base 2 logarithm of x).
$\log_2 x$ is the exponent on 2 that gives x.

2. The *logarithmic function* $y = \log_2 x$ is the inverse of the exponential function $y = 2^x$. Since $y = \log_2 x$ is another way of writing $x = 2^y$, you can rewrite an equation involving an exponent as an equation involving a logarithm.

   a. Since $32 = 2^5$, what is $\log_2 32$?

   b. Since $2^{10} = 1{,}024$, what is $\log_2 1{,}024$?

   c. Explain why $\log_2 8 = 3$.

   d. What is $\log_2 1$? Why?

There is nothing special about 2 as a base of a logarithm. Other numbers such as 5, 8, 10, or any other positive number not equal to 1 could be used as the base of a logarithm. The bases commonly used in mathematics are 2, 10, and $e \approx 2.71828\ldots$. The base e logarithm will be studied in Unit 7, "Functions and Symbolic Reasoning." The base 10 logarithm is called the *common logarithm*.

Common logarithm: $\log_{10} x = y$ if and only if $10^y = x$.

Because base 10 logarithms are so commonly used, $\log_{10} x$ is often written simply as log x. Whenever you see "log x" with no base indicated, it always means $\log_{10} x$.

Completing Activities 3 and 4 will help you become more familiar with the idea of a logarithm. As you complete these activities, think about the fundamental relationship:

$\log_a x = y$ if and only if $a^y = x$ ($a > 0$, $a \neq 1$).

3. Rewrite each expression using logarithmic notation.

   a. $10^0 = 1$ **b.** $2^4 = 16$ **c.** $10^3 = 1,000$

   d. $10^5 = 100,000$ **e.** $10^{-1} = \frac{1}{10}$ **f.** $2^{-6} = \frac{1}{64}$

4. Rewrite each expression using exponential form.

   a. $\log_2 2 = 1$ **b.** $\log 100 = 2$ **c.** $\log_2 128 = 7$

   d. $\log 0.01 = -2$ **e.** $\log 0.001 = -3$ **f.** $\log_2 0.25 = -2$

5. The log function is a built-in function on most calculators. Use your calculator to help you investigate and describe characteristics of the common log function, $y = \log x$. Start by making an easily examined graph and table of values for the function.

   a. Describe the pattern of change shown in the graph. How is that pattern shown in the table?

   b. What is the domain of $y = \log x$? What is the range? Explain why there is no logarithm of either a negative number or 0.

   c. Where does the graph cross the x-axis? Express this fact in a symbolic rule. Explain why it makes sense that the graph doesn't cross the y-axis.

   d. For what values of x is $\log x$ positive? Negative?

   e. For what value of x does $\log x = 1$?

   f. Use your calculator to find $\log 0.5$ and $\log 20$ to the nearest thousandth.

   g. Solve $1.6 = \log x$.

6. Estimate the value of the following logarithms. Check your estimates with a calculator.

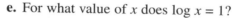

	Estimate	**Actual**
log 16		
log 1.6		
log 1,600		
log 3		
log 0.3		
log 30		

7. Now think about the relationship between a function, its inverse, and what happens when you apply them sequentially. Consider $f(x) = 10^x$ and $g(x) = 2^x$.

   a. Write symbolic rules for $f^{-1}(x)$ and $g^{-1}(x)$.

   b. On the same coordinate system, graph $y = f(x)$, $y = f^{-1}(x)$, $y = f(f^{-1}(x))$, and $y = f^{-1}(f(x))$. Explain why the graphs of $y = f(f^{-1}(x))$ and $y = f^{-1}(f(x))$ appear as they do.

   c. What would you expect the graphs of $y = g(g^{-1}(x))$ and $y = g^{-1}(g(x))$ to look like? Why?

   d. Write expressions for $f(f^{-1}(x))$, $f^{-1}(f(x))$, $g(g^{-1}(x))$, and $g^{-1}(g(x))$ in terms of logarithms and exponents. Then rewrite in a simpler equivalent form.

   e. Find the value of each of the following when $x = 5$.

     ■ $10^{\log x}$ ■ $2^{\log_2 x}$

     ■ $\log 10^x$ ■ $\log_2 2^x$

The fact that $\log_a x = y$ means $a^y = x$ is often very useful in evaluating expressions, in writing equivalent expressions, and in solving equations.

8. Use symbolic reasoning to evaluate the given expressions and to solve the given equations. Justify your answers.

   ■ Evaluate the following:

     a. $\log_2 1$ **b.** $\log_2 256$

     c. $2^{\log_2 15}$ **d.** $\log_b b^9$

     e. $\log_{10} 10{,}000$ **f.** $\log 0.01$

     g. $\log \sqrt{10}$ **h.** $\log 10^a$

   ■ Solve for x:

     i. $3^x = 81$ **j.** $\log_2 x = -4$

     k. $\log_x \frac{1}{16} = \frac{1}{2}$ **l.** $\log_7 7 = x$

     m. $\log_{10} x = 6$ **n.** $\log_x 0.0001 = -4$

     o. $\log x = -3$ **p.** $\log 1 = x$

     q. $\log x = \log 100$ **r.** $\log x = \log (2x - 3)$

9. Look back at the Dow Jones Industrial Average graph at the beginning of this lesson (page 158). The vertical axis is labeled with multiples of powers of 10. How are the distances between 60 and 80, 600 and 800, and 6,000 and 8,000 related? How can the labeling of the vertical axis and the relationship between these distances be explained by the use of logarithms?

New York Stock Exchange

Checkpoint

In this investigation, you explored a new family of functions called logarithmic functions.

a Describe how logarithmic and exponential functions with the same base are related.

b Describe the characteristics of the graph of $y = \log x$ and compare them with the characteristics of the graph of $y = 10^x$.

c Write each of the following equations in exponential form.
- $\log \sqrt{10} = a$
- $s = \log_2 r$

Write each of the following equations in logarithmic form.
- $2^{-4} = \dfrac{1}{16}$
- $10^5 = 100,000$

d Determine whether each of the following statements is true or false. Justify your answers.

- $\log 10^3 = 3$
- If $\log x = 4$, then $x = 40$.
- $\log_x x = 1$
- $2^{\log_2 5} = 5$

Be prepared to share your descriptions, equations, and reasoning with the class.

On Your Own

Use symbolic reasoning and what you have learned about logarithms to complete the following tasks.

a. Evaluate each expression without using your calculator.

   i. $\log_2 64$ **ii.** $\log_2 2$

  iii. $\log 1$ **iv.** $\log 0.001$

b. Solve each equation without using your calculator. Check your solution.

   i. $\log_3 x = 4$ **ii.** $\log_x 64 = 3$

  iii. $10^{\log 6} = x$ **iv.** $\log (10^3)^2 = x$

c. Using the definition of the common logarithm, find consecutive integers m and n such that each of the following statements is true.

- $m < \log 275 < n$
- $m < \log 3 < n$
- $m < \log 0.5 < n$

INVESTIGATION 2 Re-expression and Equation Solving with Logarithms

Originally, logarithms were developed as a tool to simplify long and cumbersome computations. To aid in this endeavor, properties of combining exponential expressions were transformed into properties of logarithms. Today, log functions are often used when answering questions about exponential models. Since logarithms undo the effects of the corresponding exponential function, you can use algebraic reasoning with logarithms to solve many exponential equations.

1. Begin by reviewing properties of exponents developed in your previous coursework. Complete each of the following statements assuming all expressions are defined. Illustrate each property with a numerical example.

   a. $b^r \cdot b^s = ?$ **b.** $\dfrac{t^r}{t^s} = ?$

   c. $(a \cdot b)^r = ?$ **d.** $(m^r)^s = ?$

   e. $d^{-s} = ?$

2. In this activity, you will investigate how the first two properties of exponents in Activity 1 can serve as a bridge to corresponding properties of logarithms.

   a. Begin by examining various ways to re-express the number 36: $30 + 6$, $18 + 18$, 4×9, 3×12, and 6^2. Find log 36 and the logarithms of the numbers into which 36 is decomposed. Describe any pattern that you see in the answers. If there is a pattern, make one or more conjectures.

   b. Decompose 16 in several ways. Test your conjectures from Part a for your factors or addends of 16. Choose another number and test your conjectures further. Compare your conjecture(s) with those of other groups.

   c. Supply reasons for each step in the following argument:

   > If $r = \log x$ and $s = \log y$, then $x = 10^r$ and $y = 10^s$;   (Why?)
   >
   > then $x \cdot y = 10^r \cdot 10^s$;   (Why?)
   >
   > then $x \cdot y = 10^{r + s}$.   (Why?)
   >
   > Therefore, $\log (x \cdot y) = r + s = \log x + \log y$.   (Why?)

   d. From your work in Part b, list examples that illustrate the relation proved in Part c.

e. Summarize the relationship in Part c in your own words.

f. Explain why the *Product Property* of common logarithms established in Part c is also a property of logarithms with base 2.

g. In Part c, you established a key property of logarithms of products. Now predict how $\log \left(\frac{x}{y}\right)$ might be related to $\log x$ and $\log y$.

h. Using a procedure similar to the deduction in Part c, derive an expression for $\log \left(\frac{x}{y}\right)$ in terms of $\log x$ and $\log y$.

i. Summarize, in words, the relationship you established in Part h.

j. Prove that the *Quotient Property* of common logarithms established in Part h also holds for base 2 logarithms.

3. The properties of logarithms you developed in Activity 2 can be used to simplify computations involving logarithms.

a. Evaluate each expression without using your calculator. Then check your result with a calculator.

- $\log 25 + \log 40$

- $\log 700 - \log 7$

b. Sharing the workload among members of your group, and without using the log function on your calculator, find the logarithm of each of the numbers 1 through 10 using the facts that $\log 2 \approx 0.3010$, $\log 3 \approx 0.4771$, and $\log 7 \approx 0.8451$.

4. The *Product Property* you established in Part c of Activity 2 leads to a particularly useful property in the case where both factors are the same number.

a. Explain why each of the following statements is true.

$\log x^2 = 2 \log x$

$\log x^3 = 3 \log x$

$\log x^5 = 5 \log x$

b. Generalize the pattern emerging in Part a.

c. The general pattern in Part b provides a powerful technique that can be used to solve exponential equations of the type found in Investigation 1. The pattern provides a way to rewrite $\log x^m$ in an equivalent form without an exponent. Give the reasons for each step in the derivation below.

If $\log x = y$, then $x = 10^y$;	(Why?)
then $x^m = (10^y)^m$;	(Why?)
then $x^m = 10^{ym}$;	(Why?)
then $\log x^m = my$.	(Why?)
Thus, $\log x^m = m \log x$.	(Why?)

d. If $\log 5 \approx 0.69897$, find $\log 5^3$, $\log 5^{1.3}$, and $\log 5^{10,000}$.

e. Could the argument using common logarithms in Part c be given using base 2 logarithms also? Explain your reasoning.

f. Summarize the relationship you found in Part c in your own words. This relationship is sometimes called the *Power Property* of logarithms.

In Activities 2–4, you discovered and proved three useful properties of logarithms. Make sure you understand and can use each one. The next two activities will illustrate the usefulness of these properties in reasoning symbolically with exponential models.

5. In your previous work, you saw that the rates at which medicines such as insulin break down in the bloodstream have predictable patterns. Although the rate varies with the drug and from individual to individual, a typical pattern for insulin is shown in the graph below. That pattern can be modeled well by the equation $y = 10(0.95^x)$.

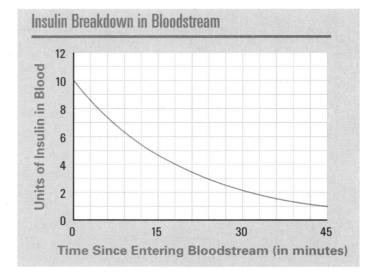

Insulin Breakdown in Bloodstream

Units of Insulin in Blood

Time Since Entering Bloodstream (in minutes)

a. What do the values 10 and 0.95 in the equation tell about the amount of insulin in the bloodstream?

b. Suppose you wanted to find the half-life of insulin in this case. Instead of estimating this value from graphs or tables of $y = 10(0.95^x)$, you could use the following symbolic reasoning strategy. Explain each step in the strategy.

$$5 = 10(0.95^x) \qquad \text{(Why?)}$$
$$0.5 = (0.95^x) \qquad \text{(Why?)}$$
$$\log 0.5 = \log (0.95^x) \qquad \text{(Why?)}$$
$$\log 0.5 = x \log 0.95 \qquad \text{(Why?)}$$
$$\frac{\log 0.5}{\log 0.95} = x \qquad \text{(Why?)}$$

Therefore, $x \approx 13.51$, and the half-life is approximately 13.51 minutes.

c. Compare the answer in Part b to the answer you get using calculator-based graphical and numerical methods.

d. Look back at the symbolic reasoning strategy in Part b. In that strategy, both sides of the equation were first divided by 10 and then the log of both sides was evaluated. What would happen if the log of both sides were taken *before* dividing both sides by 10?

6. Use symbolic reasoning and properties of logs to help answer the following questions involving exponential growth.

a. In Investigation 1 of this lesson, the number of sheets of thickness of a piece of paper repeatedly folded in half was modeled by the equation $y = 2^x$. How many folds would be needed to produce a thickness of at least 250 sheets? Compare your answer to that obtained in Part b of Activity 1 (page 160).

b. According to the 1997 *World CIA Fact Book* about 1.243 billion people lived in China in that year. At that time, the population of China was growing at the rate of 0.93% per year. Assuming the population continues to grow at the same rate, when will the population reach the 2 billion mark? (Source: www.koreanhistoryproject.org)

Crowded city street in Wuham, China.

7. Equations similar to the following arise frequently in applying exponential models.

a. Solve each equation using symbolic reasoning. Identify properties of logarithms that you use.

  i. $5 = 2 \cdot 1.3^x$

  ii. $0.75 = 2^x$

  iii. $40 = 5\left(1 + \frac{0.03}{12}\right)^x$

  iv. $3 \cdot 5^{2x} = 8$

b. Solve these exponential equations by using properties of logarithms. Then solve each equation a second way by using the definition of a logarithm. Compare your answers.

  i. $10^x = 1.7$

  ii. $2.3 = 10^{x+1}$

c. In your own words, describe a strategy for solving exponential equations.

In this investigation, you have discovered and verified three useful properties of logarithms.

ⓐ Summarize in symbols and in words each property of logarithms:
- Product Property
- Quotient Property
- Power Property

ⓑ For what kinds of equations are logarithms useful in the solution process? Explain the general solution procedure.

Be prepared to share your summary of properties of logarithms and their use in equation solving with the entire class.

On Your Own

A bank currently pays 2.75 percent annual interest compounded monthly on individual savings accounts. The amount of money after n months is given by $A = P\left(1 + \frac{0.0275}{12}\right)^n$, where P is the amount initially placed in the savings account.

a. Suppose you deposit $500 in a savings account at this bank. What will your account balance be after 5 years?

b. How long will it take your account balance to double?

c. If the annual interest rate were doubled, how long would it take your balance to double?

INVESTIGATION 3 Logarithmic Scales

In the "Think About This Situation" at the beginning of this lesson (page 159), you encountered two types of scales when the DJIA yearly averages were plotted against years. You are most familiar with linear scales, such as on a ruler or map, in which the *difference* between adjacent scale points is a constant. Logarithmic scales are used when data, such as the DJIA, follow an exponential pattern. For these scales, the *ratio* between adjacent scale points is a constant. In this investigation, you will examine logarithmic scales in more detail.

People can hear sounds over an incredible range of loudness or intensity. For example, a whisper is about 10^{-13} watt/cm^2 and the roar of a jet engine at close range is about 0.1 watt/cm^2. For this reason, loudness of sounds is reported in *decibels* (as seen in the chart below), which are based on a logarithmic scale.

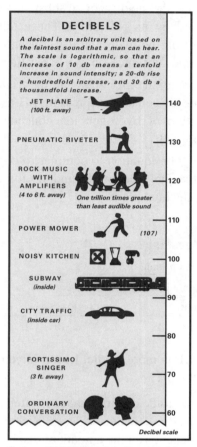

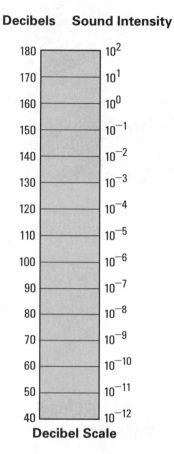

Source: ©1968 *Time* Inc. Reprinted by permission.

1. When sound I is measured in watts per square centimeter, the formula for calculating decibels is $D = 10 \log (10^{16} \cdot I)$.

   a. What is the decibel rating for a whisper? For the roar of a jet? Do your calculated ratings seem reasonable compared with those reported for similar sounds in the chart above?

   b. Using properties of logs, show that the equation for calculating decibel ratings can be rewritten as $D = 10 \log I + 160$.

   c. The chart claims that an increase in sound of 20 decibels means a hundredfold increase in sound intensity. Verify this claim in the case where one sound measures 50 on the decibel scale and another measures 70.

   d. Use the equation in Part b to show that if two sounds with decibel readings D_1 and D_2 are compared, and if the intensity of the first sound is I_1 and the intensity of the second is I_2, then $D_1 - D_2 = \log\left(\frac{I_1}{I_2}\right)$.

e. How could you use the result in Part d to show that, in general, an increase in sound of 30 decibels corresponds to a thousandfold increase in intensity?

2. You may recall from your study of chemistry that the acidity of a substance is measured by its pH rating. The acidity depends on the hydrogen ion concentration in the substance (in moles per liter).

a. Examine the pH scale at the right. Write an equation expressing pH as a function of hydrogen ion concentration, [H⁺].

b. Use your equation to complete a copy of the table below. Round results to one decimal place.

Substance	[H⁺]	pH
lemon juice	0.00501	—
apple juice	0.000794	—
milk	0.000000355	—

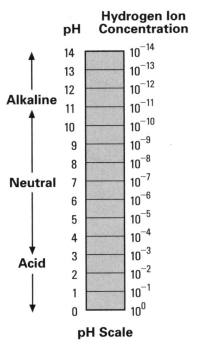

Hydrogen Ion Concentration

pH	
14	10^{-14}
13	10^{-13}
12	10^{-12}
11	10^{-11}
10	10^{-10}
9	10^{-9}
8	10^{-8}
7	10^{-7}
6	10^{-6}
5	10^{-5}
4	10^{-4}
3	10^{-3}
2	10^{-2}
1	10^{-1}
0	10^{0}

Alkaline

Neutral

Acid

pH Scale

c. Which is more acidic, lemon juice or milk? By what factor as measured by the pH?

3. The magnitude of earthquakes is often reported using the Richter scale. A Richter scale rating depends on the amount of displacement of a seismogram and the distance from the epicenter of the quake to the seismogram. The scale to the right gives the Richter scale ratings for measurements at a distance of 100 km from the epicenter.

a. Write an algebraic rule that gives Richter scale rating as a function of seismogram displacement.

b. The 1964 Alaska earthquake had a Richter scale rating of 8.6. What would have been the displacement of a seismogram 100 km away from the epicenter?

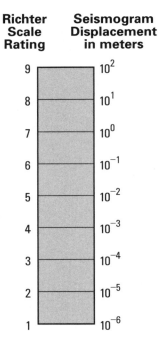

Richter Scale Rating | **Seismogram Displacement in meters**

Richter Scale Rating	Seismogram Displacement
9	10^{2}
8	10^{1}
7	10^{0}
6	10^{-1}
5	10^{-2}
4	10^{-3}
3	10^{-4}
2	10^{-5}
1	10^{-6}

c. How would the amounts of displacement be related for quakes with Richter scale ratings of 4.2 and 6.7?

d. If a seismogram showed a displacement of 0.007 m during an earthquake that is 100 km away, what Richter scale rating would be reported?

4. In this final activity, you will examine graphs of basic functions on a coordinate system in which one axis is a linear scale and the other is a logarithmic scale. In consultation with your teacher, your group should select and then complete one of tasks a–d below using *semi-log graph paper* (*x*-scale linear, *y*-scale logarithmic). You can construct such paper using the logarithmic scale construction algorithm given below. Be prepared to share a summary report with the class.

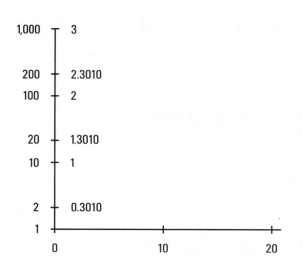

Logarithmic Scale Construction

1. Begin with $8\frac{1}{2} \times 11$ inch graph paper. Make the *y*-axis about 10 inches, the *x*-axis about 7 inches, and have them meet at the lower left hand corner.

2. Scale the *x*-axis from 0 to 20 using its complete length.

3. On the *y*-axis locate the points that divide it into thirds. Think of these points as being 1, 2, and 3 for a linear scale.

4. With your calculator verify that $\log_{10} 2 \approx 0.3010$. Locate the point on the *y*-axis representing 0.3010 and label it "2." Similarly find the logarithms of 3, 4, ..., 10 and locate them, using their logarithm, but labeling them "3," ..., "10."

5. Complete the scale by doing similarly for the remaining two thirds. Use 20, 30, ..., 100 for the middle third and 200, 300, ..., 1,000 for the top third. The result is a *y*-axis with a logarithmic scale.

a. Consider the function family $y = ax$, where $a > 0$.

- Graph $y = ax$ for $a = 0.5, 1, 5, 10,$ and $0 < x \leq 10$.

- Summarize the effect of the parameter a when $y = ax$ is graphed on semi-log graph paper.

b. Consider the function family $y = ax^2$, where $a > 0$.

- Graph $y = ax^2$ for $a = 0.5, 1, 3, 5, 10,$ and $0 < x \leq 10$.

- Summarize the effect of the parameter a when $y = ax^2$ is graphed on semi-log graph paper.

c. Consider the function family $y = x^m$, where m is a positive integer.

- Graph $y = x^m$ for integers m, $1 \le m \le 10$ and $0 < x \le 10$.
- Summarize the effect of the exponent m when $y = x^m$ is graphed on semi-log graph paper.

d. Consider the function family $y = b^x$, where b is a positive integer.

- Graph $y = b^x$ for integers b, $1 \le b \le 10$ and $0 < x \le 10$.
- Summarize the effect of changing the base b when $y = b^x$ is graphed on semi-log graph paper.

Checkpoint

In this investigation, you examined two commonly-used logarithmic scales and explored patterns in graphs of families of functions on semi-log graph paper.

a Explain how linear and logarithmic scales differ.

b When comparing numbers in a logarithmic scale, to what does an increase of one unit correspond?

c Describe the pattern of change in the graphs of each of the following functions when displayed on semi-log graph paper (linear x-scale and logarithmic y-scale). Explain why the observed patterns make sense.

- $y = ax$
- $y = ax^2$
- $y = x^m$
- $y = b^x$

Be prepared to share your ideas with the entire class.

On Your Own

Azaleas

Azaleas and blueberries require acidic soil with a pH of about 5.8. Most plants prefer slightly alkaline soil with a pH of about 7.8 to 8.2.

a. What hydrogen ion concentrations do these pH values represent?

b. What is the ratio of the hydrogen ion concentration for soil with a pH of 5.8 to that of soil with a pH of 8.2? What does this ratio mean?

Modeling

1. Shown below are the first three stages in making a triangular Sierpinski carpet. Assume that the area of the original triangle is 3 square meters.

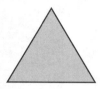

$n = 0$ $n = 1$ $n = 2$ $n = 3$

In Course 3, Unit 7, "Discrete Models of Change," you found that the area of the carpet remaining at any stage n could be modeled by the equation $y = 3(0.75^n)$.

  a. What does 3 represent? What does 0.75 represent?

  b. Explain how you could determine the number of stages required to reach the point where there is more hole than carpet remaining by reasoning with:

  ▪ the symbolic rule

  ▪ a graph of the equation

  ▪ a table of values

  Compare your answers using each of these methods.

  c. Use symbolic reasoning to determine when there is less than 0.1 m^2 of carpet remaining.

2. Atmospheric pressure is used to determine the altitude of an airplane. The relation between atmospheric pressure P (in pounds per square inch) and altitude is given by an equation of the form $P = a \cdot b^x$, where the altitude x is measured in miles.

  a. If $P = 14.7$ psi (pounds per square inch) at sea level, what is the value of a?

  b. Find b, if $P = 7.53$ psi at an altitude of 3 miles.

c. Find the pressure at 10,000 feet (1 mile = 5,280 feet).

d. Write a rule giving the altitude x as a function of pressure P.

e. Find the altitude when the atmospheric pressure is 4.55 psi. When the pressure is 10.0 psi.

f. Sketch the graph of altitude x as a function of pressure P.

3. Sea water has pH about 8.5, soft drinks have pH about 3.1, and stomach gastric juices about 1.7 pH.

a. Which of the three liquids are acidic? Which are alkaline?

b. Compare the concentration of hydrogen ions in gastric juices and sea water, and in sea water and soft drinks.

c. Explain why it is correct to say that the concentration of hydrogen ions in gastric juices is about 25 times that in some soft drinks.

d. A new soft drink has a hydrogen ion concentration that is $\frac{1}{5}$ that of most soft drinks. What is its pH?

A group of elderly Americans participate in the Chicago Square Dance Group.

4. With improved health care and advances in medicine, people in the United States continue to live longer. As a result, federal expenditures on social insurance programs such as Social Security and Medicare have been increasing rapidly. Using the data below, create a scatterplot and find an algebraic model to closely fit this data. To represent the year, let $x = 0$ correspond to 1960, $x = 5$ correspond to 1965, and so on.

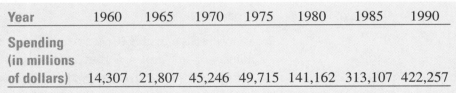

Year	1960	1965	1970	1975	1980	1985	1990
Spending (in millions of dollars)	14,307	21,807	45,246	49,715	141,162	313,107	422,257

a. Use your model to estimate expenditures in 1993. Compare your estimate against the actual amount of $534,310 million.

b. Use your model to predict expenditures on Social Security and Medicare in the year 2002. What assumptions are you making?

c. Use symbolic reasoning to estimate when expenditures were double that of 1960.

Organizing

1. For each of the following functions, denoted by $f(x)$:

   i. Sketch the graph of $y = f(x)$.

   ii. Sketch the graph of the inverse of $y = f(x)$.

   iii. Write the equation for $y = f^{-1}(x)$.

   iv. Sketch the graph of $y = f^{-1}(f(x))$.

   a. $f(x) = 2^x$ **b.** $f(x) = \log x$ **c.** $f(x) = \log_2 x$

2. With the introduction of logarithmic functions, you are now able to solve exponential equations using symbolic reasoning. Solve each of the equations below using each of the following methods and compare solutions.

   ■ Symbolic reasoning

   ■ Graphical reasoning

   ■ Numerical reasoning

   a. $100 = 4.5x - 885$

   b. $3x^2 + x + 12 = 14$

   c. $3(1.2^t) = 14$

3. Use symbolic reasoning and properties of logarithms to solve each of the following equations.

   a. $\log x = -2$ **b.** $\log 10^x = 4$ **c.** $15 = 3.21^x$

   d. $\log x = 2 \log 3 + 3 \log 2$ **e.** $\log x = \frac{1}{2}\log 36 - \log 2$

   f. $\log x = 4 \log 2 + \log 3 - 3 \log 5$ **g.** $2^{2x+2} = 8^{x+2}$

4. Write an expression for estimating the derivative of a function at a point.

   a. Estimate the derivative of $f(x) = \log x$ at $x = 1$, $x = 10$, $x = 30$, and $x = 50$.

   b. Describe two ways in which you can interpret the values in Part a.

   c. What does the graph of $f(x) = \log x$ tell you about the graph of its derivative function?

5. The calculator screen on the right shows the graphs of $y = 2^x$ and $y = \log_2 x$. The scale on both axes is 1.

   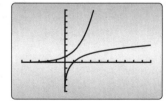

   a. Do these two graphs seem reasonable? Why?

   b. $\log_2$ is not a built-in calculator function. However, you can construct a combined-function representation of $y = \log_2 x$.

   ■ Find an expression for $\log_2 7$ in terms of $\log 2$ and $\log 7$ using the fact that if $\log_2 7 = y$, then $2^y = 7$.

   ■ What function should you graph to see a display of $y = \log_2 x$?

   c. Check your answer by producing the display shown above in Part a.

Reflecting

1. What does $\log a = b$ mean? Use this fact to explain why each of the following statements is true:

   a. $\log 1 = 0$ **b.** $\log 10 = 1$

   c. $\log 10^x = x$ **d.** $10^{\log x} = x$

2. There are some common errors that occur when students use logarithms to rewrite expressions. How could you convince someone that the following pairs of expressions are not equivalent?

   a. $\log (a + b)$ is not equivalent to $\log a + \log b$.

   b. $\log (a - b)$ is not equivalent to $\log a - \log b$.

   c. $\log (ab)$ is not equivalent to $(\log a)(\log b)$.

   d. $\log \left(\frac{a}{b}\right)$ is not equivalent to $\frac{\log a}{\log b}$.

   e. $\log ax^2$ is not equivalent to $2 \log ax$.

3. Why are logarithmic scales used when measuring sound intensity, pH levels, and earthquakes?

4. In what sense are linear scales like arithmetic sequences, and logarithmic scales like geometric sequences?

5. Logarithms are a useful tool in working with exponential models. What do you understand well about logarithms? What are some ideas about logarithms that you need to develop further?

Extending

1. Recall that a prime number, n, is an integer greater than 1 that has only 1 and n as divisors. The first eight primes are 2, 3, 5, 7, 11, 13, 17, 19. Mathematicians have proved that the number of primes less than or equal to n is approximated by $\frac{0.4343n}{\log n}$, quite an accomplishment since the primes appear irregularly among the natural numbers.

   a. Count the actual number of primes less than or equal to n to complete the table. Plot the (n, *number of primes* $\leq n$) data.

n	10	25	40	55	70	85	100	115	130	145
Number of Primes $\leq n$	4			16	19	23	25	30	31	34

   b. Graph $P(n) = \frac{0.4343n}{\log n}$, $0 < n \leq 150$. How well does this function model the data in Part a?

   c. Use the function P to estimate the number of primes less than or equal to 1,000; less than or equal to 100,000; less than or equal to 1,000,000; less than or equal to 10^{18}.

d. According to this formula, about what percent of the numbers up to 10^6 are prime? Up to 10^{18}?

2. Recall that by measuring the decay of carbon-14, scientists can estimate the age of the remains of living things. Carbon-14 decays radioactively at a rate of 0.0121% per year. Find the half-life of carbon-14.

3. Animals vary greatly in weight. Construct a logarithmic scale and locate the weight of the following 15 animals on that scale. Do this on an $8\frac{1}{2} \times 11$ inch sheet of paper.

Animal	Weight
Helena's hummingbird	0.07 oz
Shrew	3.00 oz
Gerbil	4.41 oz
Rat	16.05 oz
Guinea pig	1.54 lb
Ringtail monkey	6 lb
Otter	13 lb
Raccoon	21 lb
Porpoise	103 lb
Alligator	150 lb
Llama	375 lb
Moose	800 lb
Cow	1,800 lb
African elephant	7 tons
Blue whale	153.5 tons

4. Suppose that n is a positive integer.

   a. If $0 < \log n < 1$, what can you say about n?

   b. If $5 < \log n < 6$, what can you say about n?

   c. If $p < \log n < p + 1$, where p is a positive integer, what can you say about n?

5. In Investigation 3, you graphed various functions on graph paper with a linear x-scale and a logarithmic y-scale. Make a coordinate system where the horizontal axis is a linear scale and the vertical axis is a square root scale. Graph each of the following functions on such a coordinate system and describe its graph.

   a. $y = x^2$ **b.** $y = 3x^2$

   c. $y = 2x$ **d.** $y = x^3$

1. If $\frac{x+7}{-3} = -\frac{5}{6}$, then $x =$

   (a) -9.5 (b) -4.5 (c) $-8\frac{2}{3}$ (d) $-4\frac{2}{3}$ (e) 4.5

2. Which of the following is equivalent to $x(x^2 - 1)^2$?

   (a) $x^5 + x$ (b) $x^3 - x$ (c) $x^5 - 2x^3 + x$

   (d) $x^6 - 2x^4 + x^2$ (e) $x^5 - x$

3. The equation of the line passing through $(1, 4)$ having slope $-\frac{4}{9}$ is

   (a) $4x - 9y = 40$ (b) $4x + 9y = 40$ (c) $y = -\frac{4}{9}x - 4\frac{4}{9}$

   (d) $y = \frac{9}{4}x + 4\frac{4}{9}$ (e) $y = -\frac{9}{4}x + \frac{40}{9}$

4. If $f(x) = x^2 - 9$ and $g(x) = 2x + 1$, find $f(g(2))$.

   (a) 16 (b) 8 (c) -5 (d) 5 (e) 0

5. Which of the following could be a portion of the graph of $y = x^2 + 2x + 5$?

   (a) 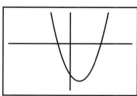   (b) 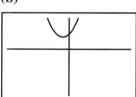   (c)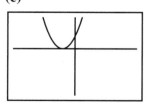

   (d) 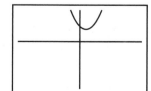   (e)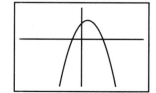

6. Which of the following is equivalent to $17 - 13x \geq 18 - 8x$?

(a) $x \leq 7$ (b) $x \leq -0.2$ (c) $x \geq 7$ (d) $x \leq -7$ (e) $x \geq -0.2$

7. If $f(x) = \frac{3 - x}{x}$, find the value of x when $f(x) = 5$.

(a) $\frac{2}{5}$ (b) $\frac{1}{5}$ (c) $\frac{2}{3}$ (d) 2 (e) none of these

8. Which equation best matches the given graph?

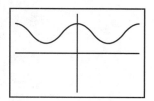

(a) $y = \sin x$ (b) $y = \cos x$ (c) $y = \cos (x - 2)$

(d) $y = \cos x + 2$ (e) $y = \sin x + 2$

9. Which of the following could be the equation for this graph?

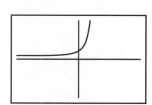

(a) $y = 3^x - 1$ (b) $y = \frac{3}{x}$ (c) $y = 1 + 3^x$

(d) $y = \sqrt[3]{x}$ (e) $y = x^3$

10. $\sqrt[5]{25.25}$ is best estimated by:

(a) 5.05 (b) 1.01 (c) 5.5 (d) 2.91 (e) 1.91

Linearizing Data

You may have heard that the population of the United States is increasing exponentially. The table and plot below give the population of the United States in the census years 1900–1990.

Year	Population (in millions)
1900	76
1910	92
1920	106
1930	123
1940	132
1950	151
1960	179
1970	203
1980	227
1990	249

Source: United States Bureau of the Census.

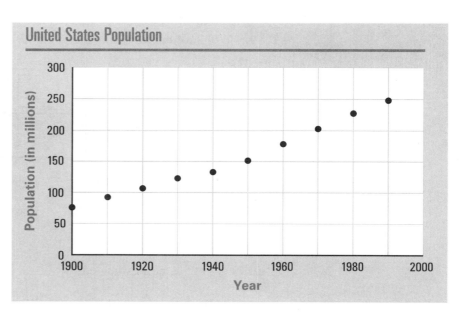

INVESTIGATION 1 ▶ Straightening Functions

In this investigation, you will learn how transforming data can change the shape of its graph. You also will investigate how transforming data can help you decide on an appropriate model as in the case of the preceding "Think About This Situation."

1. To begin, consider the data and scatterplot below that give the radii in inches of some circular tables and the surface areas in square inches of the tabletops.

Radius (in inches)	Surface Area (in square inches)
9	254.47
12	452.39
15	
18	1,017.88
21	1,385.44
24	1,809.56

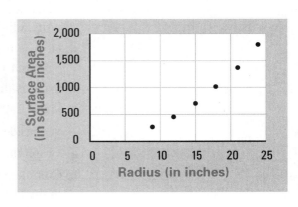

a. Find the surface area of a table with a 15-inch radius.

b. Write an equation that expresses the relationship between radius *x* and surface area *y* of a circular tabletop. Describe the shape of its graph.

c. Now transform each surface area from square inches to square feet. Predict what the plot of (*radius in inches, surface area in square feet*) will look like. Check your prediction by making a plot.

d. Will transforming the surface area from square inches to square centimeters change the basic shape of the plot? Explain your reasoning.

e. Converting square inches to square centimeters, or square inches to square feet requires multiplying or dividing by a constant. In general, will such a transformation of the y values of an (x, y) data plot change the basic shape of the plot? Why or why not?

In the following activities, you will learn how to find a transformation $y \rightarrow y*$ that **linearizes** (x, y) data; that is, when the points $(x, y*)$ are plotted, they cluster on or about a line.

2. Examine the function $y = \pi x^2$, $x \geq 0$, and the transformation $y* = \sqrt{y}$.

a. Graph the equation $y = \pi x^2$, $x \geq 0$.

b. Complete a copy of the table below. Include your own choice of x in the last row.

x	$y = \pi x^2$	$y* = \sqrt{y}$
0		
1		
3		
5		
10		

c. Make a scatterplot of the $(x, y*)$ points. Are the points collinear? If so, write a linear equation expressing $y*$ as a function of x.

d. How is the slope of the graph of the equation from Part c related to the equation $y = \pi x^2$?

e. What is the relationship between the original function and the linearizing (square root) function?

3. Next consider the exponential function $y = 2^x$ and the transformation $y* = \log y$.

a. Graph the equation $y = 2^x$.

b. Complete a copy of the table on the next page. Include your choice of input in the last row.

x	$y = 2^x$	$y^* = \log y$
0		
1		
3		
5		
10		

   c. Make a scatterplot of the (x, y^*) points in the table above. Are the points collinear? If so, write a linear equation expressing y^* as a function of x.

   d. How is the slope of the graph of the equation from Part c related to the equation $y = 2^x$?

   e. What is the relationship between the original function $y = 2^x$ and the linearizing (log) function?

4. Suppose a set of points (x, y) falls along the graph of $y = 4 \cdot 5^x$.

   a. Graph the equation $y = 4 \cdot 5^x$.

   b. How can you transform each value of y to linearize the set of points?

   c. What is the relationship between the original function and the linearizing function?

   d. Write an equation that expresses the relationship between x and y^*. What type of equation is this?

   e. How is the slope of the graph of the equation from Part d related to the equation $y = 4 \cdot 5^x$?

5. Now suppose a set of points (x, y) falls along the graph of $y = 6\sqrt{x}$.

   a. Graph this equation.

   b. How can you transform each value of y to linearize the set of points?

   c. What is the relationship between the original function and the linearizing function?

   d. Imagine a scatterplot of the transformed points. Along the graph of what equation would the transformed points fall? What type of equation is this?

   e. How is the slope of the graph of the equation from Part d related to the equation $y = 6\sqrt{x}$?

In the next activity, you will discover how transforming data can help you determine which type of equation is a reasonable model for a set of paired data.

6. For a science experiment, students have dropped a small weight and measured how far it falls in various lengths of time. Their data are given in the table below.

Time (in seconds)	Distance (in centimeters)
0.1	5
0.2	20
0.3	44
0.4	78
0.5	122
0.6	176
0.7	240
0.8	314

    a. Based on your work in previous courses, what type of function model do you think would be a good fit for these data? Compare your conjecture to those of other groups.

    b. Based on your answer to Part a, what transformation y^* would linearize the (*time, distance*) data? Check your conjecture by making a scatterplot of the (*time, y^**) data.

    c. When given the (*time, distance*) data, students in a class in California thought an exponential model would be reasonable. Compute the log of each distance. Make a scatterplot of the (*time, log distance*) data. Explain why an exponential model is not reasonable.

    d. Find the power model that best fits the (*time, distance*) data. Use symbolic reasoning to determine the time it would take for the weight to drop 100 cm.

7. Think back on your work with the data transformations $y^* = \log y$ and $y^* = \sqrt{y}$.

    a. If a set of points (x, y) cluster on or about the graph of an exponential equation $y = a(b^x)$, what is the equation of the graph the points $(x, \log y)$ will cluster on or about?

    b. If a set of points cluster on or about the graph of a quadratic power rule $y = ax^2$, $x \geq 0$, what is the equation of the graph the points $(x, \sqrt{y})$ will cluster on or about?

In this investigation, you have learned how to transform data to check whether a set of points is modeled reasonably well by an exponential equation or by a quadratic power rule.

ⓐ How would you check if an exponential function is a reasonable model for a set of data points (x, y)?

ⓑ How would you check if a quadratic power function is a reasonable model for a set of data points (x, y)?

ⓒ What is the relationship between a function and its linearizing function?

Be prepared to explain your methods and thinking to the entire class.

On Your Own

The table and plot below give the estimated population of the world for various years.

Year	Estimated Population (in millions)
1650	550
1750	725
1850	1,175
1900	1,600
1950	2,564
1980	4,478
1991	5,423

Source: World Almanac and Book of Facts, 1994.

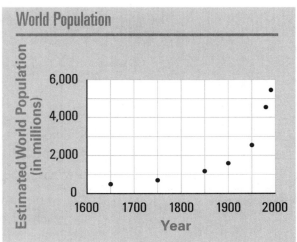

a. Make a scatterplot of $(x, \log y)$.

b. Is the population of the world increasing exponentially, slower than exponentially, or faster than exponentially? Explain.

INVESTIGATION 2 Fitting Exponential Functions Using Log Transformations

In previous courses, you have used least squares regression to model data that has a linear pattern. You may recall that the least squares regression line is the one that minimizes the sum of the squared vertical distances from the data points to the line. These distances are called **residuals**. To find the equation of the least squares regression line, your calculator or computer uses an algorithm based on calculus. How this algorithm works for small data sets is the focus of Extending Tasks 4 and 5. If you take a calculus course, where you study general methods to find minimum and maximum values of functions, you will learn more about the mathematics of the algorithm. For now, think about the meaning of least squares regression as you complete the following two activities.

1. The graph below displays a set of points and the least squares regression line, $y = 1.6x$, for the points.

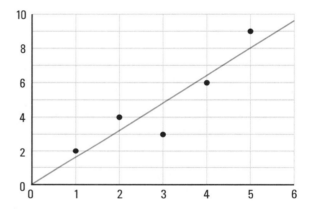

   a. Find the residual for each of the points. Show each residual on a copy of the plot above.

   b. What is the sum of the squared residuals?

2. One of the two lines on the graph below is the least squares regression line for the given set of four data points. Use the idea of least squares to determine which line it is. (Do not use your calculator to compute the regression line.)

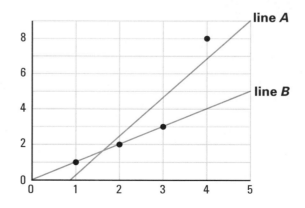

Now that you have reviewed the meaning of least squares regression, you are ready to explore how your calculator uses the method of least squares to fit an exponential model to a set of data points.

3. Examine the data and scatterplot below:

x	y
1	1
2	5
3	7
4	17

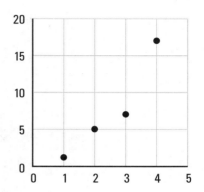

Consider these two candidates for an exponential model:

$$y = 2^x$$
$$y = 0.5423 \cdot 2.4196^x$$

a. Graph these two functions on a scatterplot of the above data. Does one appear to fit the data better than the other?

b. Find the sum of the squared residuals for each model by completing two copies of the table below. Record at least three decimal places in each step.

x	y	Predicted $\hat{y}$	Residual $(y - \hat{y})$	Squared Residual $(y - \hat{y})^2$
1	1			
2	5			
3	7			
4	17			

c. Which model has the smaller sum of squared residuals?

d. One of these models is the exponential function given by your calculator. Explain which one you think it will be and why.

e. Use your calculator to fit an exponential function to the data using exponential regression. Which function does it give?

4. In Activity 3, you found that your calculator did *not* give the function with the smaller sum of squared errors. In this activity, you will find out what criterion the calculator does use to fit an exponential function.

a. If an exponential model is appropriate for a set of data, what transformation would you use to linearize the data?

b. For the data from Activity 3, make a scatterplot of (*x, log y*). What pattern do the points seem to follow?

c. Since the transformed points are reasonably linear, you can find the least squares linear regression line for the points (*x, y**). Do this using your calculator. Write the equation in the form $y^* = a + bx$.

d. Substitute log *y* for *y** in your equation from Part c and then solve for *y*. Where have you seen this equation before?

e. Describe how your calculator actually does use the principle of least squares to fit an exponential function.

Checkpoint

In this investigation, you examined how a graphing calculator fits an exponential function to data.

ⓐ What is the purpose of transforming data?

ⓑ Write a summary of the method your calculator appears to use to fit exponential functions to data. At what stage does the calculator minimize the sum of the squared residuals?

Be prepared to share your summary and thinking with the class.

There are several reasons for fitting functions to data. One is that you want a model for the situation that you can use to build a theory. For example, you might want to describe under what situations a population increases exponentially. The most important thing to consider when fitting a function to data for this purpose is whether there is any contextual, scientific, or theoretical reason why the data might follow that model. You should not just go searching for any function that comes close to the points. After all, if you look hard enough, you are bound to find some function that comes reasonably close to the points in any set of data.

Another reason for fitting a function to data is that you would like to use that function for estimation purposes. For example, suppose you just want a reasonable estimate of the United States population in the year 1955. By fitting several different types of functions to the populations known from the census years and selecting the one that seems to fit the best, you would get a reasonable estimate. If you select an exponential function and the United States population isn't in fact growing exponentially, your estimate for the year 1955 would not be off by much. However, if the population isn't growing exponentially and you were to use that exponential function to predict the United States population in the year 2050, you might be off by a lot.

Reproduced below is the United States population data reported at the beginning of this lesson.

Year	Population (in millions)
1900	76
1910	92
1920	106
1930	123
1940	132
1950	151
1960	179
1970	203
1980	227
1990	249

a. Let $x = 0$ correspond to the year 1900, $x = 10$ correspond to the year 1910, and so on. Make a scatterplot of (*year, log population*). Does an exponential model appear to be a reasonable fit to the original data?

b. Use your calculator to fit an exponential function to the original population data. What does this function say about the yearly growth rate in the United States?

c. Compute this same exponential function another way by fitting a linear equation to (*year, log population*) and then solving that equation for population.

d. What estimate would you give for the United States population in 1955? In the year 2000?

e. Use your exponential model to estimate the year in which the population of the United States was about 50 million; about 140 million.

Modeling • Organizing • Reflecting • Extending

Modeling

1. The table on the right gives the number of deaths from AIDS in the United States for the years 1981 through 1994.

  a. In the late 1980s, people were worrying about whether the number of deaths from AIDS was increasing exponentially. Does that appear to be the case for 1981 through 1989? Decide by making a suitable transformation of the number of cases from 1981 through 1989 and analyzing the resulting scatterplot.

  b. Now consider the data for all the years 1981 through 1994. Does the number of deaths from AIDS appear to be increasing exponentially from 1981 through 1994? Explain your reasoning.

  c. In 1992, the definition of AIDS was expanded to include more symptoms. Would this fact affect your answer in Part b? If so, how?

Year	Number of Deaths from AIDS
1981	128
1982	460
1983	1,501
1984	3,497
1985	6,961
1986	12,056
1987	16,336
1988	21,040
1989	27,691
1990	31,402
1991	36,307
1992	40,516
1993	42,992
1994	46,050

Source: United States Centers for Disease Control and Prevention, *HIV/AIDS Surveillance Report,* Year-End Edition 1995.

2. In 1905, when the study of radioactivity was just beginning, Meyer and Schweidler reported data giving the time in days and the relative radioactivity for a radioactive substance. The data below are a modification of their data as given by the statistician John Tukey, who invented box plots and stem-and-leaf plots.

Time (in days)	0.2	2.2	4	5	6	8	11	12	15	18	26	33	39	45
Relative Activity	35.0	25.0	22.1	17.9	16.8	13.7	12.4	10.3	7.5	4.9	4.0	2.4	1.4	1.1

Source: John Tukey, *Exploratory Data Analysis,* Addison-Wesley, 1977.

a. Make a scatterplot of these data.

- Do the data appear to follow an exponential pattern, $y = a \cdot b^x$?

- If so, what is a reasonable estimate for a?

- Is the value of b less than 1 or greater than 1?

b. Make a scatterplot of (*time, log relative activity*). Does an exponential function appear to be a reasonable fit to the data?

c. Use your calculator to fit an exponential function to these data. Graph this function on the plot of the data.

d. Compute this same exponential equation another way by first taking the log of the relative activity (y), fitting a linear equation to (x, *log y*), and then solving that equation for y.

e. What estimate would you give for the relative activity at 10 days? At 47 days?

3. Reproduced below are data on federal expenditures on social insurance programs that you first encountered in Modeling Task 4 in Lesson 2 on page 174. In that task, you may have modeled the data with an exponential function.

Year	Spending (in millions of dollars)
1960	14,307
1965	21,807
1970	45,246
1975	49,715
1980	141,162
1985	313,107
1990	422,257

a. What is it about this context that would suggest that the data *might* follow an exponential model?

b. If the pattern in the data is exponential, what transformation should linearize the data? Try it. What did you find?

4. The data below give the results of an experiment to determine how long it takes people to make a given number of choices.

Number of Choices N	1	2	3	4	5	6	7	8	9	10
Reaction Time R (in seconds)	0.17	0.34	0.37	0.42	0.48	0.52	0.56	0.58	0.59	0.57

Source: Bernice Kastner, *Space Mathematics*, NASA, page 91.

a. After examining the plot below, list some transformations that might linearize these data.

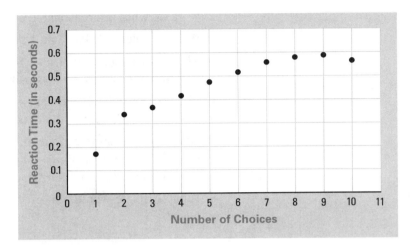

b. Try the transformations you suggested. Do any of them linearize the data? Explain what you think is going on.

Organizing

1. Reproduced below is the (*time, distance*) data reported for a weight-dropping experiment in Investigation 1, Activity 6 (pages 183–184). In that activity, you reasoned from the scatterplot of (*time, log distance*) data to conclude that an exponential model is not reasonable.

Time (in seconds)	Distance (in centimeters)
0.1	5
0.2	20
0.3	44
0.4	78
0.5	122
0.6	176
0.7	240
0.8	314

Suppose a student did not try to linearize the data first, and simply assumed the data pattern was exponential.

a. Use your calculator to find the equation of an exponential model for these data and note the value of the correlation coefficient *r*.

b. Does a large value of *r* indicate that an exponential function is a good model for the data?

2. If you want to linearize data points that fall roughly along the graph of $y = x^2$, $x \geq 0$, you could take the square root of each of the y values. You could also linearize the points by transforming each of the x values or by a different transformation of the y values. How would you do this?

3. Take the log of both sides of $y = a \cdot b^x$ and show that the resulting equation gives a linear relationship between x and log y.

4. Solve each equation below for y. Write the equation in the form $y = k^x$, where k is a constant.

   a. log $y = 4x$ **b.** log $y = -3x$ **c.** log $y = ax$

5. Solve each equation below for y. Write the equation in the form $y = c \cdot d^x$, where c and d are constants.

   a. log $y = 3x + 2$ **b.** log $y = 3x - 4$ **c.** log $y = ax + b$

Reflecting

1. What is the connection between linearizing a function and the inverse of that function? Which functions can you linearize?

2. How do you think your calculator finds the value of the correlation coefficient r that can be displayed when you fit an exponential model to data? (Some calculators or computer software display r^2 or R^2 instead.)

3. Why isn't it a good idea for a scientist to use his or her computer to fit many possible functions to a set of data and select the function that seems to fit the best as a model for the data?

4. What kinds of functions have graphs that (eventually) grow faster than the graph of an exponential function?

Extending

1. In earlier coursework, you discovered that transforming a set of single-variable data by adding a constant or multiplying by a constant affected measures of center and variation in predictable ways. Suppose you have a set of data that consists of positive numbers and the mean is $\bar{x}$.

   a. If c is added to each data value, what is the mean of the transformed data?

   b. If each data value is multiplied by c, what is the mean of the transformed data?

   c. Suppose the data is transformed by taking the square root of each data value. Is the mean of the transformed data equal to $\sqrt{\bar{x}}$? Explain your reasoning.

d. Suppose the data is transformed by taking the common logarithm of each data value. Is the mean of the transformed data equal to log $\bar{x}$? Explain your reasoning.

2. Reproduced below is the plot of the world population data from the "On Your Own" in Investigation 1 (page 185). The second plot was made by checking the box for the option "logarithmic scale" on the spreadsheet program Microsoft Excel Version 4.0.

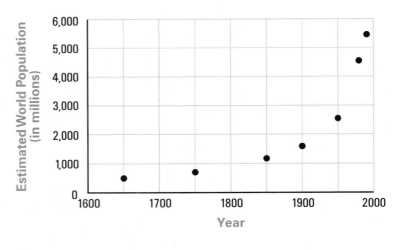

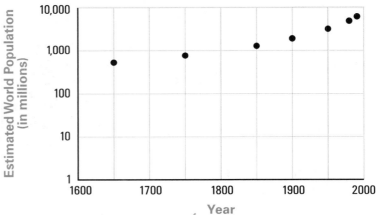

a. Describe how the spreadsheet program made this second plot.

b. The points on this plot appear to follow a path that is slightly *concave up* (curved upwards). Explain what this means as to whether or not an exponential model is appropriate for these data.

c. Make a similar plot for the AIDS data in Modeling Task 1 on page 190. What does this plot suggest about the appropriateness of modeling these data with an exponential function?

3. In this task, you will use the method of least squares and symbolic reasoning to find the equation of the regression line, $\hat{y} = ax + 7$, for the three points (1, 12), (2, 15), and (3, 21). (You are given the y-intercept of 7 to simplify the computations.)

a. Using the equation $\hat{y} = ax + 7$, the residual for the point (1, 12) is $y - \hat{y} =$ $12 - [a(1) + 7] = 12 - a - 7 = 5 - a$.

Find the residuals for the points (2, 15) and (3, 21).

b. Complete the table below.

x	y	Residual	Squared Residual
1	12	$5 - a$	$(5 - a)^2 = 25 - 10a + a^2$
2	15		
3	21		

c. What is the sum of the squared residuals?

d. What value of a gives you the smallest possible sum of the squared residuals?

e. Using your results from Parts c and d, write the equation of the least squares regression line in the form $\hat{y} = ax + 7$. What is the sum of the squared residuals for this equation?

f. Compare your answer to that found by using the least squares linear regression feature on your calculator.

4. In this task, you will use the method of least squares directly on the data below to find an equation of the form $\hat{y} = ax^2$ that minimizes the sum of the squared residuals. Note that your calculator fits $\hat{y} = ax^2 + bx + c$, which has three parameters a, b, and c. The equation $\hat{y} = ax^2$ has just one parameter to find, a.

a. Complete the following chart.

x	y	$\hat{y} = ax^2$	Residual	Squared Residual
1	4			
2	12	$4a$	$12 - 4a$	$144 - 96a + 16a^2$
3	26			

b. What is the sum of the squared residuals?

c. What value of a gives you the smallest possible sum of the squared residuals?

d. Write the equation of the least squares equation of the form $\hat{y} = ax^2$.

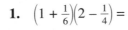

1. $\left(1 + \frac{1}{6}\right)\left(2 - \frac{1}{4}\right) =$

   (a) $2\frac{11}{12}$ (b) $1\frac{7}{12}$ (c) $2\frac{1}{24}$ (d) $\frac{2}{21}$ (e) $\frac{2}{3}$

2. Simplify: $\dfrac{\frac{3+x}{2}}{\frac{2x+6}{4}}$

   (a) $\frac{3+x}{x+6}$ (b) 2 (c) $\frac{1}{4}$ (d) $\frac{1}{2}$ (e) 1

3. What is the y-intercept of the line $2x - 9y = 36$?

   (a) 4 (b) 18 (c) -4 (d) -18 (e) 36

4. If a and b are in the domain of a function f and $f(a) > f(b)$, which of the following must be true?

   (a) $a = 0$ or $b = 0$ (b) $a < b$ (c) $a \leq b$

   (d) $a \neq b$ (e) $a = b$

5. What is the axis of symmetry of the graph of $y = 2x^2 + 5x - 3$?

   (a) $x = -2$ (b) $x = -1$ (c) $x = -\frac{5}{4}$ (d) $x = -1.5$ (e) $x = \frac{3}{4}$

6. If $\log_2 (x + 1) = 3$, then $x =$

   (a) 5 (b) 7 (c) $\sqrt{3} - 1$ (d) 8 (e) 0

7. What is the largest solution of $3x^4(x^2 - 5)(x - 7)(x + 9) = 0$?

    (a) –5   **(b)** 0   **(c)** 7   **(d)** 9   **(e)** 5

8. Which graph below could be a portion of the graph of $y = 2.5 \sin x$?

    (a)   **(b)**   **(c)**

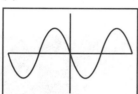 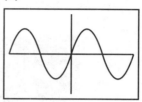 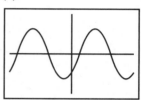

    (d)   **(e)**

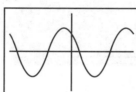 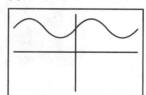

9. Evaluate $\log_5 125$.

    (a) 4   **(b)** 25   **(c)** 2.63   **(d)** 2   **(e)** 3

10. Solve: $\sqrt[3]{2x} = 4$

    (a) 32   **(b)** 2   **(c)** 8   **(d)** 64   **(e)** $\sqrt[3]{\dfrac{4}{2}}$

INVESTIGATION 3 Fitting Functions Using Log-Log Transformations

One outstanding example of the power of blending algebraic and geometric methods in modeling physical phenomena was the description by Johannes Kepler of the behavior of the planets. By looking at data from the astronomer Tycho Brahe (1546–1601), Kepler (1571–1630) deduced many laws of astronomical motion.

The path of the orbit of each planet in our solar system is an *ellipse* with the sun located a bit off center. The table below provides some data on the orbits of planets. The variable x is the length of half the longer axis of the elliptical orbit of the planet around the sun. The variable y is the length of time it takes a planet to orbit the sun.

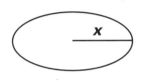

Planet	Half Length of Longer Axis x (in millions of miles)	Orbit Time y (in Earth years)
Mercury	36	0.241
Venus	67	0.615
Earth	93	1.000
Mars	142	1.88
Jupiter	483	11.9
Saturn	886	29.5
Uranus	1,782	84
Neptune	2,793	165
Pluto	3,670	248

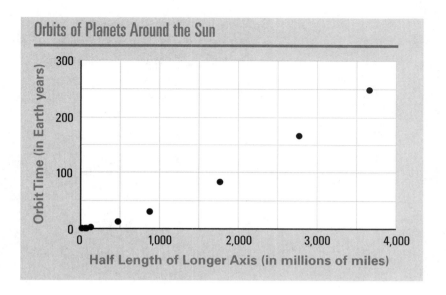

Orbits of Planets Around the Sun

Orbit Time (in Earth years) vs *Half Length of Longer Axis (in millions of miles)*

1. For these data, Kepler proposed a power model of the form $y = a \cdot x^b$.

   a. Which of the values *a, b,* and *x* will be positive in this model?

   b. As you have seen, the inverse function can be used to linearize. What is the inverse function of $y = a \cdot x^b$ for $x \geq 0$, $a > 0$, $b > 0$?

   c. Try to linearize the planet data by applying an inverse power transformation. Were you successful? Why or why not?

   d. Now try a log transformation. Find the log of each value of *y*. Make a scatterplot of (*x, log y*). Did the log transformation linearize the data?

   e. Now try a **log-log transformation.** Find the log of each value of *x*. Make a scatterplot of (*log x, log y*). Did the log-log transformation linearize the data?

   f. Take the log of both sides of $y = a \cdot x^b$ and show that the resulting equation gives a linear relationship between log *x* and log *y*.

   g. Compare your scatterplot from Part e to the plot of the original data above. On which plot is it easier to distinguish all of the points? What made this possible?

When your calculator fits a power model to data, it does a log-log transformation of the data. It then fits a linear equation to the points (*log x, log y*) using least squares linear regression and solves that equation for *y*.

2. What is known today as Kepler's third law states that the square of the length of time y it takes a planet to orbit the Sun is proportional to the cube of half the length of the longer axis of the ellipse.

a. Represent the length of half of the longer axis by x. Write Kepler's third law as an equation. Use k as the constant of proportionality.

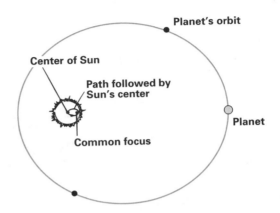

b. Solve this equation for y. Why don't you have to worry about multiple roots?

c. Use your calculator to fit a power model to the planet data. How closely does it match Kepler's third law?

3. In Investigation 1 Activity 6 (pages 183–184), you found a power model for the data on the right for the distance a small weight falls in given lengths of time.

a. What method did you use to linearize these data in Investigation 1?

b. Does a log-log transformation linearize these data? If so, why? If not, why not?

Time (in seconds)	Distance (in centimeters)
0.1	5
0.2	20
0.3	44
0.4	78
0.5	122
0.6	176
0.7	240
0.8	314

Checkpoint

In this investigation, you explored log-log transformations of data.

a What is a log-log transformation? Why is it useful?

b Describe the steps you should follow to decide on an appropriate model for a set of data.

Be prepared to explain your group's responses.

On Your Own

The data and scatterplot below give the average distance from the Sun and the length of a "year" for the planets in our solar system.

Planet	Average Distance from Sun (in millions of miles)	Length of a "Year" (in Earth days)
Mercury	36	88
Venus	67	225
Earth	93	365
Mars	142	687
Jupiter	484	4,333
Saturn	887	10,759
Uranus	1,783	30,685
Neptune	2,794	60,189
Pluto	3,661	90,465

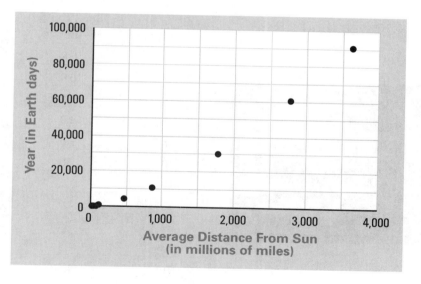

a. Transform the data using a log-log transformation.

b. Make a scatterplot of $(\log x, \log y)$. Why can you see more points on this scatterplot than on the plot above? Does the log-log transformation appear to linearize the data?

c. Use your calculator to find a power model for these data. Use this function to predict the length of a year if a new planet is discovered that is 600 million miles from the Sun.

d. How are these data related to the planet data at the beginning of this investigation on page 198?

MORE
Modeling • Organizing • Reflecting • Extending

Modeling

1. The following table and scatterplot give the age and diameter of 27 chestnut oak trees planted on a poor site. Try to find a model of how diameter increases with age.

Chestnut Oak Trees

Age (in years)	Diameter at Chest Height (in inches)	Age (in years)	Diameter at Chest Height (in inches)
4	0.8	23	4.7
5	0.8	25	6.5
8	1.0	28	6.0
8	2.0	29	4.5
8	3.0	30	6.0
10	2.0	30	7.0
10	3.5	33	8.0
12	4.9	34	6.5
13	3.5	35	7.0
14	2.5	38	5.0
16	4.5	38	7.0
18	4.6	40	7.5
20	5.5	42	7.5
22	5.8		

Source: From *Quantitative Literacy Series: Exploring Data* by James M. Landwehr and Ann E. Watkins © 1986 by Bell Telephone Laboratories, Inc. Published by Dale Seymour Publications, an imprint of Pearson Learning. Used by permission.

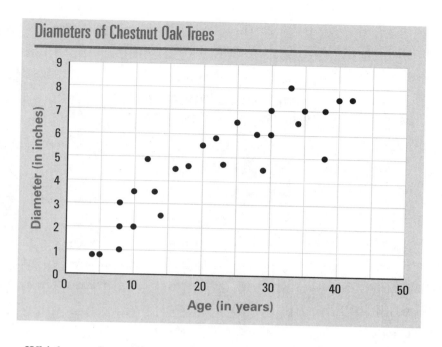

Diameters of Chestnut Oak Trees

a. Which transformation seems to best linearize these data?

b. Use your calculator to find a function that fits the relationship between age and diameter of chestnut oak trees planted on a poor site.

c. Use your function to predict the diameter of a 15-year-old chestnut oak tree planted on a poor site.

d. How does the circumference of the trees increase with age?

e. How does the cross-sectional area of the trees increase with age?

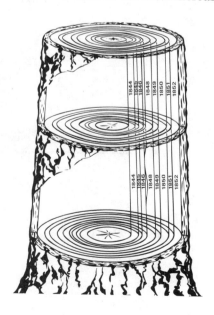

2. The following table and scatterplot give the brain weight and body weight for various species of animals.

Species	Brain Weight (in grams)	Body Weight (in kilograms)	Species	Brain Weight (in grams)	Body Weight (in kilograms)
Canary	0.848	0.0171	Skunk	10.3	1.7
Crow	9.3	0.337	Tiger	302	209
Flamingo	8.05	1.598	Wolf	152	29.94
Loon	6.12	1.53	Greyhound	105.9	24.49
Ostrich	42.11	123	Seal	442	107.3
Pheasant	3.289	0.625	Walrus	1,126	667
Pigeon	2.694	0.282	Porpoise	1,735	142.43
Stork	16.24	3.35	Blue Whale	6,800	58,059
Vulture	19.6	5.27	Bat	0.936	0.028
Catfish	1.84	2.894	Mole	1.16	0.0396
Barracuda	3.83	5.978	Baboon	140	7.9
Mackerel	0.64	0.765	Grey Monkey	66.6	4.55
Salmon	1.257	3.93	Chimpanzee	440	56.69
Brown Trout	0.57	0.292	Human	1,377	74
Tuna	3.09	5.21	Mouse	0.551	0.0177
Northern Trout	1.233	2.5	Squirrel	3.97	0.183
Grizzly Bear	233.9	142.88	Rhinoceros	655	763
Cheetah	2.449	22.2	African Elephant	5,712	6,654
Lion	106.7	28.79	Horse	618	461.76
Raccoon	40	5.175			

Source: *Data Analysis: An Introduction* by Witmer, ©1993. Reprinted by permission of Prentice-Hall, Inc., Upper Saddle River, NJ.

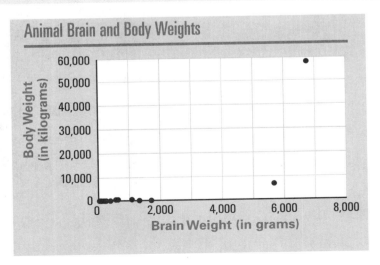

a. From observing the plot on the preceding page, what conclusions can you make about the relationship between brain weight and body weight?

b. Scientific theory suggests that an equation of the form $y = a \cdot x^b$ should model these data well. Decide whether or not that appears to be the case. Summarize your findings and conclusions. Include a plot that is easier to interpret.

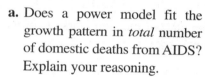

AIDS quilt on display.

3. The table to the right gives the *total* number of deaths from AIDS in the United States from 1981 to 1994.

In Modeling Task 1 on page 190, you should have determined that the number of deaths from AIDS was not increasing exponentially. Some epidemiologists have suggested that a power function might be a good model for the growth of deaths due to AIDS in the United States.

Years Since 1981	Total Number of Deaths from AIDS
1	588
2	2,089
3	5,586
4	12,547
5	24,603
6	40,939
7	61,979
8	89,670
9	121,072
10	157,379
11	197,895
12	240,887
13	286,937

a. Does a power model fit the growth pattern in *total* number of domestic deaths from AIDS? Explain your reasoning.

b. If a power model $y = ax^b$ passes through the points (1, 588) and (9, 121,072), find a and b. Compare your equation to that found by using the regression feature of your calculator.

c. What is the total number of AIDS deaths by the year 2000 predicted by the power regression feature of your calculator? On what assumption is this prediction based?

Organizing

1. In Organizing Task 1 on page 192, you should have found that a large value of the correlation coefficient r does not necessarily indicate that a linear model is a good one for the data. Similarly, a small value of r does not rule out the possibility that a linear model may be a good one for the data.

a. Construct a set of points that should not be modeled by a linear equation but has correlation of $r \geq 0.9$ when a linear equation is fit to the points.

b. Construct a set of points that is best modeled by a linear equation but has a positive correlation of $r \leq 0.5$.

2. Rewrite each equation in the form $y = a \cdot x^b$.

  a. $\log y = \log x + 2$

  b. $\log y = -2 \log x + 3$

  c. $\log y = 3 + 2 \log x$

  d. $\log y = a \log x + b$

3. Re-express each of the following equations in the linear form $y^* = ax + b$, where a and b are constants and y^* is a transformation of y.

  a. $y = 2 \cdot 3^x$

  b. $y = 5 + 2^x$

  c. $y = 3x^2, x \geq 0$

4. Represent each situation below with an algebraic equation. Use k for the constant of proportionality.

  a. The distance d an object falls is proportional to the square of the time t it has been falling.

  b. The volume v of a sphere is proportional to the cube of the radius r.

  c. The speed s a car was traveling is proportional to the square root of the length l of the skid marks.

  d. The length l of the skid marks is proportional to the square of the speed s a car was traveling.

Reflecting

1. In what ways is it easier to work with data that is linear than with data that is nonlinear?

2. Sometimes in a scatterplot some of the points are clustered together near the origin. You have seen how taking a log-log transformation can spread out the points in a scatterplot so you can see them all. It has been said that in this case, the wrong scales were used for the original measurements. What would a person who said this mean?

3. Kepler thought at first that the Earth moves in a circle with the sun at the center. Although the orbit is almost circular, it is, in fact, an ellipse. What phenomena have orbits that are distinctly elliptical?

4. What does the value of the correlation coefficient r (or r^2) tell you about a model?

Extending

1. Investigate what happens if you use a log-log transformation on data that have an exponential relationship. Write a summary of your findings.

2. Reproduced on the next page are the planet data from "On Your Own" on page 201.

Planet	Average Distance from Sun (in millions of miles)	Length of a "Year" (in Earth days)
Mercury	36	88
Venus	67	225
Earth	93	365
Mars	142	687
Jupiter	484	4,333
Saturn	887	10,759
Uranus	1,783	30,685
Neptune	2,794	60,189
Pluto	3,661	90,465

a. Fit a power function to these data by using the same algorithm that your calculator does:

Step 1 Take the log of each value of x and each value of y.

Step 2 Fit a linear equation to the points (log x, log y). This equation will be of the form log $y = a + b$ log x.

Step 3 Solve the equation for y.

b. Compare your equation to that produced by your calculator. Resolve any differences.

3. You have learned that points that follow the graph of a power function, $y = a \cdot x^b$, can be linearized by taking the log of the values of both x and y. Now you will consider sets of points that follow the graph of a function of the form $y = a \cdot x^b + c$.

a. The points in the table to the right lie on the graph of a function of the form $y = a \cdot x^b + c$. Find the values of a, b, and c.

x	y
0	1.6000
1	3.9000
2	5.3364
3	6.5627

b. Suppose you drop a marble from a window halfway up a building that is 1,000 feet tall. Ignoring air resistance, the distance d of the marble in feet from the roof of the building at any time t seconds is given by $d = 16t^2 + 500$. Make a table showing the distance d of the marble at times $t = 1, 2, 3, 4,$ and 5 seconds. Does a log-log transformation linearize these values?

c. Take the log of both sides of the function $y = 16x^2 + 500$ and simplify if possible. Is the resulting function linear in log x and log y?

d. Subtract 500 from each of the values of d in your table of part b. Does a log-log transformation linearize these points? Explain why or why not.

e. When you have data that you suspect is modeled by a function of the form $y = a \cdot x^b + c$, sometimes you may have a good estimate of the constant c. In this case, what transformation should you make before doing the log-log transformation?

1. Find $16\frac{2}{3}\%$ of 9,600.

   (a) 160,000   (b) 57,600   (c) 1,594   (d) 3,200   (e) 1,600

2. Which of the following is a factor of $6x^2 + 8x - 12y^2x - 16y^2$?

   (a) $x - 2y^2$ (b) $3y - 4$ (c) $x^2 - y^2$

   (d) $x + 2y^2$ (e) $2x + 4y$

3. An equation of the line in the figure shown is

   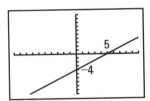

   (a) $\frac{x}{5} - \frac{y}{4} = 1$ (b) $\frac{x}{4} - \frac{y}{5} = 1$ (c) $\frac{x}{4} + \frac{y}{5} = 1$

   (d) $y = \frac{5}{4}x - 4$ (e) $y = -\frac{4}{5}x - 4$

4. If $f(x) = 2x + 5$ and $g(x) = x^2 - 2$, then $g(f(x)) =$

   (a) $4x^2 + 23$ (b) $4x^2 + 20x + 27$ (c) $4x^2 + 20x + 23$

   (d) $4x^2 + 20x + 25$ (e) $4x^2 + 10x + 23$

5. If the equation for the flight of a ball is $y = -2x^2 + x + 12$, approximately when will the ball hit the ground?

   (a) 10.8 seconds   (b) 4.1 seconds   (c) 2.5 seconds

   (d) 2.7 seconds   (e) 3 seconds

6. If $P = 2v + 2w$, then $w =$

   (a) $\frac{1}{2}(P - v)$ (b) $\frac{P}{2} + v$ (c) $\frac{P - 2v}{2}$ (d) $\frac{P}{2} - 2v$ (e) $\frac{2v - P}{2}$

7. The function $f(x) = \frac{(x + 1)(x - 4)}{(x + 1)(x + 5)}$ is not defined when $x =$

   (a) 5   (b) -5 or 4   (c) 1 or 5   (d) 1 or -5 (e) -1 or -5

8. $\sin(\alpha + 2\pi) =$

   (a) $\sin \alpha$ (b) $-\sin \alpha$ (c) $\sin 2\alpha$ (d) $\cos \alpha$ (e) $-\cos \alpha$

9. Find x if $\log_8 512 = x$.

   (a) $x = 64$ (b) $x = 3$ (c) $x = 1.8$ (d) $x = 2.7$ (e) $x = 3.6$

10. If $x \geq 0$, which of the following is equivalent to $\sqrt{4x^2} + \sqrt[3]{8x^6} - \sqrt[4]{16x^8}$?

    (a) $2x^2$ (b) $6x^2$ (c) x^2 (d) $2x$ (e) $-2x^2$

Looking Back

In this unit, you have continued to deepen your understanding of functions and the patterns of change that they model. You revisited the basic types of functions relating quantitative variables and explored conditions under which these functions have inverses. You also developed strategies for finding symbolic rules for inverses of functions. Two special inverse functions, the square root function and the logarithmic function were found to be particularly useful in transforming data sets to help determine the most appropriate regression models. You also saw how common logarithms are useful in scaling data and in solving exponential equations.

In this final lesson, you will review the big ideas of this unit in contexts that may be slightly different from those you already encountered.

1. Suppose the population of a small town is modeled by a function $P = f(t)$ where P is the number of people in thousands and t is the number of years since 1980.

   a. What does $f(20)$ mean in this context? What does $f^{-1}(20)$ mean?

   b. How would you interpret the equation $f(t) = 32$ in this context? How would you rewrite this equation using f^{-1}?

2. Sketch the graph of each function. Then, explain why the function does or does not have an inverse. Sketch the graph of the inverse if it exists.

   a. $f(x) = -2x + 3$

   b. $g(x) = 10^x$

   c. $h(x) = 0.6x^2$

   d. $j(x) = \log_2 x$

3. Light, radio and television signals, x-rays, and the waves produced by alternating current are forms of electromagnetic radiation. The alternating current used in North America has a frequency of 60 cycles per second. The following table gives the frequencies (in cycles per second) of several electromagnetic waves.

Type of Wave		Frequency
Alternating current		60
AM Radio ranges	from	540,000
	to	1,600,000
Television and FM Radio range	from	54,000,000
	to	216,000,000
Light ranges	from infrared	390,000,000,000,000
	to ultraviolet	770,000,000,000,000
X-rays range	from	30,000,000,000,000,000
	to	100,000,000,000,000,000,000

Represent these wave frequencies on a logarithmic scale.

4. Find an equation for the inverse of each given function.

   a. $f(x) = 3x - 2$ **b.** $h(x) = \log x$ **c.** $i(x) = 7^x$

5. In computer science, the efficiency of computational algorithms is often analyzed in terms of the time necessary to perform the operation on n objects. There are several algorithms that put a list of names in alphabetical order. The times needed by two algorithms that order a list of n names are modeled by $f(n) = \frac{1}{2}n^2$ and $g(n) = n \log n$. Which algorithm is faster? Explain your reasoning.

6. Solve each equation using symbolic reasoning. Make sure to check your answers.

   a. $10^x = 2.75$ **b.** $10^x = -2.75$ **c.** $16.2 = 9.3^x$

   d. $16.2 = 2 \cdot (3.7^x)$ **e.** $\log x = -2.3$

7. Crew rowing is a popular sport in many areas of the United States. There are contests for boats with one, two, four, or eight rowers. The following data give the average speed over a 2,000-meter course for boats in several world rowing competitions. The theory of fluid mechanics indicates that the speed should be proportional to $\frac{1}{9}$th the power of the number of rowers.

a. Plot the data. Does it appear that the speed is proportional to $\frac{1}{9}$th the power of the number of rowers?

b. Write a function that represents the scientific theory. Use k for the constant of proportionality. Let x represent the number of rowers and y represent the speed.

c. Make the appropriate transformation and graph the transformed data. Do the transformed data appear linear?

d. Compute the least squares linear regression line for the transformed data, $y^* = ax^* + b$. Solve this equation for y.

e. Now use the regression feature of your calculator to fit the appropriate model to the original data. Compare the equation your calculator computes with the one you found in Part d.

Number of Rowers	Speed (in meters/minute)
1	279
1	276
1	275
1	279
2	291
2	289
2	287
2	295
4	316
4	312
4	309
4	326
8	341
8	338
8	343
8	349

Source: Helen Skala, "Will the real best fit curve please stand up?" *College Mathematics Journal,* 27 (1996) 220–223.

8. Plot **I** below shows the pattern of change in the number of reported cases of a disease over a seven-year period. Least squares regression lines for the transformed data are shown in Plots **II** and **III**.

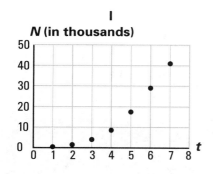

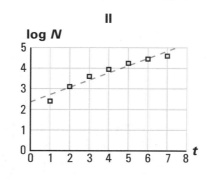

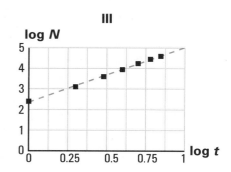

a. The points (1, 2.6953) and (4, 3.7651) are on the regression line for Plot **II**. Using this information, write an equation expressing N as a function of t.

b. The points (0, 2.3607) and (0.5, 3.6882) are on the regression line for Plot **III**. Using this information, write an equation expressing N as a function of t.

c. Which of the functions in Parts a and b provides the better fit to the data in Plot **I**? Why?

Checkpoint

When modeling a situation with a function $y = f(x)$, you often are interested not only in the question, "What is $f(a)$?" but also in the inverse question, "For what value of x is $f(x) = b$?" In this unit, you drew on concepts and methods from both geometry and algebra to answer the inverse question in a general way and to extend your understanding of function models to include logarithmic functions.

a Describe how you can determine whether a function has an inverse.

b For functions represented by algebraic rules, illustrate and describe how the rule for the inverse function, if it exists, can be found.

c Identify and describe the characteristics of the inverse of each of these functions.
- $f(x) = ax + b$
- $h(x) = a^x$
- $j(x) = 2^x$
- $k(x) = \log x$

d This unit introduced a new family of functions: logarithmic functions. What are three important ways in which logarithms are used?

e Logarithms have properties that are similar to those for exponents. Use your understanding of basic properties of logarithms to determine which of the following statements are true and which are false.
- $\log M \cdot N = \log M + \log N$
- $\log M^N = (\log M)^N$
- $\log_a M = \dfrac{\log M}{\log a}$
- If $\log y = 3x + 2$, then $y = 100 \cdot (1,000^x)$.

f What are the goals and steps involved when using logarithms to transform data?

g Explain how your graphing calculator fits a nonlinear model to paired data.

Be prepared to share your responses with the entire class.

On Your Own

Write, in outline form, a summary of the important mathematical concepts and methods developed in this unit. Organize your summary so that it can be used as a quick reference in future units and courses.

Counting Models

Lesson 1

Methods of Counting

Counting is a basic skill that you learned early and use often. It helps you answer the question, "How many?" You may be surprised by the wide variety of situations that require counting and the amount of mathematics that has been developed to help solve counting problems.

In previous units and courses, you studied how to model population growth. Population growth within a community or region affects many variables—from availability of housing and schools to assignment of license plates and telephone numbers. Fundamental to each of these situations is the question, "How many?" Consider the notice to telephone customers in Fairfield, Iowa, shown above.

> ### Important Notice to Fairfield Customers
>
> Effective October 3, 1992, telephone customers establishing new telephone service in Fairfield may be assigned a new telephone number prefix—469.
>
> Existing 472 prefix numbers in Fairfield are currently filled to capacity, making this addition necessary.
>
> New GTE customers in Fairfield will be assigned a new 469 telephone prefix or a 472, if available.
>
> Customers who are currently assigned a 472 prefix will continue with that number.

Source: *The Fairfield Weekly Reader,* October 15–21, 1992.

Think About This Situation

Until October 3, 1992, all telephone numbers in Fairfield began with the prefix 472.

a Besides population growth, what other factors might have made it necessary to create new telephone numbers in Fairfield?

b Does the community in which you live have more than one telephone number prefix? If you know the population of a town or city, how could you estimate the number of prefixes?

c How many different phone numbers can be created using the 472 prefix? How many different phone numbers will be available in Fairfield with the introduction of the 469 prefix?

d Describe some other situations that require careful counting to answer the question, "How many?" Think of situations from school, from business and industry, and from daily life outside of school.

Answering questions like those in the "Think About This Situation" requires careful, systematic, and sometimes clever counting. The branch of mathematics that deals with systematic methods of counting is called **combinatorics.** In this unit, you will learn some of the basic concepts, techniques, and proof methods in combinatorics.

INVESTIGATION 1 Careful Counting

In the "Think About This Situation," you briefly considered several counting situations, including assigning telephone numbers. In this investigation, you will examine a few situations in more depth, and in the process you will develop some useful counting strategies. At the end of the investigation, you will use the strategies to carry out a more complete analysis of telephone numbers.

1. Most computer systems require individual users to have passwords so that access can be controlled and security can be maintained. The number and type of characters allowed in a computer password varies from system to system.

   a. Suppose a password consists of only two characters: one letter from A to D, followed by one digit from 0 to 2. How many different passwords are possible? Explain the method you used to get your answer. Describe at least one other method that could be used.

   b. Do you think the password format in Part a is practical? Explain your answer.

   c. In one computer system, passwords consist of five characters: three digits from 0 to 9, followed by two letters from A to Z. How many different passwords are possible? Suppose an unauthorized user tries to gain access to the system simply by trying different passwords. If the person can try one password every second, and the system does not cut her off, what is the longest it could take to get into the system? (For this problem, ignore the need to also know the correct user name.)

   d. Personal Identification Numbers (PINs) used in Automated Teller Machines (ATMs) are similar to computer passwords. You must insert your card and then enter the correct PIN in order to get access to your bank account and withdraw money. A PIN consists of four digits, 0–9. Some ATMs will confiscate your card if you enter the wrong PIN too many times. Use a counting argument to explain why you think this is done.

2. Outdoor Adventure Clothing and Gear stocks windproof ski jackets in a different style for men and women. For each of these styles, there are 4 colors (purple, teal, yellow, blue), in each of 3 sizes (small, medium, large).

a. How many different jackets could be displayed?

b. Students in one class proposed the following methods for answering this question. Examine each method. Do they all work? Explain.

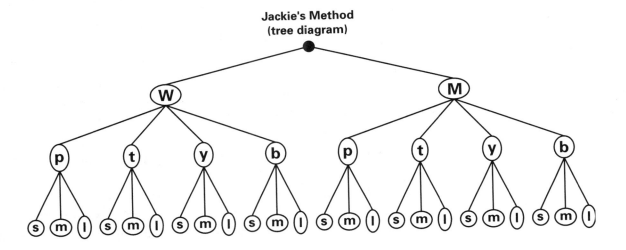

**Jackie's Method
(tree diagram)**

Antonio's Method

M-b-s	W-b-s
M-b-m	W-b-m
M-b-l	W-b-l
M-y-s	W-y-s
M-y-m	W-y-m
M-y-l	W-y-l
M-t-s	W-t-s
M-t-m	W-t-m
M-t-l	W-t-l
M-p-s	W-p-s
M-p-m	W-p-m
M-p-l	W-p-l

Dwight's Method

W-b-l M-p-s W-y-s W-t-s
W-t-m   M-y-s   M-y-m
M-t-l W-p-s M-p-l W-t-l
W-b-s   W-p-l   M-y-l
M-b-s W-p-m M-t-m
W-b-m   W-y-m M-t-s
M-b-l

```
┌──────────────────────────────────────────────────────┐
│                   Marsha's Method                    │
│                                                      │
│      2       ×       4       ×      3     = 24 different │
│   2 choices:      4 choices      3 choices     jackets │
│   men or          for color      for size            │
│   women                                              │
└──────────────────────────────────────────────────────┘
```

```
┌─────────────────────────┐   ┌──────────────────────────────┐
│      Sam's Method        │   │        Billie's Method       │
│  There are 2 genders     │   │   There are 4 colors for     │
│     plus 4 colors        │   │   both men and women;        │
│     plus 3 sizes.        │   │   that makes 4 × 4 = 16.      │
│     So there are         │   │   Then there are 3 sizes;     │
│     2 + 4 + 3 = 9        │   │   that makes 16 × 3 = 48.     │
│   different jackets      │   │   So there are 48            │
│     possible.            │   │   different jackets          │
│                          │   │     possible.                │
└─────────────────────────┘   └──────────────────────────────┘
```

    c. For those methods that work, describe similarities among them.

    d. Which method makes the most sense to you? Why? Describe any other methods that you can think of.

    e. Suppose the men's and women's jackets are available in four sizes—small, medium, large, and extra large. Modify the correct methods in Part b to determine the number of different jackets that could be displayed in this case.

3. Now that you've thought about a variety of different counting methods, return to an analysis of computer passwords.

    a. Look back at Activity 1 Part a on page 217. Count the number of passwords in this situation using each correct method from Activity 2 that you did not previously use.

    b. Which of the methods in Activity 2 would be most effective for answering the first question in Part c of Activity 1? Explain your reasoning and illustrate how the method can be used to determine the answer.

    c. Consider another type of password that consists of just two characters. One character is a letter from A to C and the other character is 0 or 1. The two characters can be in either order, letter-digit or digit-letter. How many such passwords are there?

    d. In one computer system, a password consists of any 7 letters followed by any 2 digits. How many passwords are possible? Suppose that no letters or digits can be repeated. In this case, how many passwords are possible?

    e. In another computer system, a password consists of 4 letters and 1 digit in any order. How many passwords are possible?

4. Marsha's reasoning in Activity 2 illustrates the **Multiplication Principle of Counting.** If you want to count all the ways a sequence of events can happen, just count how many ways each event can happen and multiply those numbers together. More precisely, suppose the first event in a sequence can happen in n_1 ways; for each of these, the second event can happen in n_2 ways; for each of these, the third event can happen in n_3 ways; and so on. Then the whole sequence of events can happen in $n_1 \times n_2 \times n_3 \times \ldots$ ways.

    a. Consider the counting situations in Activities 2 and 3. What are the "events" in each situation? What is the "sequence of events" in each situation?

    b. If you have not already done so, apply the Multiplication Principle of Counting to the counting situations in Activity 3. Compare these answers to the answers you got before.

5. These days there is a high demand for telephone numbers. Besides regular telephones, many individuals and businesses have fax machines, pagers, cellular phones, and separate lines for accessing the Internet. The high demand has caused a shortage of telephone numbers! Read the article below about new area codes.

Number Please: New Area Codes Create Confusion

A wave of new area codes hitting the country is short-circuiting business switchboards.

Most residential telephone users should have no trouble dialing the new area codes because their calls are routed through local telephone networks equipped to handle them, the Federal Communications Commission said.

But private business switch-boards, known as PBXs can't recognize the new codes unless they've been upgraded, making it impossible to dial calls to them. That's because unlike existing area codes, the new ones don't have a zero or a one in the middle; instead, they use two through nine.

Businesses and other PBX users can call 1 (281) 792-9999, at no cost, to test whether their equipment can reach the new codes.

Those whose PBX systems fail the test can get help by calling another toll-free number— 1 (800) 218-6436.

Since the beginning of this year, 11 sections of the country, including Alabama, Colorado, Virginia and Washington state, have begun implementing new area codes.

Beginning this month, through next year, nine areas—Chicago, Dallas, Miami, Missouri, northern Florida, Ohio, Oregon, South Carolina and southern California—will add new codes. By next year, a total of 23 new codes—including one for toll-free 800 service—are slated to be in operation, affecting millions of people.

The new area codes are being instituted because all codes under the old plan, which dates back to the 1940s, have been exhausted thanks to the explosion of such services as cellular phones, fax machines

> Some of the new area codes (the existing code is listed first, followed by the new code and the date of implementation):
>
> **Miami: 305; 954—November.**
> **Oregon: 503; 541—Nov. 5.**
> **South Carolina: 803; 864—Dec. 3.**
> **North Florida: 904; 352—Dec. 3.**
> **Missouri: 314; 573—Jan. 7.**
> **Suburban Chicago: 708; 847—Jan. 20 and 630—Aug 3.**
> **Dallas: 214; 972—Feb. 1.**
> **Ohio: 216; 330—first quarter 1996.**
> **Southern California: 310; 562—Feb. 1.**

and pagers, and the need for second telephone lines for personal computers.

The new area code plan will make it possible to create 640 new area codes and up to five billion new telephone numbers, the FCC said. The FCC doesn't expect the new area codes to be depleted until well beyond 2000.

Source: *Capper's*, Vol 117, No. 126, 11/14/95, page 2.

a. According to the newspaper article, what is the difference between the new area codes and old area codes?

b. A new area code is constructed according to the following rules: The first digit cannot be a 0 or a 1. The second digit is restricted according to what you found out in Part a. The third digit can be any number from 0 to 9. Under these rules, how many new area codes are possible? Does your answer match the number given in the article? If not, go back and examine your work.

6. The article about area codes mentions the old telephone numbering plan from the 1940s. This plan was devised by AT&T, which was the only telephone company in the United States until 1984.

a. A standard telephone number in the United States has a three-digit area code, followed by a three-digit local prefix, followed by a four-digit local number. Thus there are 10 digits: ddd-ddd-dddd. If 0–9 could be used for each digit, how many telephone numbers would be possible?

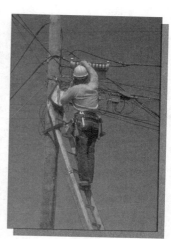

b. The original AT&T numbering restrictions are listed below. Under these restrictions, how many different ten-digit phone numbers were available?

Original Telephone Numbering Policies

• 0 cannot be used as the first digit of an area code or a local prefix, since dialing 0 is reserved for reaching the operator.

• Phone numbers beginning with 1 are reserved for internal use within the telephone system, so 1 cannot be used as the first digit of an area code or a local prefix.

• Early phone numbers included letters, for example PYramid4-1225 instead of 794-1225. In order to be able to dial letters, most numbers on a telephone have letters associated with them. However, to avoid confusing the numbers 0 and 1 with the letters O and I, the numbers 0 and 1 on a telephone do not have associated letters. So 0 and 1 cannot be the second digit of a local prefix.

• The telephone system used the second digit to distinguish an area code from a local prefix. Since the second digit of a local prefix can be anything *except* 0 and 1, the second digit of an area code *must* be 0 or 1.

• The third digit of an area code can be any number. The third digit of a local prefix can be any number except 0 or 1.

• The four digits of the local number can be anything.

On Your Own

Think about how many different automobile license plates can be made under certain constraints. For example, in 1997 in Iowa, a license plate had six characters. The first three characters were numbers and the last three were letters.

a. How many different license plates were possible in Iowa in 1997?

b. Suppose that no letters or numbers can be repeated. How many license plates are possible?

c. Suppose that the three letters were used to represent the county, with GUT used for all license plates issued to residents of Guthrie County. Do you think this is a good plan? Explain.

d. What license plate configurations are used in the state where you live? How many different license plates are possible using one of those configurations?

INVESTIGATION 2 Permutations and Combinations

In the last investigation, you solved a variety of counting problems using the Multiplication Principle of Counting and some careful thinking. It is possible and useful to formalize some of the work you have been doing. In particular, in this investigation you will analyze two important characteristics of counting problems—*order* and *repetition*. These two characteristics lie at the heart of many counting problems and applications.

1. Read the newspaper article from 1995 below.

Take Note: Counting Their Chickens

A national restaurant chain that boasts about its tasty chicken is eating crow after a high school mathematics class cried foul over a television ad.

The ad shows Joe Montana, the National Football League quarterback, standing at the counter at a Boston Chicken restaurant puzzling over side-dish choices when an announcer says that more than 3,000 combinations can be created by choosing three of the restaurant's 16 side dishes.

But Bob Swaim, a math teacher at Souderton Area High School near Philadelphia, and his class did the math and told the Colorado-based chicken chain that there were only 816 combinations.

"We goofed," said Gary Gerdemann, a spokesman for Boston Chicken, explaining that the restaurant had confused "combinations" with "permutations."

"Apparently we didn't listen to our high school math teachers," Mr. Gerdemann said.

The company has, however, listened to Mr. Swaim and corrected its ads. For their eagle eyes, the students were awarded free meals and $500 to expand the math menu at Souderton.

Source: Reprinted with permission from *Education Week*. Vol. 14, No. 20, February 8, 1995, p. 3

a. Describe how the issues of order and repetition are involved in this situation.

b. The announcer claimed that more than 3,000 combinations can be created by choosing three of the restaurant's 16 side dishes. How do you think this number of combinations was determined?

c. Why is the claim of more than 3,000 combinations too high?

In the newspaper article above, a spokesman stated that the restaurant had confused combinations with permutations (Later you will see if what he said is correct—see Extending Task 5 on page 237.). In order to understand combinations and permutations, it is important to consider two key questions:

Are repetitions allowed?
Do two different orderings count as two different possibilities?

2. Suppose that a local convenience store has 5 flavors of ice cream—chocolate (C), vanilla (V), pecan fudge (F), mint chocolate chip (M), and cookie dough (D). Some friends want to try all possible two-dip cones. Think about the two preceding questions as you count the different ice cream cones.

a. John loves ice cream, any ice cream. He just wants a two-dip cone. It doesn't matter to him which flavor is on top, or even if both scoops are the same flavor. For example, he will gladly accept cookie dough on top of cookie dough (D-D), and for him there is no difference between pecan fudge on top of mint chocolate chip (F-M) or vice versa (M-F).

- Are repetitions allowed in this situation?
- Should two different orderings be counted as different possibilities?
- Based on his preferences, how many different ice cream cone choices does John have? List all the possibilities.

b. Shrita is much more discriminating. She definitely wants two different flavors on her cone, and she cares about which flavor is on top.

- Are repetitions allowed in this situation?
- Should two different orderings be counted as different possibilities?
- Based on her preferences, how many different ice cream cone choices does Shrita have? List all the possibilities.

c. Jeong-Woo also wants two different flavors on his cone, but it makes no difference to him which flavor is on top.

- Are repetitions allowed in this situation?
- Should two different orderings be counted as different possibilities?
- Based on his preferences, how many different ice cream cone choices does Jeong-Woo have? List all the possibilities.

d. Like John, Deborah will gladly accept two scoops of the same flavor, but when she has two different flavors it matters to her which one is on top.

- Are repetitions allowed in this situation?
- Should two different orderings be counted as different possibilities?
- Based on her preferences, how many different ice cream cone choices does Deborah have? List all the possibilities.

e. Which person has the most possibilities from which to choose? Which person has the fewest possibilities? Why does this make sense?

3. The table below is one way to organize information about counting situations where order and repetition are important. In each cell of a large copy of the table, enter the student name from the corresponding part of Activity 2. If you

Analyzing Counting Situations

	No Repetitions	Repetitions OK
Different Orderings Count As Different Possibilities		
Different Orderings Do Not Count As Different Possibilities		

used some formula or computation to determine the number of ice cream cone possibilities, then enter that as well. (You will enter several more items into each cell later, so write neatly and leave some space.)

You will now take a closer look at the cells in the "No Repetitions" column of the table. Situations that fit in these cells involve the ideas of *permutations* and *combinations*. These ideas were referred to in the newspaper article at the beginning of this investigation. In the next several activities, you will investigate permutations and combinations.

Suppose a club with 15 members decides to hold an election to elect three officers. Consider two possibilities. The club members might elect a President, Vice-President, and Treasurer, as indicated by the French Club ballot below. Or the club might elect an executive committee consisting of three members of equal rank, as indicated by the Ski Club ballot.

French Club Elections Ballot
President
_____
Vice-President
_____
Treasurer
_____

Ski Club Elections Ballot
Executive Committee
_____
_____
_____

In the following activities, you will seek an answer to this question:

How many different possibilities are there in each case?

4. First, consider the number of different possibilities for President, Vice-President, and Treasurer in the French Club.

   a. In which cell of the table in Activity 3 does this problem belong? Enter "P-VP-T" in the appropriate cell of your table.

   b. How many different three-person groups are possible for President, Vice-President, and Treasurer? Explain.

5. There are several possible strategies for answering the question in Activity 4. Think about the strategy below.

There are 15 choices for President. Once the President is chosen, then there are 14 members left who could be chosen for Vice-President. Once the President and Vice-President have been chosen, then there are 13 members left who could be Treasurer. So, by the Multiplication Principle of Counting, there are $15 \times 14 \times 13 = 2{,}730$ different possibilities for the 3 club officers.

  a. Does the answer given above agree with your answer in Activity 4? If not, resolve any differences.

  b. Use this strategy to count the number of possibilities if the French Club has 20 members.

  c. Use this strategy to count the number of possibilities if the 15-member French Club decides to elect four officers—President, Vice-President, Treasurer, and Secretary.

6. Factorial notation is a compact way of writing certain products of consecutive nonnegative integers. For example, $5 \times 4 \times 3 \times 2 \times 1 = 5!$ which is read as "5 factorial." In general, $n! = n \times (n-1) \times \cdots \times 2 \times 1$. For convenience, $0!$ is defined to be 1.

  a. Explain how the method in Activity 5 for computing the number of possibilities for the three people who will be President, Vice-President, and Treasurer in a 15-member club is related to factorials.

  b. What factorial-type computation would you use to compute the number of possibilities if the French Club has 30 members and they decide to elect four officers—President, Vice-President, Treasurer, and Secretary?

The methods in Activities 5 and 6 generalize to useful counting formulas that will be developed in Activities 7 and 8.

7. If there are n club members and k ranked officers will be elected, then the number of possible k-member officer slates is

$$n(n-1)(n-2) \cdots (n-k+1)$$

  a. Apply this formula to the counting problems in Parts b and c of Activity 5. Verify that you get the same answers that you got before.

  b. Explain why this formula is a generalization of the method described in Activity 5.

  c. How many factors are in this product?

  d. Explain why the last factor is equivalent to $[n - (k-1)]$.

8. Consider another counting formula for this situation. If there are n club members and k ranked officers will be elected, then the number of possible k-member officer slates is

$$\frac{n!}{(n-k)!}$$

a. Apply this formula to the counting problems in Parts b and c of Activity 5, and verify that you get the same answers you got before.

b. Prove that the formulas in Activities 7 and 8 are equivalent by showing that
$$n(n-1)(n-2) \cdots (n-k+1) = \frac{n!}{(n-k)!}.$$

c. In addition to using and proving formulas, it is important to explain formulas in words. Explain why the expression $\frac{n!}{(n-k)!}$ makes sense as the number of possible k-member ranked officer slates.

9. Now consider the Ski Club election. Recall that in this situation the club will elect a 3-person executive committee instead of a President, a Vice-President, and a Treasurer. All three members of the executive committee are equal in rank. The problem is to determine how many different 3-person executive committees can be chosen from the 15 club members.

a. Before you actually count the possibilities, compare this election to the French Club election. Do you think the number of possible 3-person groups in this election is *more than, less than,* or *the same as* the number of possible 3-person groups in the French Club election? Explain your reasoning.

b. In terms of order and repetition, what is the difference between the Ski Club problem and the French Club problem?

c. Which cell of the table in Activity 3 corresponds to the Ski Club problem? Enter "committee" in the appropriate cell of your table.

d. Now solve the problem: How many different 3-person executive committees can be chosen from a club with 15 members? Compare your answer and your solution method to those from the similar French Club problem in Activity 5. Explain the differences.

10. As you may have discovered in Activity 9, the methods used in Activities 5–8 to solve the French Club problem can be modified to solve the Ski Club problem. First, consider the following modification of the strategy used in Activity 5:

There are 15 choices for the first executive committee member. This leaves 14 club members who could be chosen as the second executive committee member, and 13 choices for the third executive committee member. So far this yields 15 × 14 × 13 possibilities, just as in Activity 5 with the French Club. However, in this situation different orderings do *not* count as different possibilities. For example, a committee of *ABC* is the same as a committee of *BAC*. In fact, for a committee consisting of *A*, *B*, and *C*, there are 6 different orderings that make the same committee, so you must divide the first calculation by 6. This gives a final answer of $\frac{15 \times 14 \times 13}{6} = 455$ possible committees.

a. List the 6 different orderings of a committee *ABC* mentioned in the strategy above. Explain how to use the Multiplication Principle of Counting to count the number of different orderings without listing them.

b. Does the final answer given in the description of the strategy agree with your answer in Activity 9? If not, resolve any differences.

c. Suppose the Ski Club has 24 members. Use the above strategy to determine how many different 3-person executive committees can be chosen from the club.

d. Suppose the 15-member Ski Club decides to elect a 4-person executive committee.

■ Use the above strategy to determine the number of 4-person executive committees that can be chosen from the club.

■ By what number do you divide in this situation? Use the Multiplication Principle of Counting to show how to compute this divisor.

e. Now consider the use of factorials in these committee-counting problems.

■ Explain how the method for computing the number of 3-person executive committees that can be chosen from a club with 15 members is related to factorials.

■ Use a similar method involving factorials to count the number of different 5-person executive committees that can be chosen from a club with 30 members.

Checkpoint

You have explored two major types of counting problems in this investigation:

■ Count the number of possible ranked-officer slates, like President, Vice-President, and Treasurer.

■ Count the number of possible executive committees.

ⓐ Describe how these problems are similar and different, in terms of the key issues of order and repetition.

ⓑ In Activities 7 and 8, you examined general formulas for the ranked-officer problem. Modify these two general formulas so that they apply to the committee problem. Write down the two new formulas.

ⓒ Use each new formula in Part b to determine how many 5-person executive committees can be chosen from a club with 30 members. In each case, verify that you get the same answer as in Activity 10 Part e.

ⓓ Prove that the two new formulas are equivalent.

Be prepared to compare your group's descriptions, formulas, and proofs to those of other groups.

An arrangement like President, Vice-President, and Treasurer, where different orderings count as different possibilities and repetitions are not allowed, is called a **permutation**. An arrangement like a 3-person executive committee, where different orderings are *not* counted as different possibilities and repetitions are not allowed, is called a **combination**.

On Your Own

Solve the following two counting problems noting similarities and differences in the methods you use.

a. Find the number of different 4-person executive committees that can be chosen from a club with 27 members.

b. Find the number of possibilities for four people who can be chosen President, Vice-President, Treasurer, and Secretary in a 27-member club.

11. In counting situations, the term "combination" is used in the very precise way described below the preceding Checkpoint. This may be different from how it is often used in everyday language. Revisit some of your earlier work, thinking about permutations and combinations.

    a. Which of the ice cream cone problems in Activity 2 involves permutations? Which ice cream cone problem involves combinations?

    b. Enter "permutation" and "combination" into the appropriate cells of your table in Activity 3.

    c. In general, which yields a greater number of possibilities—permutations or combinations? Explain your reasoning.

12. A common notation for the number of different permutations of k objects taken from n objects is $P(n, k)$. Similarly, a common notation for the number of different combinations of k objects chosen from n objects is $C(n, k)$. We sometimes read $C(n, k)$ as "n choose k," because $C(n, k)$ is the number of ways of choosing k objects from n objects (when order doesn't matter and repetition is not allowed).

A general formula for the number of permutations, from Activity 8, is

$$P(n, k) = \frac{n!}{(n - k)!}$$

A general formula for the number of combinations is

$$C(n, k) = \frac{n!}{(n - k)!k!}$$

    a. Compute $P(9, 2)$ and $C(9, 2)$ using the methods below. Compare methods and answers.

      ■ Compute without a calculator using the formulas given above and writing the fractions in simplest form.

      ■ Compute using the permutation and combination features on your calculator. (Note that the notation used on your calculator may be slightly different than that used here.)

    b. Compare the formula for $C(n, k)$ with the formulas you stated in the Checkpoint. If one of your formulas in the Checkpoint does not match the formula for $C(n, k)$ given here, resolve the differences.

    c. What restrictions must be placed on n and k for these formulas to make sense?

    d. Write a formula for $C(n, k)$ using $P(n, k)$.

13. It is often helpful, both for using and remembering a formula, to have a verbal description of the formula.

   a. Below is a description of how to compute $P(n, k)$.

   Start with n and carry out a factorial-type computation using exactly k factors.

   Explain how this description fits the formula above. Explain how this description fits the counting situation in the club officers example.

   b. Below is a description of how to compute $C(n, k)$.

   Start with n and carry out a factorial-type computation using exactly k factors. But then you've counted too many, so divide by k!.

   Explain how this description fits the formula above. Explain how this description fits the counting situation in the executive committee example.

14. Solve each of the counting problems below. In each case, state whether the problem involves combinations, permutations, or neither.

   a. How many different 13-card hands can be made from a deck of 52 cards?

   b. Seven people are running for three unranked positions on the school board. In how many different ways can these three positions be filled?

   c. Three of seven people will be seated on stage at a banquet in a row of chairs. How many different seating arrangements are possible?

   d. Information is stored in computers as strings of 0s and 1s, because 0 and 1 can be interpreted as off and on settings for switches inside the computer. A *bit* is a 0 or a 1. A *binary string* is a sequence of bits. A *byte* is an 8-bit binary string.

   ■ How many different bytes are possible?

   ■ How many 8-bit strings contain exactly 2 zeroes?

15. A set A is a **subset** of a set B if every element of set A is an element of set B. For example, if $B = \{1, 2, 3\}$, then the subsets of B are

$$\varnothing, \{1\}, \{2\}, \{3\}, \{1, 2\}, \{1, 3\}, \{2, 3\}, \{1, 2, 3\}.$$

(The symbol $\varnothing$ denotes the **empty set**—the set with no elements. The empty set is a subset of every set.)

How many different subsets of 5 elements can be constructed from a set containing 12 elements?

In this investigation, you developed concepts, techniques, and formulas related to permutations and combinations.

a Examine your copy of the "Analyzing Counting Situations" table from Activity 3. Bring the table up to date by entering as much of the following information as you can into each cell of the table. (You have already entered some of this information during the investigation.)

- Mathematical term for the problem type
- Notation for the problem type
- Formula for the problem type
- Example of the problem type in addition to the ice cream cone example

b Permutations and combinations can be thought of in terms of sets and subsets.

- Explain why a subset of a set is a combination.
- Explain why an ordered sequence of distinct elements of a set is a permutation.

c Describe similarities and differences between permutations and combinations.

Be prepared to explain your group's completed table and thinking to the entire class.

On Your Own

Consider the following counting situations.

a. Four of the 11 members of a championship gymnastics team will be chosen at random to stand in a row on stage during an awards ceremony. Assuming it is more prestigious to stand closer to the podium, how many different arrangements of gymnasts on stage are possible?

b. A bicycle lock has four number dials. Each dial ranges from 0 to 9. How many different lock combinations are possible? Are these lock combinations actually combinations in the mathematical sense of the word? Explain.

Modeling • Organizing • Reflecting • Extending

Modeling

1. Dominoes are rectangular tiles used to play a game. Each tile is divided into two squares with a number of dots in each square, as in the figure below.

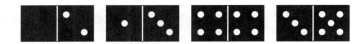

   The standard set of dominoes has from 0 to 6 dots in each square. A deluxe set of dominoes has from 0 to 9 dots in each square. How many different standard dominoes are possible? How many different deluxe dominoes are possible? How many dominoes are possible in a set that has 0 to n dots in each square?

2. Most radio stations in the United States have 3 or 4 call letters.

   a. Historically, radio stations west of the Mississippi river had call letters starting with K. How many different sets of call letters like this are possible?

   b. Today, radio station letters can begin with K or W. How many different call letters like this are possible?

3. The following television commercial aired nationwide in 1993.

Customer:	So what's this deal?
Pizza Chef:	Two pizzas.
Customer:	[Looking towards a four-year-old boy.] Two pizzas. Write that down.
Pizza Chef:	And on the two pizzas choose any toppings—up to five [from the list of 11 toppings].
Older Boy:	Do you . . .
Pizza Chef:	. . . have to pick the same toppings on each pizza? No!
4-Year-Old Boy:	Then the possibilities are endless.
Customer:	What do you mean? Five plus five are ten.
4-Year-Old Boy:	Actually, there are 1,048,576 possibilities.
Customer:	Ten was just a ballpark figure.
Old Man:	You got that right.

a. Do you think the customer's "ballpark figure" is too low?

b. Suppose you order just one pizza and you must choose exactly 5 different toppings from 11 choices. How many different pizzas are possible?

c. Suppose you order just one pizza and you must choose exactly 3 different toppings from 11 choices. How many different pizzas are possible?

d. Suppose you order just one pizza and you can choose from 0 to 5 different toppings. How many different pizzas are possible?

e. In the TV commercial on the previous page, does the 4-year-old boy have the correct answer? If so, explain how to compute his answer. If not, explain why it is incorrect and determine the correct answer.

f. Jeremy reasoned as follows:

There are 1,024 possibilities for one pizza. Since 2 pizzas are ordered, that makes $(1,024)^2$ possibilities for a two-pizza order. But order doesn't matter for the two pizzas, so divide by 2. Thus, the correct answer is 524,288.

Explain the error in Jeremy's reasoning.

4. The original plan for assigning telephone numbers that you investigated in Activity 6 on page 221 was implemented in 1947. At that time, the supply of numbers was expected to last for 300 years. However, by the 1970s the numbers were already starting to run out! So the numbering plan had to be modified. In this task, you will count the number of different phone numbers that were available in the late 1990s.

a. As of 2000, local seven-digit phone numbers could have the form XZZ-ZZZZ, where X is any digit 2 through 9 and Z is any digit 0 through 9. (Of course, the Zs don't necessarily all represent the same digit.) How many seven-digit numbers are possible under this plan?

b. After the AT&T breakup in 1984, Bellcore became responsible for administering the numbering plan for all telephone numbers in World Zone 1, which includes the United States, Canada, and about a dozen Caribbean countries. In 1993, Bellcore allocated the last of the original area codes. Beginning in 1995, new area codes went into service. In Activity 5 on pages 220–221, you counted the number of new area codes. In Part a above, you counted the number of local seven-digit phone numbers under the new plan. Use this information to determine how many ten-digit telephone numbers are available under the new plan. Does your answer match the estimate given in the newspaper article in Activity 5? If not, go back and examine your work.

Organizing

1. Consider matrices that have only 0 or 1 as entries.

   a. How many 3×2 matrices are possible that have 0 or 1 as entries?

   b. How many $n \times m$ matrices are possible that have entries of 0 or 1?

2. At many private schools, students are required to wear uniforms. Suppose the boys must wear navy or khaki pants; a short-sleeve or long-sleeve white shirt; and a sweater, vest or blazer.

   Explain how the Multiplication Principle of Counting can be used to determine that in any group of at least 13 boys two will be wearing the same type of uniform. How big would the group need to be to guarantee that three boys would be wearing the same type of uniform?

3. Use counting methods to help answer each of the following geometric questions.

   a. Given a set of n points, how many distinct line segments can be formed with two of the n points as endpoints? Does it make any difference if all of the points are not in the same plane? Explain your reasoning.

   b. How many points of intersection are formed by n coplanar lines if no two are parallel and no three intersect in a common point?

   c. Using combinations, explain why the questions in Parts a and b are essentially the same.

4. There are several different notations used for counting combinations. One of the most common notations is the one used in this lesson, namely, $C(n, k)$. Other notations that mean the same thing include $_nC_k$ and $\binom{n}{k}$. Practice with different notation by computing $C(12, 5)$, $_8C_3$, and $\binom{12}{7}$.

Reflecting

1. Two important issues to consider in counting are order and repetition. How do you decide whether "order" should be considered in counting? If it is important, what approach do you use? How do you decide whether repeti-

tions are involved in a counting situation? If they are, how do you account for them in the approach you use?

2. Combinatorics is sometimes described as "methods for counting without counting." In what sense is this an apt description of the mathematics you have been doing in this lesson?

3. Recall or listen to the song "The Twelve Days of Christmas." How many gifts have accumulated after the 12th day?

4. Find a counting problem in your daily life or in a newspaper whose solution involves combinations or permutations. Describe the problem and explain how it can be solved.

Extending

1. In the book *The Man Who Counted* by Malba Tahan, a story is told of Beremiz Samir, a man with amazing mathematical skills. Read at least the first chapter of this book. Then describe and explain at least one counting feat performed by Beremiz. (From *The Man Who Counted: A Collection of Mathematical Adventures* by Malba D. Tahan, translated by Leslie Clark and Alastair Reid. Cover art and illustrations by Patricia Reed Bagnero. Used by permission of W.W. Norton and Company, Inc.)

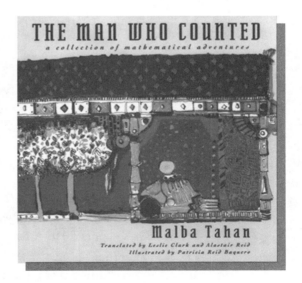

2. RNA (ribonucleic acid) is a messenger molecule associated with DNA (deoxyribonucleic acid). RNA molecules consist of a chain of *bases*.

Each base is one of 4 chemicals: U (uracil), C (cytosine), A (adenine), and G (guanine). It is difficult to observe exactly what an entire RNA chain looks like, but it is sometimes possible to observe fragments of a chain by breaking up the chain with certain enzymes. Armed with knowledge about the fragments, you can sometimes determine the makeup of the entire chain.

Computer-rendered molecular model of t-RNA

One type of enzyme that breaks up an RNA chain is a "G-enzyme." The G-enzyme will break an RNA chain after each G link. For example, consider the following chain:

AUUGCGAUC

A G-enzyme will break up this chain into the following fragments:

AUUG CG AUC

a. What fragments result when a G-enzyme is applied to the following chain?

CGUUGGAUCGAU

b. Unfortunately, the fragments of a broken-up chain may be mixed up and in the wrong order. Explain why a fragment that does not end in G must be the last fragment in the chain.

c. In Parts c–e, you will use information about fragments to reconstruct the complete chain. Suppose an RNA chain is broken by a G-enzyme into the following fragments (although not necessarily in this order):

AUG AAC CG AG

How many different ways can these fragments be combined into a complete RNA chain of 10 bases?

d. Another enzyme, the U-C enzyme, breaks up an RNA chain after every U and every C. This enzyme breaks the unknown RNA chain in Part c into the following fragments:

GC GAAC AGAU

How many different ways can these fragments be combined into a single RNA chain of 10 bases?

e. Parts c and d give you information about fragments of a particular RNA chain. Putting that information together, what is the complete chain?

3. In Modeling Task 1, you counted the number of standard dominoes. To play the game of dominoes, you take turns trying to place dominoes end-to-end by matching the number of dots. For example, for the three dominoes pictured below, the 3-5 domino can be placed next to the 1-3 domino, but the 0-2 domino cannot be placed next to either of the other dominoes.

   a. Is it possible to make a chain of all the dominoes in a standard 6-dot set? Justify your answer.

   b. Is it possible to make a chain of all the dominoes in an n-dot set? One way to tackle this question is to use a vertex-edge graph model. Let the vertices be the number of dots and let an edge between two vertices, or from a vertex to itself, represent a domino with dots corresponding to the vertices. Then consider paths through the graph model. Construct a graph model like this for domino sets using a few different values of n. Then figure out, and explain, how to use the graph model to determine whether it is possible to make a chain using all the dominoes in the set.

4. Think about all possible positive integers. What proportion of all positive integers contain the digit 3?

5. Reread the newspaper article on page 223. The counting problem discussed in the article is to determine the number of different 3-side-dish choices that can be made from 16 side dishes.

> ### Sides
> *(served after 10:30 A.M. until 8:00 P.M.)*
>
> | | |
> |---|---|
> | Tomato Bisque | Macaroni and Cheese |
> | Caesar Salad | Black Beans and Rice |
> | House Salad | Sweet Potato Fries |
> | Potato Salad | Cornbread |
> | Green Beans | Mashed Potatoes |
> | Vegetable Medley | Cranberry Relish |
> | Cole Slaw | Cinnamon Apples |
> | Creamed Spinach | Fruit Salad |

   a. Are repetitions allowed in this situation? Does order matter? Are the 3-side-dish choices examples of permutations, combinations, or neither?

   b. The correct answer given by the math teacher and his students is 816. Explain how to determine this answer.

1. $\frac{1}{5} + \frac{7}{8} - \frac{3}{10} =$

    (a) $\frac{5}{3}$ **(b)** $\frac{9}{10}$ **(c)** $\frac{39}{40}$ **(d)** $\frac{31}{40}$ **(e)** $\frac{11}{8}$

2. Which of the following is equivalent to $(x^3 - y^2)^2$?

    (a) $x^6 + y^4$ **(b)** $x^9 - 2x^3y^2 + y^4$ **(c)** $x^6 + 2x^6y^4 + y^4$

    (d) $x^9 + y^4$ **(e)** $x^6 - 2x^3y^2 + y^4$

3. Find the slope of the line shown below.

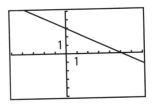

    (a) 1 **(b)** $\frac{3}{5}$ **(c)** $-\frac{5}{3}$ **(d)** $\frac{5}{3}$ **(e)** $-\frac{3}{5}$

4. If $f(x) = 3x^4 + 2x^2 - 5x + 6$, then $f(-4)$ is

    (a) 826 **(b)** 862 **(c)** 786 **(d)** -786 **(e)** -826

5. Solve $6b^2 = 12b$ for b.

    (a) $b = 2$ **(b)** $b = \frac{1}{2}$ or $b = 0$ **(c)** $b = 0$ or $b = 2$

    (d) $b = -2$ or $b = 0$ **(e)** $b = 0$

6. Solve $|x - 7| > 9$.

    (a) $x < -2$ or $x > 16$ **(b)** $x < -16$ or $x > 16$ **(c)** $x > -16$ or $x < 16$

    (d) $x > -2$ or $x < 16$ **(e)** $x > 16$

7. If $f(x) = \frac{2x + 6}{x + 2}$, then $f(2a)$ is

    (a) $\frac{2a + 3}{a + 1}$ **(b)** $\frac{2a + 6}{a + 1}$ **(c)** $2a + 3$ **(d)** $\frac{a + 3}{a + 1}$ **(e)** 5

8. Which of the following is the best approximation of the measure of angle A?

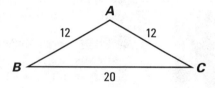

    (a) $56.4°$ **(b)** $67.11°$ **(c)** $73.74°$ **(d)** $112.89°$ **(e)** $134.22°$

9. Simplify $125^{\frac{2}{3}}$.

    (a) $\sqrt[6]{125}$ **(b)** 10 **(c)** 75 **(d)** 5 **(e)** 25

10. Simplify $\sqrt{4x + 16}$.

    (a) $2\sqrt{x + 4}$ **(b)** $2\sqrt{x} + 4$ **(c)** $2x + 4$

    (d) $x\sqrt{2} + 4$ **(e)** $4\sqrt{x + 4}$

Lesson 2

Counting Throughout Mathematics

You saw in the last lesson that counting problems arise in many different contexts, for example, clothing and menu choices, telephone numbers, computer passwords, automobile license plates, club committees, card games, and binary strings. The counting methods you learned are used throughout mathematics—in algebra, geometry, probability, graph theory, and other areas.

Think About This Situation

Consider the question "How many?" in the following mathematical contexts.

a Suppose you write $(a + b)^2$ in standard polynomial form. How many terms are in the expanded form? How many terms would be in the expansion of $(a + b)^3$? In the expansion of $(a + b)^n$?

b Given five points, no three of which are collinear, how many different triangles can be formed?

c Suppose you flip a coin three times. How many sequences of heads and tails are possible? How many of the possible sequences have exactly two heads? What is the probability of getting exactly two heads when you flip a coin three times?

d Recall that a complete graph is a vertex-edge graph with exactly one edge between each pair of vertices. How many edges does a complete graph with four vertices have? How about a complete graph with five vertices? What would be the generalized counting question?

Paul Erdös (1913–1996) is regarded as one of the top 10 mathematicians of the last century. He did significant work in combinatorics, number theory, geometry, graph theory, and set theory, writing over 1,500 mathematical papers. He helped create the probabilistic method and much of discrete mathematics.

In this lesson, you will investigate applications of counting in probability and algebra. In the MORE set and in Lesson 3, you will explore counting applications in geometry and discrete mathematics.

INVESTIGATION 1 Counting and Multiplication Rules for Probability

Counting methods are often useful when trying to determine probabilities. This is especially true when there are a finite number of outcomes, all of which are equally likely. In this case, the **probability of an event** A can be defined as

$$P(A) = \frac{\text{number of favorable outcomes}}{\text{total number of possible outcomes}}$$

Thus, when all the outcomes are equally likely, you can determine the probability of an event by counting the number of favorable outcomes and dividing by the number of possible outcomes.

1. Consider the experiment of rolling two dice, one red and one blue, where an outcome is the number of spots showing on each die face up. For example, (3, 5) denotes the outcome of getting 3 on the red die and 5 on the blue die.

   a. Are all the outcomes equally likely? What is the total number of possible outcomes?

   b. Consider the event of getting doubles. How many outcomes are "favorable" to this event?

   c. What is the probability of getting doubles when rolling two dice?

2. In a state lottery, a player fills out a ticket by choosing five "regular" numbers from 1 to 45, without repetition, and one PowerBall number from 1 to 45. The goal is to match the numbers with those drawn at random at the end of the week. The regular numbers chosen do not have to be in the same order as those drawn.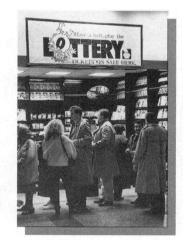

   a. How many different ways are there to fill out a ticket?

   b. A player wins the jackpot by matching all five regular numbers plus the PowerBall number. This is called "Match 5 + 1." How many different ways are there to fill out a ticket that is a "Match 5 + 1" winner? What is the probability of the event "Match 5 + 1"?

   c. A player won $100,000 by matching the five regular numbers but not the PowerBall number. This was called "Match 5." What was the probability of getting a "Match 5" winner?

d. A player won $5,000 for "Match 4 + 1." What was the probability of getting a "Match 4 + 1" winner?

3. Suppose you toss a fair coin four times and observe the sequence of heads and tails.

a. How many possible outcomes are there? Describe two ways of determining this number. Are the outcomes equally likely?

b. Suppose you record the number of heads from the four tosses. Find the following probabilities.

- P(four heads)

- P(exactly one head)

- P(at least three heads)

c. Recall that the Multiplication Rule for independent events states that if A and B are independent events, then $P(A \text{ and } B) = P(A) \times P(B)$. Show how to calculate the probabilities in Part b using the Multiplication Rule. (You may also use the Addition Rule for probability.)

4. Suppose you have the names of six boys and four girls on slips of paper in a hat. You draw a slip of paper, note the name, and return the slip of paper to the hat. You then draw again and note the name.

a. Can you use the Multiplication Rule for independent events to find the probability that the first name drawn is a girl's name and the second name is a boy's name? If so, explain. If not, explain why not.

b. Compute this probability using the Multiplication Principle of Counting and the definition of probability given at the beginning of this investigation.

5. Suppose again you have the names of six boys and four girls on slips of paper in a hat. You draw one name, but this time you do not return the slip of paper to the hat. Then you draw a second name.

   a. Explain why you cannot use the Multiplication Rule for independent events to find the probability that the first name drawn is a girl's name and the second name is a boy's name.

   b. To find the probability that the first name drawn is a girl's name and the second name drawn is a boy's name, you can use the **General Multiplication Rule** for any two events:

   > If A and B are events, then $P(A \text{ and } B) = P(A) \times P(B \text{ given } A)$.

   $P(B \text{ given } A)$ is sometimes written as $P(B|A)$. Answer the following questions for drawing two names from a hat without replacement.

   ▪ What will you use as event A? Find $P(A)$.

   ▪ What will you use as event B? Find $P(B|A)$.

   ▪ Find the probability that the first name drawn is a girl's name and the second name is a boy's name.

   c. Find this probability using the Multiplication Principle of Counting and the definition of probability given at the beginning of this investigation.

   d. Compare the probability you determined in this activity to the probability you determined in Activity 4. The events are the same in the two activities, yet the probabilities are different. Explain why it makes sense that one probability is larger than the other.

   e. Extend the General Multiplication Rule to find the probability that all names drawn are those of girls if you draw four names without replacement. Also, find this probability using the Multiplication Principle of Counting and the definition of probability given at the beginning of this investigation.

6. Suppose that there are 50 people in a jury pool and 15 of them are Native Americans. Jurors are selected at random without replacement.

   a. What is the probability that the first and second people selected are both Native Americans?

b. What is the probability that neither of the two people selected is a Native American?

c. What is the probability that exactly one person of two selected is a Native American?

Checkpoint

In this investigation, you used counting methods to help calculate probabilities.

ⓐ Under what conditions can you calculate the probability of an event by using the following ratio?

$$\frac{\text{number of favorable outcomes}}{\text{total number of possible outcomes}}$$

ⓑ What is the difference between "with replacement" and "without replacement" in a probabilistic (chance) situation? What is the connection to independent trials? What is the connection to "repetition" and "no repetition"?

ⓒ When can you calculate probabilities using the Multiplication Rule $P(A \text{ and } B) = P(A) \times P(B)$? When do you need to use the General Multiplication Rule?

ⓓ How are the Multiplication Rule and the General Multiplication Rule for probability similar to the Multiplication Principle of Counting? How are they different?

Be prepared to explain your group's thinking to the entire class.

On Your Own

Consider the following probability and counting situations.

a. Suppose you roll a die three times.

■ What is the probability that you get an even number on the first roll, a number greater than four on the second roll, and a number less than six on the third roll? Show how to use the Multiplication Rule for independent events to find this probability.

■ Explain how to use the Multiplication Principle of Counting to find this probability.

b. In Iowa in 1997, a license plate had six characters. The first three characters were numbers and the last three were letters. Suppose that no numbers or letters could be repeated. What is the probability that a randomly-chosen license plate had three even numbers?

INVESTIGATION 2 Combinations, the Binomial Theorem, and Pascal's Triangle

In this investigation, you will explore some of the properties of combinations and their applications in algebra. One of the most interesting and useful properties of combinations is found in the analysis of *binomial* expressions of the form $(a + b)^n$.

1. Think about expanding $(a + b)^n$. In particular, think about the coefficients of the terms in the expansion. For example, $(a + b)^2 = (a + b)(a + b) = a^2 + 2ab + b^2$. The coefficients are 1, 2, and 1. There is an important connection between combinations and the coefficients of the terms in the expansion of $(a + b)^n$.

Investigate this connection by expanding $(a + b)^n$ for several values of n. Use at least $n = 0, 1, 2, 3,$ and 4. See the computer algebra system output below for the cases of $n = 5$ and $n = 6$. Examine and organize the coefficients of the expansions. Describe any patterns in the coefficients. Describe any connections you see to combinations.

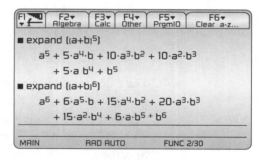

2. You might organize your work from Activity 1 as follows:

coefficients of $(a + b)^0$					1				
coefficients of $(a + b)^1$				1		1			
coefficients of $(a + b)^2$			1		2		1		
coefficients of $(a + b)^3$		1		3		3		1	
coefficients of $(a + b)^4$	1		4		6		4		1

a. Continue this array of numbers, using the coefficients from $(a + b)^5$ and $(a + b)^6$.

b. Describe any patterns you see in this array of numbers. In particular, describe how you could compute the numbers in a specific row of the array by using the numbers in the previous row.

c. Based on the pattern in the array, what do you think is the expansion of $(a + b)^7$? Check your conjecture by carrying out the expansion, by hand or with a computer algebra system.

3. The triangular array of numbers in Activity 2 is called *Pascal's triangle*. It is named for the French philosopher and mathematician Blaise Pascal (1623–1662). He explored many of its properties, particularly those related to the study of probability. Although the triangle is named for Pascal, other mathematicians knew about it much earlier. For example, the triangular pattern was known to Chu Shih-Chieh in China in 1303. (See Reflecting Task 2 on page 253.)

Pascal's Triangle   Blaise Pascal

row 0   1

row 1   1   1

row 2   1   2   1

row 3   1   3   3   1

row 4   1   4   6   4   1

The rules for constructing **Pascal's triangle** (which you probably discovered in Activity 2) are as follows: The top row, which is the top vertex of the triangle, consists of the single number 1. Each succeeding row starts and ends with 1. The remaining entries are constructed by looking at the row above. Specifically, each number in a given row is found by computing this sum:

(the number just above and to the left) + (the number just above and to the right).

This is illustrated by the connector lines between 2, 1, and 3 in the triangle above.

You can add rows to the triangle indefinitely. Use the rules above to add rows 5 and 6 to the triangle. Compare to the rows for $(a + b)^5$ and $(a + b)^6$ that you determined in Activity 2.

4. In Activity 3 you saw a remarkable connection. On the one hand, you have the coefficients of $(a + b)^n$, which can be computed using algebraic multiplication. On the other hand, you have the numbers in Pascal's triangle, which are computed using the specific arithmetic rules given in Activity 3.

You have seen that these two very different procedures generate the same rows of numbers! Later in this lesson you will see why this connection holds. But first, you need to consider a related connection between Pascal's triangle and combinations.

The rows of Pascal's triangle are numbered starting with row 0. The entries in a given row are also numbered beginning with 0. So the initial entry in each row is labeled "entry 0," the next entry is labeled "entry 1," and so on.

a. Compute $C(4, 2)$. Where is this number found in Pascal's triangle (which row and which entry)? What is the coefficient of the a^2b^2 term in $(a + b)^4$?

b. Compute $C(6, 4)$. Where is $C(6, 4)$ found in Pascal's triangle? What is the coefficient of the a^2b^4 term in $(a + b)^6$?

c. Now try to generalize your work in Parts a and b. Describe how to find $C(n, k)$ in Pascal's triangle. Describe where in Pascal's triangle you can find the coefficient of the $a^{n-k}b^k$ term in $(a + b)^n$.

5. So far in this investigation you have studied connections among three seemingly different mathematical topics: coefficients in the expansion of $(a + b)^n$, numbers in Pascal's triangle, and values of $C(n, k)$. One of the most important of these connections involves using combinations to expand $(a + b)^n$.

Analyze the following reasoning that uses combinations to find the coefficient of the $a^{54}b^{46}$ term in $(a + b)^{100}$.

You know that $(a + b)^{100} = (a + b)(a + b)(a + b) \cdots (a + b)$ (100 factors). To do this multiplication, you multiply each term in the first factor, that is, a and b, by each term in the second factor, then by each term in the third factor, and so on. You must multiply through all 100 factors. To get $a^{54}b^{46}$, you need to multiply by b in 46 of the factors. That is, you must choose 46 of the 100 factors to be those where you use b as the multiplier (and in the other factors a will be the multiplier). So the total number of ways to get $a^{54}b^{46}$ is the number of ways of choosing 46 factors from the 100 factors, which is $C(100, 46)$. Hence, the coefficient of the $a^{54}b^{46}$ term in $(a + b)^{100}$ is $C(100, 46)$.

a. Use similar reasoning to find the coefficient of the $a^{29}b^{71}$ term in $(a + b)^{100}$.

b. Discuss this reasoning with some of your classmates. Resolve any questions you may have. Based on this reasoning, use combinations to find the coefficients for the expansion of $(a + b)^5$. Confirm that your coefficients match those in the computer algebra system display on page 245.

c. Use similar reasoning to find the coefficient of the a^3b^5 term in $(a + b)^8$.

d. What is the coefficient of the $a^{n-k}b^k$ term in $(a + b)^n$?

6. The work in Activity 5 suggests the following general result, called the **Binomial Theorem.** For any positive integer n,

$$(a + b)^n = C(n, 0)a^n + C(n, 1)a^{n-1}b + C(n, 2)a^{n-2}b^2 + \ldots + C(n, k)a^{n-k}b^k + \ldots + C(n, n-2)a^2b^{n-2} + C(n, n-1)ab^{n-1} + C(n, n)b^n.$$

a. Use the Binomial Theorem to expand $(a + b)^4$. Verify that you get the same answer as in Activity 1.

b. Use the Binomial Theorem to find the coefficient of a^3b^5 in $(a + b)^8$. Compare to the answer you found using combinatorial reasoning in Part c of Activity 5.

c. Explain why the sum of the exponents of a and b in each term of $(a + b)^n$ is n.

d. Explain why the coefficient of the $a^{n-k}b^k$ term is the same as the coefficient of the a^kb^{n-k} term.

e. Use the Binomial Theorem to expand $(2x - 3y)^5$. What are a and b in this case?

7. Now that you've observed that the entries in Pascal's triangle are values of $C(n, k)$, you can make conjectures about properties of combinations by looking for patterns in Pascal's triangle. Based on the symmetry and other patterns in Pascal's triangle, make at least two conjectures about properties of combinations. State your conjectures using $C(n, k)$ notation. Compare your conjectures to those of other groups.

8. If you have not already done so in Activity 7, use the line symmetry in Pascal's triangle to make a conjecture about the precise relationship between $C(n, k)$ and $C(n, n - k)$. You might find it helpful to examine a few examples using specific values of n and k.

a. State the relationship you found in the specific instance when $n = 8$ and $k = 3$. Prove this relationship in the following two ways:

- ■ Use the factorial formula for $C(n, k)$.

- ■ Use combinatorial reasoning. That is, rather than using formulas, think about how you might choose and count combinations. In this case, you might find it helpful to think about how choosing 3 objects from 8 objects is the same as *not* choosing a number of objects.

b. Now prove the general property: $C(n, k) = C(n, n - k)$, in two ways, as in Part a.

- ■ Use factorial formulas and algebraic reasoning.

- ■ Use combinatorial reasoning by thinking about ways of choosing objects.

c. Which of the arguments in Part b was most convincing for you? Most appealing? Why?

▶**On Your Own**

Think about the relative advantages of algebraic, visual, and combinatorial approaches to binomial expansions as you complete these tasks.

a. Expand $(x + 2)^3$ in three ways:

■ Multiply by hand.

■ Use Pascal's triangle.

■ Use the Binomial Theorem.

b. Find the coefficient of the a^4b^2 term in $(a + b)^6$ in three ways:

■ Reason with combinations.

■ Use Pascal's triangle.

■ Use the Binomial Theorem.

Modeling • Organizing • Reflecting • Extending

Modeling

1. Monograms on jewelry, clothing, and other items consist of the initials of your name. Examine the three-initial monogram offer below.

> **Monogram Pins by Max**
>
> *FDL*
>
> *Your initials hand made in all sizes.*
>
> *Available in gold and silver.*
>
> *ALL 17,576 COMBINATIONS!*

a. Is the number of different three-initial monograms given in the ad correct? Explain.

b. What is the probability that a randomly selected three-initial monogram has all three initials the same?

c. Now consider the case where two of the initials are the same.

   ■ How many three-initial monograms are possible if the first two initials are the same and the third is different?

   ■ How many three-initial monograms are possible if *any* two initials are the same and the other is different?

   ■ What is the probability that a randomly selected three-initial monogram will have two initials the same and the other initial different?

d. What is the probability that a randomly selected three-initial monogram has all three initials different?

e. Describe the relationship among the probabilities in Parts b, c, and d.

2. Suppose you have 10 blue socks and 8 white socks in a drawer. You reach in and draw two socks at random.

a. Find the probability that both socks are blue, if you replace the first sock before drawing the second.

b. Find the probability that both socks are blue, if you do not replace the first sock before drawing the second.

c. Why is it reasonable that the answer to Part a is larger than the answer to Part b?

3. The Chess Club at Asiniboyne High School consists of 6 seniors and 11 juniors. Presently, the club president and the club secretary are both seniors. (They must be different people.) If the students were selected randomly for these offices, what is the probability both would be seniors?

a. Show how to find the answer to this question using the General Multiplication Rule for probability.

b. Show how to find the answer using the Multiplication Principle of Counting and the definition of probability given at the beginning of Investigation 1 on page 241.

4. Consider the experiment of flipping a fair coin four times and counting the number of heads.

a. Out of the possible sequences of heads and tails, how many sequences contain no heads? How many contain exactly 1 head? Exactly 2 heads? Exactly 3 heads? Four heads?

b. Show or describe where you can find the answers to these questions in Pascal's triangle.

c. Explain how you can reason about combinations to find the answers to the questions in Part a.

d. Find the probability of getting more than three heads.

5. There are many interesting patterns in Pascal's triangle. For example, consider the sum of each row of Pascal's triangle.

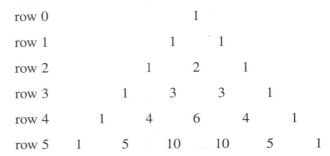

row 0						1					
row 1					1		1				
row 2				1		2		1			
row 3			1		3		3		1		
row 4		1		4		6		4		1	
row 5	1		5		10		10		5		1

a. Compute the sum of each of the first 5 rows of Pascal's triangle. Describe any patterns you see. What kind of sequence is this?

b. Make a conjecture about the sum of row n in Pascal's triangle.

c. Consider row 3 of Pascal's triangle. Express each entry as a combination; then express the sum of the entries as a sum of combinations. This should suggest a property of combinations. State that property.

Organizing

1. Reexamine the General Multiplication Rule: $P(A \text{ and } B) = P(A) \cdot P(B|A)$, where A and B are events.

   a. $P(B|A)$ is sometimes called a *conditional probability*. $P(B|A)$ is often found directly from information in the problem situation. Explain why $P(B|A)$ can also be found by calculating $\frac{P(A \text{ and } B)}{P(A)}$, provided $P(A) \neq 0$.

   b. How can you use the result in Part a to show that if A and B are independent, then $P(B|A) = P(B)$?

2. Prove that $C(2n, 2) = 2C(n, 2) + n^2$, for $n \geq 2$, using two methods:

   a. The factorial formula for $C(n, k)$ and algebraic reasoning.

   b. Combinatorial reasoning.

3. In Investigation 2, you saw that there is a close connection between the coefficients of the expansion of $(a + b)^n$ and the entries in row n of Pascal's triangle. This connection allows you to use technology to quickly generate any row of Pascal's triangle.

   a. Using combinations, express the entries in row 4 of Pascal's triangle.

   b. How could you use the sequence command on your calculator to generate row 4 of Pascal's triangle?

   c. Use the sequence command to generate the coefficients for $(a + b)^{10}$.

4. In this lesson, you have primarily studied counting situations in probability and algebra. Combinatorial questions also arise in geometry.

   a. Given a set of n points, no three of which are collinear, how many distinct triangles can be formed with three of the n points as vertices? Does it make any difference if all the points are not in the same plane? Explain your reasoning.

   b. Given a set of n points, no four of which are coplanar (that is, no four of which lie in the same plane), how many distinct tetrahedra can be found using four of the n points as vertices?

   c. Suppose a map is formed by drawing n lines in a plane, no two of which are parallel and no three of which intersect in a common point. What is the fewest number of colors needed to color this map so that no two regions with a common boundary are the same color?

5. There are many counting problems related to vertex-edge graphs. Consider the three problems below.

    a. Recall that a **complete graph** is a graph in which there is exactly one edge between each pair of vertices. How many edges are there in a complete graph with 5 vertices? How many edges are there in a complete graph with n vertices?

    b. A **cycle graph** is a graph consisting of a single cycle, as in the graphs below.

    In a previous course, you studied vertex coloring as a means to model situations involving potential conflicts. Now consider *edge coloring*. To **color the edges of a graph** means to assign colors to the edges in such a way that if two edges share a vertex, then they must be different colors. What is the fewest number of colors needed to color the edges of a cycle graph with n vertices ($n \geq 3$)?

    c. What is the fewest number of colors needed to color the edges of a complete graph with n vertices ($n \geq 2$)?

Reflecting

1. Which Multiplication Rule for probability must you use if you have a situation that does not have replacement? Explain why.

2. Shown at the left is the triangular pattern pictured in Chu Shih-Chieh's book written in 1303 and entitled *Precious Mirror of the Four Elements*.

    a. What do you think the symbols in the first six rows of the pattern mean?

    b. How do you think this pattern is related to the title of the book?

3. Describe any connections you see between the General Multiplication Rule for probability and the ideas of permutations and combinations.

4. In their article, "The Evolution with Age of Probabilistic, Intuitively Based Misconceptions," in *Journal for Research in Mathematics Education* (January 1997, pp. 96–105), Efraim Fischbein and Ditza Schnarch reported on a survey in which 100 high school students were asked the following question: "When choosing a committee composed of 2 members from among 10 candidates, is the number of possibilities smaller than, equal to, or greater than the number of possibilities when choosing a committee of 8 members from among 10 candidates?"

    a. What is the correct answer? State this answer using combinations.

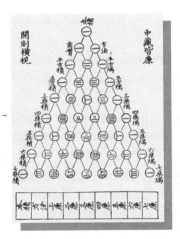

b. Eighty-five percent of the high school students surveyed stated that the correct answer is "greater than." Why do you think that so many students believed that there are more two-member committees than eight-member committees?

Extending

1. Poll your class to find the number of students who have been to the movies in the last week. Suppose you select two students at random from your class using the following method: Write the name of each student on a slip of paper. Select a slip at random. Do not replace that slip. Select another slip at random.

   a. What is the probability that both students you select have been to the movies in the past week? If you had replaced the first slip of paper, what would be the probability that each name you select is a student who has been to the movies in the past week?

   In the remainder of this task, you will investigate whether the probability of selecting a student who has been to the movies in the last week is the same on the first draw as on the second draw if you don't replace the slip of paper.

   b. Make a conjecture about whether the probability of selecting a student who has been to the movies in the last week is the same on the first draw as on the second draw, when you don't replace the slip of paper. Then check your conjecture by completing the parts below.

   c. What is the probability of selecting a student on the first draw who has been to the movies in the last week?

   d. What is the probability of selecting a student on the first draw who has *not* been to the movies in the last week and a student on the second draw who has been to the movies in the last week?

   e. What is the probability of selecting a student on the first draw who has been to the movies in the last week and a student on the second draw who has been to the movies in the last week?

   f. Use results from Parts d and e to find the probability of selecting a student on the second draw who has been to the movies in the last week. Is this the same as or different from the first-draw probability you found in Part c?

2. Prove that $rC(n, r) = nC(n - 1, r - 1)$, for $n \geq r \geq 1$ using two methods:

   a. The factorial formula for $C(n, k)$ and algebraic reasoning.

   b. Combinatorial reasoning.

3. Consider the following example of a certain property of combinations:

$$C(5, 3) = C(4, 2) + C(3, 2) + C(2, 2).$$

   a. Show that this statement is true by using the factorial formula for $C(n, k)$.

   b. Another example of this property is the following:

   $$C(6, 2) = C(5, 1) + C(4, 1) + C(3, 1) + C(2, 1) + C(1, 1)$$

   Based on the two examples that you now have, make a conjecture for the general statement of this property.

   c. Explain how this property appears as a pattern in Pascal's triangle.

   d. Prove this property using combinatorial reasoning.

   e. Justify the property by giving an argument in terms of coefficients in the expansion of $(a + b)^n$.

4. In this lesson, you have seen that there is a close correspondence between the entries of Pascal's triangle and values of $C(n, k)$, but you have only seen this correspondence as a pattern; you have not yet proven it. The reason for the close correspondence is because the construction rule for Pascal's triangle is the same as an important recursive property of combinations.

Rule for Pascal's triangle:	(number in any row)	=	(number above and to the left)	+	(number above and to the right)
Combination property:	$C(n, k)$	=	$C(n - 1, k - 1)$	+	$C(n - 1, k)$

   a. Think about this correspondence. Using the fact that entry k in row n of Pascal's triangle is $C(n, k)$, explain why $C(n - 1, k - 1)$ corresponds to the "number above and to the left" and $C(n - 1, k)$ corresponds to the "number above and to the right."

   b. Verify the combination property for some specific values of n and k.

   c. Now prove that the combination property is true. That is, prove $C(n, k) = C(n - 1, k - 1) + C(n - 1, k)$, where $k > 0$ and $k < n$.

5. At the beginning of this lesson, there is a photograph of the famous mathematician Paul Erdös. Read one of the following books (or at least some of the chapters) about Erdös and write a short report about what you have read.

   ■ Paul Hoffman, *The Man Who Loved Only Numbers: Mathematical Truth.* New York: Hyperion, 1998.

   ■ Bruce Schecter, *My Brain is Open: The Mathematical Journeys of Paul Erdös.* New York: Simon and Schuster, 1998.

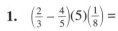
1. $\left(\frac{2}{3} - \frac{4}{5}\right)(5)\left(\frac{1}{8}\right) =$

   (a) $-\frac{5}{8}$ (b) $-\frac{16}{75}$ (c) $-\frac{11}{12}$ (d) $-\frac{1}{12}$ (e) $-\frac{3}{10}$

2. Simplify $\frac{x}{2y} - \frac{5}{y} + \frac{1}{3y}$.

   (a) $\frac{3x - 28}{6y}$ (b) $\frac{x - 4}{4y}$ (c) $\frac{3x - 28}{6y^3}$ (d) $\frac{xy - 14}{3y}$ (e) $\frac{x - 28}{2y}$

3. The equation of a line parallel to the line $y = \frac{7}{3}x + 1$ is

   (a) $7y - 3x = 7$ (b) $7x + 3y = 3$ (c) $3x + 7y = -7$

   (d) $3y - 7x = -3$ (e) none of these

4. Which one of the following is a function?

   (a) $\{(3, -8), (-8, -6), (3, -9)\}$ (b) $\{(3, -8), (-9, -9), (-9, -6)\}$

   (c) $\{(3, -8), (-8, 3), (-8, -8)\}$ (d) $\{3, -8, -6, -9\}$

   (e) $\{(-6, -8), (-8, 3), (3, -8)\}$

5. Which of the following equations could represent the graph shown?

   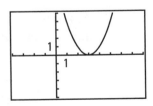

   (a) $f(x) = x^2 + 3$ (b) $f(x) = x^2 - 3$ (c) $f(x) = -(x - 3)^2$

   (d) $f(x) = (x - 3)^2$ (e) $f(x) = (x + 3)^2$

6. Solve $\frac{2}{3}(x + 4) - 4 = 8x$.

(a) -5.5 (b) $-\frac{2}{11}$ (c) $\frac{22}{3}$ (d) 14 (e) $-\frac{2}{3}$

7. How many x-intercepts does the graph of $f(x) = x(x^2 - 9)(x^2 + 10)$ have?

(a) 5 (b) 4 (c) 3 (d) 2 (e) 1

8. $\cos(-\alpha) =$

(a) $-\cos\alpha$ (b) $-\sin\alpha$ (c) $\frac{1}{\cos\alpha}$ (d) $\sin\alpha$ (e) $\cos\alpha$

9. Solve the equation $\log_2 x = 9$ for x.

(a) $x = 4.5$ (b) $x = 18$ (c) $x = 81$ (d) $x = 256$ (e) $x = 512$

10. Simplify $\left(\sqrt[3]{y}\right)\left(\sqrt{y}\right)$.

(a) y^2 (b) $\sqrt[3]{y}$ (c) $\sqrt[3]{y^2}$ (d) $\sqrt[6]{y}$ (e) $\sqrt[6]{y^5}$

The Principle of Mathematical Induction

In previous lessons, and throughout the *Contemporary Mathematics in Context* program, you discovered and described general patterns that seem to hold for infinitely many values of *n*. For example, you investigated and made conjectures about the number of diagonals in a regular polygon with *n* sides, the number of two-scoop ice cream cones when *n* flavors are available, and the expansion of expressions of the form $(x + y)^n$.

It is not only important to discover patterns, but also to prove that a particular pattern *must* be true for *all* the stated values of *n*. Consider the Sierpinski triangle at various stages as shown below. Starting with a solid triangular figure one unit on a side, smaller and smaller equilateral triangles are cut out of the original.

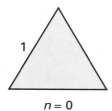
$n = 0$

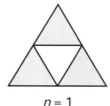
$n = 1$

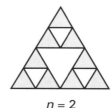
$n = 2$

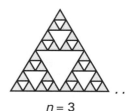
$n = 3$

. . .

Think About This Situation

By looking for patterns in the sequence of figures above, one might conjecture that the perimeter P_n and area A_n of the Sierpinski triangle at any stage *n* are given by the following formulas:

$$P_n = \frac{3^{n+1}}{2^n} \quad \text{and} \quad A_n = \frac{3^n \sqrt{3}}{4^{n+1}}$$

a Do you think the conjecture for the perimeter formula is correct? Why or why not?

b Do you think the conjecture for the area formula is correct? Explain.

c If you think that the conjectures are true, how might you convince a skeptic that each of the formulas is correct for *every* nonnegative integer *n*?

d If some students think that one of these conjectures is false, how could they *prove* that it is false?

e How is the perimeter of the Sierpinski triangle at any stage P_n ($n \geq 1$) related to the perimeter at the previous stage P_{n-1}? How is A_n related to A_{n-1}?

INVESTIGATION 1 ▸ Infinity, Recursion, and Mathematical Induction

You have to be very careful when thinking about a statement that is supposed to be true for infinitely many values of *n*. The statement may seem true, and in fact it may be true for many values of *n,* but then it can turn out to be false. For example, in Course 3 you investigated an algebraic expression for generating prime numbers: $n^2 - n + 41$. You may recall that for integers *n* such that $1 \leq n \leq 40$, this expression does indeed produce prime numbers:

$$1^2 - 1 + 41 = 41$$
$$2^2 - 2 + 41 = 43$$
$$3^2 - 3 + 41 = 47$$
$$\vdots$$

This might lead one to conjecture that for every integer $n \geq 1$, $n^2 - n + 41$ is a prime number. But for $n = 41$, $n^2 - n + 41$ is *not* a prime number. Why? Thus the conjecture is false, even though it may have seemed plausible at first.

In this investigation, you will learn a technique for proving that a statement is true for all integer values of *n* larger than some starting value. This technique, called *mathematical induction,* is closely connected to the work you have done with recursion.

1. As you have previously seen, exponential functions and factorial functions can both output numbers that are very large. Think about which type of function grows faster. In particular, compare the sizes of 5^n and $n!$ for positive integer values of *n*.

   a. Consider the following conjecture: $5^n > n!$ for $n \geq 1$. Do you think this conjecture is true or false? Explain.

   b. Next, consider this conjecture: $n! > 5^n$ for $n \geq 1$. Is this conjecture true? Would it be true if the condition $n \geq 1$ were modified and, if so, how?

   c. Now consider the conjecture: $n! > 5^n$ for $n \geq 12$. Is this conjecture true or false? How do you know for sure?

A single counterexample will prove that a statement claimed for infinitely many integers *n* is not true. But what if you feel certain that such a statement is true? How do you *prove* that it's true for *every n*? Using a computer, you might verify the statement for thousands of values of *n*. But that doesn't necessarily mean that the statement is true. Maybe you haven't yet found a counterexample; it might be the next value of *n* that doesn't work. You might generate a table and find a pattern. But how do you know for sure that the pattern will always be valid? In the next activities, you will learn an ingenious technique for proving an assertion about infinitely many integers. This powerful technique is based on a simple idea that is illustrated in the next activity.

2. Think about setting up a number of dominos on edge, and then making them all fall over, one after another. This is like proving a statement for all values of *n,* one after another.

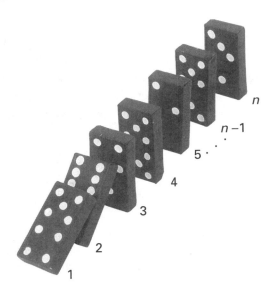

a. Set up five dominos or books and then make them all fall over, one after another.

b. Suppose you set up a line of *n* dominos in such a way that when any given domino falls, it will knock over the next domino. Then knock over the first domino. What will be the result?

c. List the two conditions that are required for the entire line of *n* dominos in Part b to fall down. Explain why neither one of the conditions alone is sufficient.

d. The idea in Parts b and c is the basic idea behind a *proof by mathematical induction,* as seen below.

Dominos	Proof by Mathematical Induction
(a) Set up the dominos in such a way that whenever any given domino falls over, it will knock over the next domino.	**(a)** Show that whenever a statement is true for $n-1$, it is also true for n.
(b) Knock over the first domino.	**(b)** Show that the statement is true for some initial value of n.

Result
    All the dominos fall over.
	Conclusion
	    The statement is true for all values of n greater than or equal to the initial value.

Explain each step of the correspondence above between dominos and proof by mathematical induction.

The validity of a proof by mathematical induction rests, in part, on the Principle of Mathematical Induction stated in the following box, which is just a formalization of the scheme in Activity 2 Part d on the previous page. The Principle of Mathematical Induction is a basic property of integers. It can be used to prove that a statement about integers, $S(n)$, is true for every integer $n \geq n_0$, where n_0 is the initial value (starting value).

Principle of Mathematical Induction

Suppose $S(n)$ is a statement about integers. If

(a) $S(n)$ is true whenever $S(n-1)$ is true, for each $n > n_0$, and

(b) $S(n_0)$ is true,

then $S(n)$ is true for all integers $n \geq n_0$.

In the next several activities, you will examine how the Principle of Mathematical Induction can be applied to a problem you may have investigated previously. You may recall that a **complete graph** is a vertex-edge graph in which there is exactly one edge between every pair of vertices.

Question: *How many edges does a complete graph with n vertices have?*

Goal: Determine an answer to this question and prove that the answer is correct.

3. A common first step in determining and proving the answer to a general question like the one above is to examine several special cases and look for patterns. Draw several complete graphs and count the number of edges in each. How many edges do you think there are in a complete graph with *n* vertices?

4. Let E_n be the number of edges in a complete graph with *n* vertices. As you have seen many times in the *Contemporary Mathematics in Context* curriculum, there are two fundamental ways to think about E_n: You could find a function rule that describes E_n as a function of *n*, or you could find a recursion equation that describes E_n in terms of E_{n-1}. In the situation here, you need to do both. It is the function rule that you will prove using the Principle of Mathematical Induction. An essential tool used in the proof, as you can see from condition (a) in the Principle of Mathematical Induction, will be the recursion equation.

   a. Find a recursion equation that describes the relationship between E_n and E_{n-1}. Explain why this equation is valid.

   b. Find a function rule that describes E_n as a function of *n*.

   c. One function rule is $E_n = \frac{n(n-1)}{2}$. If necessary, transform your function rule from Part b into this form.

5. Now you will use the Principle of Mathematical Induction to *prove* that the function rule in Part c of Activity 4 is true for every $n \geq 1$. There are two steps in a proof by mathematical induction, corresponding to the two conditions of the Principle of Mathematical Induction. These steps may be done in either order.

Induction Step: Prove the statement is true for n whenever it is true for $n - 1$.

You must show that *if* the statement is true for $n - 1$, then it will be true for n. (In terms of dominos, you are showing that the dominos are set up in such a way that if the previous domino falls, then it will knock over the current domino.)

Thus, in a proof by mathematical induction, you may assume that the statement is true for n − 1 while you try to prove it for n.

a. In this situation, this means that you may assume that the function rule for E_{n-1} is true. Write the function rule for E_{n-1} by replacing n with $n - 1$ in the equation $E_n = \frac{n(n-1)}{2}$.

b. Complete the induction step of the proof by filling in the requested details below.

You must prove that $E_n = \frac{n(n-1)}{2}$.

You may assume that $E_{n-1} = \frac{(n-1)(n-2)}{2}$. Why?

Here's one way to lay out the proof. Start with E_n, use the recursion equation and the assumption of the function rule for E_{n-1}, and try to end with $\frac{n(n-1)}{2}$, as shown in the following outline of a proof.

$$E_n = E_{n-1} + (n-1)$$ Use the recursion equation from Activity 4.

$$= \frac{(n-1)(n-2)}{2} + (n-1)$$ Why?

$$= \frac{n^2 - 3n + 2}{2} + (n-1)$$ Why?

$$= \, ?$$ Why?

$$= \, ?$$ Why?

$$\vdots$$ (You may use more or fewer steps.)

$$= \frac{n(n-1)}{2}$$ Why?

Thus, you are done with the induction step. Now you need to do the base step.

Base Step: Prove the statement is true for the initial value of n.

In the induction step, you have shown that the function rule for the number of edges in a complete graph is true for n whenever it is true for $n - 1$. Now you need to show that the function rule is true for the initial value of n, in this case $n = 1$.

c. Prove that $E_n = \frac{n(n-1)}{2}$ is true for $n = 1$. That is, prove that a complete graph with $n = 1$ vertex has $\frac{n(n-1)}{2}$ edges. How is this step related to the dominos analogy?

You have now completed the two steps of a proof by mathematical induction, and thus you have satisfied the two conditions of the Principle of Mathematical Induction. Therefore, by these two conditions and the Principle of Mathematical Induction, you can conclude that $E_n = \frac{n(n-1)}{2}$, for every $n \geq 1$.

6. This activity is another example of the process of experimenting, conjecturing, and writing a proof by mathematical induction. Consider the following question: How many regions are formed by n lines in the plane ($n \geq 1$), all of which pass through a common point?

   a. Experiment with this situation. Look for patterns and make a conjecture. Express your conjecture as a function of the number of lines n. Compare your conjecture to those of other groups. Resolve any differences.

   b. Find a recursion equation that describes the relationship between the number of regions formed by n lines and the number of regions formed by $(n-1)$ lines.

   c. Use the Principle of Mathematical Induction to prove the function rule you conjectured in Part a.

7. The Principle of Mathematical Induction is often used to prove statements about finite sums. For example, consider the sum of the first n odd positive integers:

   $$S_n = 1 + 3 + 5 + 7 + \ldots + (2n - 1).$$

   a. Compute S_n for a few values of n. Make a conjecture for a concise formula for S_n as a function of n.

   b. Use mathematical induction to prove your conjecture.

Checkpoint

In this investigation, you learned how to prove statements using mathematical induction.

a Explain the domino analogy for proof by mathematical induction.

b Typically there were two equations related to each of the problem situations you worked on in this investigation—a function rule and a recursion equation. Explain the role of each of these equations in a proof by mathematical induction.

c Consider the induction step in a proof by mathematical induction. In this step you must show that the "n statement" $S(n)$ is true whenever the "$(n-1)$ statement" $S(n-1)$ is true. Describe a good strategy for doing this part of the proof.

Be prepared to explain your group's thinking to the entire class.

Prove by mathematical induction that the number of diagonals in a regular n-gon is $\frac{n(n-3)}{2}$, for $n \geq 3$.

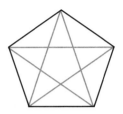

MORE

Modeling • Organizing • Reflecting • Extending

Modeling

1. In Activity 6 of this lesson, you investigated the number of regions formed by n lines in the plane, all of which pass through a common point. Now remove the restriction that all the lines pass through a common point. What is the maximum number of regions formed by n lines in the plane if no two lines are parallel and no three intersect in a common point? Prove your answer using the Principle of Mathematical Induction.

2. The Towers of Hanoi is a mathematical game featured in an old story about when the world will end. As the story goes, a group of monks in a secluded temple is working on this game, and when they are finished the world will end! The game is played with 3 pegs mounted on

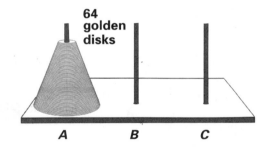

a board and 64 golden disks of successively larger sizes with holes in the center. The game begins with all 64 disks stacked on one peg, graduated in size from largest to smallest.

   The goal is to move the disks one at a time from peg to peg until all the disks are stacked, largest to smallest, on another peg. You must follow these rules:

   (1) Only one disk may be moved at a time.

   (2) You are not allowed to put a larger disk on top of a smaller disk.

   (3) A disk may be moved more than once.

   (4) During the course of the game, you may move a disk to any peg, including the one on which the disks were originally stacked.

   a. What is the fewest number of moves needed to finish a game with 2 disks? How about a game with 3 disks? 4 disks?

   b. Consider the Towers of Hanoi game with n disks. Make a conjecture for the fewest number of moves needed to finish the game. Express your conjecture as a function of n.

c. Use the Principle of Mathematical Induction to prove your conjecture in Part b.

d. What is the fewest number of moves needed to finish a game with 64 disks, as in the original story? If the monks in the story move one disk every second and work nonstop, should you worry about the world ending soon?

3. Recall that a tree is a vertex-edge graph that is connected and has no circuits. Use mathematical induction to prove that a tree with n vertices has exactly $(n - 1)$ edges. You may find it useful to use the fact that every tree has at least one "dangling vertex," that is, a vertex of degree one.

4. Reproduced below are the first four stages of the Sierpinski triangle you considered in the "Think About This Situation" at the beginning of this lesson.

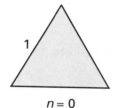

$n = 0$

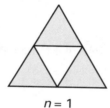

$n = 1$

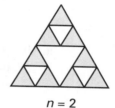

$n = 2$

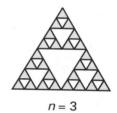

$n = 3$

a. Use mathematical induction to prove that the area of the figure at stage n is given by

$$A_n = \frac{3^n \sqrt{3}}{4^{n+1}} \text{ for } n \geq 0$$

b. Use mathematical induction to prove that the perimeter of the figure at stage n is given by

$$P_n = \frac{3^{n+1}}{2^n} \text{ for } n \geq 0$$

c. What happens to the perimeter and area of the figure as n gets very large?

5. Use mathematical induction to prove that the sum S_n of the first n positive integers is equal to $\frac{n(n + 1)}{2}$. That is, prove that

$$S_n = 1 + 2 + 3 + \ldots + (n - 1) + n = \frac{n(n + 1)}{2}, \text{ for } n \geq 1$$

Organizing

1. In Activity 4 of the investigation in this lesson, you found a function rule for the number of edges in a complete graph on n vertices. Now, determine function rules for $C(n, 2)$ and for the sum of the first $(n - 1)$ natural numbers. Explain the connections among the three function rules by reasoning about the three contexts.

2. Recall that a set A is a subset of a set B if every element of set A is an element of set B. For example, if $B = \{1, 4, 9\}$, then the subsets of B are

$$\varnothing, \{1\}, \{4\}, \{9\}, \{1, 4\}, \{1, 9\}, \{4, 9\}, \{1, 4, 9\}$$

a. Examine some sets and their subsets and formulate a conjecture about the number of subsets of a set with n elements.

b. Prove your conjecture using the Principle of Mathematical Induction.

3. Use mathematical induction to prove that $n! > 2^n$, for $n \geq 4$.

4. Use mathematical induction to prove that $\log x^m = m \log x$, where m is a non-negative integer. Compare your proof with the derivation of this property in Lesson 2 of Unit 3. (See page 165.)

5. In Course 3, Unit 7, "Discrete Models of Change," you investigated geometric series of the form $a_0 + a_0 r + a_0 r^2 + \ldots + a_0 r^{n-1} + a_0 r^n$, where $r \neq 1$ and $n \geq 0$. Consider the sum S_n of the geometric series with $a_0 = 1$:

$$S_n = 1 + r + r^2 + \ldots + r^{n-1} + r^n$$

a. Use the Principle of Mathematical Induction to prove that the following statement is true:

$$1 + r + r^2 + \ldots + r^{n-1} + r^n = \frac{1 - r^{n+1}}{1 - r} \text{ for } n \geq 0 \text{ and } r \neq 1$$

b. There is often more than one way to prove a mathematical statement. To prove the statement in Part a, explain why a reasonable alternate strategy would be to multiply both sides by $(1 - r)$. Use this strategy to carry out such a proof.

Reflecting

1. Mathematical induction is a powerful method of proof, but it must be used correctly. What is wrong with the following "proof"?

Proposition: Every positive integer is equal to its successor. That is,
$$n = n + 1.$$

Proof: $n = (n - 1) + 1$ This is the recursion equation relating n to $n - 1$.

$= (n) + 1$ When proving by induction, you assume that the statement is true for the $(n - 1)$ case. Here, this means that $n - 1 = n$.

$= n + 1$ Done

2. How does proof by mathematical induction relate to the ideas of sequences and recursive and function formulas that you studied in Course 3, Unit 7, "Discrete Models of Change"?

3. The French mathematician Henri Poincaré (1854–1912) stated that the Principle of Mathematical Induction cannot be denied by the human mind. What do you think he meant? Do you agree?

4. Often there is more than one way to prove a statement. For example, consider the mathematical induction proof from the "On Your Own" task on page 264. Provide a counting argument that also proves this statement. (*Hint:* A diagonal can be determined by the two vertices that are its endpoints, so you can count the diagonals by counting pairs of appropriate vertices.) Which proof is more convincing to you? Which proof is easier for you? Why?

Henri Poincaré

Extending

1. In Lesson 2 you investigated the Binomial Theorem. Use the Principle of Mathematical Induction to prove this special case:

$$(x + 1)^n = C(n, 0)x^n + C(n, 1)x^{n-1} + C(n, 2)x^{n-2} + ... + C(n, n-1)x^1 + C(n, n)x^0$$

You may find it useful to use the fact from Extending Task 4 in Lesson 2 (page 255) that $C(n, k) = C(n-1, k-1) + C(n-1, k)$.

2. Prove that $\sum_{k=0}^{n} C(n, k) = 2^n$, $n \geq 0$ using mathematical induction. Explain how this statement is related to the counting of subsets in Organizing Task 2 on page 266. You may find it useful to use the fact from Extending Task 4 in Lesson 2 that $C(n, k) = C(n-1, k-1) + C(n-1, k)$.

3. Consider the Bernoulli inequality, named after the Swiss mathematician Jacob Bernoulli (1654–1705): $(1 + x)^n \geq 1 + nx$, for every integer $n \geq 0$ and every real number $x > -1$.

   a. Prove the Bernoulli inequality using mathematical induction.

   b. Use the Binomial Theorem to prove this inequality when $x > 0$.

4. In Unit 7 of Course 3, you studied arithmetic sequences and series. Examine the following formula for the sum of the first n terms of an arithmetic sequence with initial term a_1 and common difference d:

$$S_n = a_1 + (a_1 + d) + (a_1 + 2d) + ... + [a_1 + (n-1)d]$$
$$= \tfrac{1}{2}n[2a_1 + (n-1)d], \text{ for } n \geq 1$$

   a. Verify that this formula is true for $n = 1, 2,$ and 3.

   b. Prove the formula using the Principle of Mathematical Induction.

   c. Prove the formula in a different way without using the Principle of Mathematical Induction.

1. If $\frac{15}{x} = \frac{2}{11}$, then $x =$

    (a) 24   **(b)** 20.5   **(c)** 90   **(d)** 330   **(e)** 82.5

2. Simplify $\dfrac{4A}{4 + \frac{1}{2}}$.

    (a) $\frac{9}{8A}$ **(b)** $\frac{A}{2}$ **(c)** $2A$ **(d)** $\frac{8A}{9}$ **(e)** $\frac{2A}{3}$

3. An equation of the line containing $(-4, 1)$ and $(0, 8)$ is

    (a) $y = \frac{7}{4}x + 8$ **(b)** $y = \frac{4}{7}x + 8$ **(c)** $y = -\frac{7}{4}x + 8$

    (d) $y = -\frac{4}{7}x - 8$ **(e)** $y = -\frac{4}{7}x + 8$

4. Which of the following is the domain of the function $y = \sqrt{x^2 - 49}$?

    (a) all real numbers   **(b)** $x \le -7$ or $x \ge 7$ **(c)** $x > 7$

    (d) $x \ge 7$ **(e)** $-7 \le x \le 7$

5. Which of the following could be a portion of the graph $y + 3x^2 = 7$?

    (a)   **(b)**   **(c)**

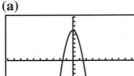 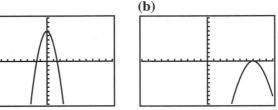 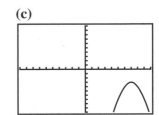

    (d)   **(e)**

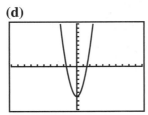 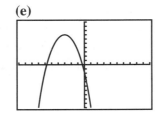

6. If $C = \frac{5}{9}(F - 32)$, then $F =$

    (a) $\frac{9}{5}(C + 32)$ **(b)** $\frac{9}{5}C - 32$ **(c)** $\frac{5}{9}(C + 32)$

    (d) $\frac{5}{9}C + 32$ **(e)** $\frac{9}{5}C + 32$

7. The solutions to $\frac{(2x - 12)(x + 4)}{x - 3} = 0$ are $x =$

    (a) 6, 4, or 3   **(b)** −6, −4, or 3   **(c)** 6, −4, or 3

    (d) 6 or −4   **(e)** 6, −4, or −3

8. If two small pizzas, each with a radius of 4.5 inches, fit exactly on a baking pan as shown, what are the dimensions of the pan?

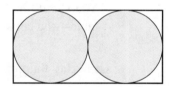

    (a) 9 × 9 inches   **(b)** 4.5 × 9 inches   **(c)** 9 × 18 inches

    (d) 162 square inches   **(e)** 40.5π square inches

9. Simplify $\frac{x^{4a + 1}}{x^{a - 1}}$.

    (a) $x^{3a + 2}$ **(b)** x^{3a} **(c)** x^3 **(d)** $x^{3a - 2}$ **(e)** x^{5a}

10. Simplify $\frac{18}{\sqrt{2}}$.

    (a) $\frac{9\sqrt{2}}{2}$ **(b)** 3   **(c)** 9   **(d)** $9\sqrt{2}$ **(e)** $18\sqrt{2}$

Looking Back

In this unit, you have learned several counting strategies and two new methods of proof. The counting strategies include work with the Multiplication Principle of Counting, combinations, and permutations. The new proof techniques are combinatorial reasoning and proof by mathematical induction. These strategies and techniques enable you to reason about combinatorial situations both within and outside of mathematics. Within mathematics, your work led to several important results that have wide-ranging applications, including the Binomial Theorem, Pascal's triangle, and the General Multiplication Rule for probability. In this final lesson, you will review and pull together all these ideas and apply them in new contexts.

1. Reproduced below is the "Analyzing Counting Situations" table from Lesson 1. You should have entered formulas in at least two cells of your copy of that table—the cells corresponding to permutations and combinations.

Analyzing Counting Situations

	No Repetitions	Repetitions OK
Different Orderings Count As Different Possibilities		
Different Orderings Do Not Count As Different Possibilities		

   a. Make sure you have the correct entries for permutations and combinations in your copy of the table.

   b. Consider a counting situation in which repetition is allowed and order matters.

   ■ Give an example of such a situation. Does this situation directly involve combinations, permutations, or neither?

   ■ Determine a general formula for counting the number of ways of choosing k objects from n objects when order matters and repetitions are allowed. Enter this formula into the appropriate cell of the Analyzing Counting Situations table.

c. Now reread the newspaper article about side dishes on page 223 in Lesson 1. The counting problem discussed in that article is to determine the number of different 3-side-dish choices that can be made from 16 side dishes. Are the 3-side-dish choices examples of permutations, combinations, or neither? Enter "side dishes" into the cell of the table that corresponds to this problem.

2. DNA molecules are found in every cell of a living organism. A single molecule of DNA is a pair of chains twisted together into a spiral. Each chain consists of many links or *bases*. Each base is one of four chemicals: T (thymine), C (cytosine), A (adenine), and G (guanine). The base chemicals can occur in any order on a DNA chain. For example, one of the chains shown in the diagram at the right begins GGTC. The ordered sequence of bases encodes genetic information.

a. Amino acids, which are building blocks of proteins, are encoded by short segments on a DNA chain. There are 20 basic amino acids, and each one is encoded by a segment consisting of the same number of bases. What is the minimum number of bases needed per segment to ensure that there are enough different segments to encode all 20 amino acids?

b. How many possible DNA segments of length 5 contain exactly 2 thymines (T)?

c. You have probably heard that no two people are exactly alike. The number of different DNA chains can help make this statement more understandable. A human has 2.1×10^{10} bases per DNA chain. (Source: Spector, W. S. (ed.), *Handbook of Biological Data,* Philadelphia: Saunders, 1956.) How many human DNA chains are possible? Estimate this as a power of 10. Try to give some description of the size of this number.

Tamar Schlick, an applied mathematician, with a joint appointment in the chemistry department at New York University, is investigating the way DNA twists and turns in response to chemical forces.

3. Examine the following information from an Iowa Daily Millions lottery ticket.

How to Play

- To play, choose 2 numbers from 1 to 21 from each section (Red, White, and Blue).
- Each play costs $1 including sales tax.

How to Win

Every day, 2 numbers will be drawn from each of 3 colored ball sets (Red, White, and Blue). Each set has 21 balls numbered from 1 to 21. Win a prize for the following matches (you MUST match both number AND color).

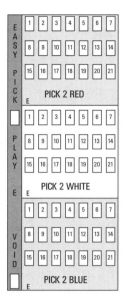

Match	Prize	Number of winning choices
6	$1,000,000	1 (out of 9,261,000)
5	$5,000	114 (out of 9,261,000)
4	$100	4,845 (out of 9,261,000)
3	$5	93,860 (out of 9,261,000)
2	$2	828,495 (out of 9,261,000)

a. Verify at least two of the entries in the column entitled "Number of winning choices." Explain your reasoning and show your calculations.

b. Determine the probability of each of the different types of matches. State the probability definition that you are using and explain why it is appropriate to use in this situation.

c. Do you think a state lottery like this is an effective way for the state to make money? Do you think it is an effective way for players to make money? Explain.

4. Prove that $C(n, 3) = C(n, n - 3)$ for $n \geq 3$, using two different methods:

- The factorial formula for $C(n, k)$
- Combinatorial reasoning (by reasoning about ways to choose combinations)

5. The following identity exhibits several connections among combinatorial ideas.

$$C(n, 0) + C(n, 1) + ... + C(n, n) = 2^n \ (n \geq 0)$$

To uncover some of these connections, complete at least two of the following tasks:

a. Explain how this statement appears as a pattern in Pascal's triangle.

b. Use the Binomial Theorem to prove this statement.

c. Use combinatorial reasoning about the number of subsets of a set with n elements to prove this statement.

6. Spirals are a common form in nature and in the man-made world. Pine cones, spider webs, shells, drill bits, DNA models, screws, and many works of art are examples of spiral designs.

Spider web

Seashell

Examine the spiral-like design below which was generated by starting with the isosceles right triangle OAB in which $OA = AB = 1$ unit. Each of the remaining triangles outlined in the figure also is an isosceles right triangle.

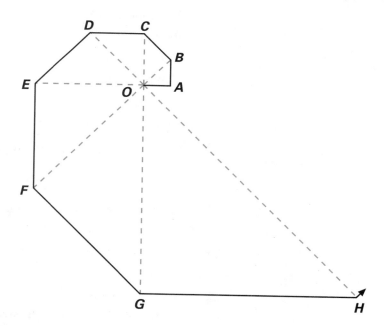

a. Let L_n = the length of the nth segment. The design begins with $\overline{AB}$, so $L_0 = 1$. Find rules that describe the patterns relating L_n and L_{n-1} and relating n and L_n. For what values of n do you think your conjectures are true?

b. Use the Principle of Mathematical Induction to prove your conjectured function rule relating n and L_n.

c. Consider the total length of a growing spiral like the one shown in the figure.

   ▪ What is the total length of a spiral with 5 segments?

- Explain why the sequence of segment lengths in this spiral design is a geometric sequence.

- In Organizing Task 5 (page 266) of Lesson 3, you were asked to prove the following formula for the sum of a geometric series with initial term 1 and constant multiplier r:

$$1 + r + r^2 + \ldots + r^n = \frac{1 - r^{n+1}}{1 - r}, \text{ for } n \geq 0 \; (r \neq 1)$$

Use this formula to determine the total length of a spiral like the one in the figure, but with 25 segments.

Checkpoint

In this unit, you have investigated many situations where systematic counting methods and combinatorial reasoning are useful.

ⓐ Below is a list of some of the combinatorial ideas you have studied. Add other important ideas and topics to the list. Then give a brief explanation and describe an application for each topic on the list.

- Multiplication Principle of Counting
- Permutations
- Combinations
- Combinatorial Reasoning
- Binomial Theorem
- General Multiplication Rule for Probability

ⓑ Why are order and repetition important when deciding how and what to count in a situation? How are these ideas related to permutations and combinations?

ⓒ Describe at least one counting situation or application in each of the following areas of mathematics: algebra, probability, geometry, and graph theory.

ⓓ How are Pascal's triangle and the Binomial Theorem related to each other and to the ideas of counting?

ⓔ When is mathematical induction a useful method of proof? How is the Principle of Mathematical Induction used in a proof?

Be prepared to share your group's examples and thinking with the class.

On Your Own

Write, in outline form, a summary of the important mathematical concepts and methods developed in this unit. Organize your summary so that it can be used as a quick reference in future units and courses.

Binomial Distributions and Statistical Inference

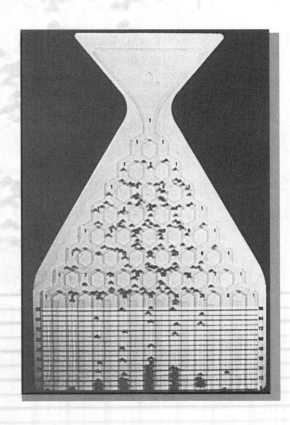

Unit **5**

Binomial Situations

The ethnicity, gender, age, and other demographic characteristics of juries has been of great interest in recent trials in the United States. When the composition of a jury doesn't appear to reflect the demographic characteristics of the surrounding community, both ethical doubts about the jury selection process and legal challenges can arise.

It is unlikely that a jury of 12 people will reflect exactly the demographic characteristics of the surrounding community. Some characteristic of interest is bound to be over- or underrepresented. The jury may have too many Hispanics, too few seniors, too many college graduates, too few parents, or too many unemployed people.

Although juries aren't selected by chance, comparing the actual jury to the composition of juries that would occur if jurors *were* selected at random can tell lawyers whether there are grounds to investigate the jury selection process.

Think About This Situation

Suppose that in a large judicial district, 30% of the eligible jurors are college graduates.

a On a particular jury of 12 people, only one is a college graduate. Do you think having only one juror who is a college graduate can reasonably be attributed to chance? What strategies could you use to support your view?

b If 12 jurors are selected at random from those eligible, what do you think the probability distribution of the number of jurors who are college graduates would look like?

c How do you think the shape, mean, and spread of the probability distribution of the number of jurors who are college graduates would change if the jury were a grand jury of 24 people rather than a 12-person jury?

INVESTIGATION 1 ▸ Constructing Binomial Distributions Using Simulation

In this first investigation, you will review some ideas about probability distributions. Recall that a probability distribution is a table, graph, or formula that gives all possible outcomes for a chance situation and the probability associated with each outcome.

1. One strategy for approximating the probability distribution for the number of college graduates on a jury is to use simulation.

   a. Describe how to use random digits to simulate the selection of one juror from a large pool where 30% of the people are college graduates. How would you use your calculator or computer software to generate the random digits?

   b. Use your method to select 12 jurors. How many were college graduates? Add your result to a copy of the frequency table below, which shows the results from 490 simulations.

Number of College Graduates, x	Frequency, f
0	9
1	28
2	90
3	126
4	104
5	76
6	44
7	9
8	4
9	0
10	0
11	0
12	0

c. Repeat your simulation nine more times placing each result in your copy of the table. This will result in a total of 500 trials.

d. Use your frequency table to estimate the probability that a jury will contain no more than one college graduate.

e. What is your estimate of the probability that a jury will contain at least four college graduates?

f. Make a histogram of the frequency distribution. Describe its shape. From the histogram, estimate the mean and standard deviation. (Recall that the mean is the balance point of the histogram. Also, if a distribution is approximately normal, about 68% of the values will be within one standard deviation of the mean and about 95% will be within two standard deviations.)

2. In Course 2, Unit 7, "Patterns of Chance," a **rare event** was defined as an outcome that falls in the upper 5% of a waiting-time distribution. In the case of this jury, there are two types of rare events: getting too many college graduates or getting too few. Thus, to estimate the cut-off points for a rare event, you must split the outer 5% of the frequency distribution into two parts of 2.5% each. Each of these outer regions of the distribution is called a **tail** of the distribution.

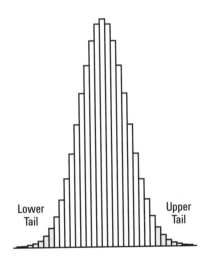

a. Use your frequency distribution to estimate the number of college graduates a jury would need to have to be in the upper 2.5% of juries; in the lower 2.5%.

b. Suppose a lawyer in a large city keeps track of the number of college graduates on the next 1,000 juries. She uses your cutoff points from Part a and finds that 52 of the 1,000 juries qualify as rare events. She plans to recommend that the jury selection process be investigated. What would you say to her?

c. Suppose a jury for a high profile case about biotechnology turns out to have no college graduates. Can this event reasonably be attributed to chance or should another explanation be considered?

3. The table you finished constructing in Activity 1 listed the values of (*number of college graduates x, frequency f*). Sometimes it is more useful if a table gives the *proportion of successes $\hat{p}$* rather than the number of successes *x*. (The symbol $\hat{p}$ is read "*p* hat.")

   a. Make a table giving ($\hat{p}, f$).

   b. Change the scale on the horizontal axis of your histogram from Activity 1 Part f so that it shows the proportion $\hat{p}$ of college graduates.

   c. From the histogram, estimate the mean and standard deviation of the proportion of college graduates.

The jury-selection situation in Activity 1 was treated as a *binomial situation*. You were interested in counting the number of "successes" (jurors who are college graduates) that occur in a fixed number of trials (12). A **binomial situation** has four characteristics:

■ There are a fixed number of individual trials, *n*.

■ Each trial is classified as a "success" or a "failure."

■ Each trial is independent of the others. (Recall that trials are independent if the result of one trial does not change the probability of a success on any other trial.)

■ On each trial, the probability of a success is a fixed (but possibly unknown) value *p* and the probability of a failure is $1 - p$.

4. Sometimes situations can be considered binomial even though technically they are not. Suppose the large judicial district actually has 30,000 eligible jurors, 30% of whom are college graduates, and that a 12-person jury is picked at random from this pool. No person can be picked more than once.

   a. Which of the four characteristics of a binomial situation does not hold in the case of this jury selection?

   b. What is the probability that the first juror picked is a college graduate?

   c. What is the probability that the second juror picked is a college graduate given that the first juror picked was a college graduate? What is the probability that the second juror picked is a college graduate given that the first juror picked was not a college graduate?

   d. To six decimal places, what is the difference in the probabilities from Part c?

e. If the first eleven jurors picked were all college graduates, what is the probability that the twelfth juror picked is also a college graduate? If none of the first eleven jurors picked were college graduates, what is the probability the twelfth juror picked is a college graduate?

f. To six decimal places, what is the difference in the probabilities from Part e?

g. Does the fact that the trials are not independent make much difference in the probabilities in this situation?

5. Now suppose that there are only 50 eligible jurors in a judicial district and that 30% of them are college graduates. A 12-person jury is selected at random from this pool and again no person can be picked more than once. Repeat Parts a–g of Activity 4 for this new situation. Then compare your answers for Part g. What explains the difference?

In juror selection, once a person has been selected to be on a jury, their name is removed from the pool for that jury. Consequently, the probability of getting a college graduate for any juror after the first depends on who has been selected before. As you saw in Activity 4, this probability doesn't change much if the size of the jury is small compared to the population. But it changes quite a bit if the size of the jury is large compared to the population (as in Activity 5). Here is a practical guide used by statisticians.

Sample-Size Guideline

If the size of the sample (jury) is less than 10 percent of the size of the population (jury pool), then the situation can be treated as a binomial situation without much loss of accuracy in the probabilities computed.

6. Which of the following are binomial situations or can be treated as binomial situations? Explain your thinking.

a. Next Monday, select 20 students at random without replacement from a large high school and ask each if they have a driver's license.

b. Roll a die 35 times and count the number of times an even number appears on top.

c. Place the names of the students in your classroom on slips of paper. Draw 10 slips at random without replacement and determine the number of students who have their own phone.

d. Place the names of the students in your classroom on slips of paper. Draw one slip at random and note whether the student is male or female. Replace the name in the hat. Repeat until you have 10 trials.

Distributions from samples and the related idea of a rare event are useful not only in examining composition of juries, but also in many other situations.

a Why is it important to identify rare events?

b How are frequency distributions for the number and for the proportion of successes related?

c How does a binomial situation differ from a situation that produces a waiting-time (geometric) distribution? How is it the same?

Be prepared to compare your group's thinking to that of other groups.

On Your Own

The table below gives the results from a simulation of the number of women on 998 12-member juries in a large city. Half of the eligible jurors are women.

Number of Women, x	Proportion of Women, $\hat{p}$	Frequency, f
0	0.00	0
1	0.08	4
2	0.17	18
3		63
4		115
5		193
6	0.50	246
7	0.58	171
8	0.67	112
9	0.75	62
10	0.83	10
11	0.92	3
12	1.00	1

a. Can this situation be treated as a binomial situation? Why or why not?

b. Describe a simulation to select a jury at random from the eligible jurors in this city.

c. Perform your simulation twice and add your results to a copy of the table, completing and, as necessary, adjusting all columns.

d. Make a frequency histogram of the proportion of jurors who are women.

e. Which juries qualify as rare events?

f. How are the center, spread, and shape of this frequency distribution different from those of the frequency distribution in Activity 3?

INVESTIGATION 2 The Binomial Probability Formula

In Investigation 1, you used simulation to approximate binomial probabilities. Estimating binomial probabilities using simulation can be time-consuming. In this investigation, you will learn how to use counting methods to compute binomial probabilities exactly.

1. About 51% of all babies born in the United States are boys. Suppose that a couple is going to have four children. Assume that having children and noting their genders is a binomial situation.

   a. Compute the probability that all four children will be boys. Is having a family of four boys a rare event?

   b. Name the rule that was used for the computation in Part a. What condition needs to be in place in order to use this rule?

   c. Compute the probability that all four children will be girls.

d. Place your results from Parts a and c in a probability distribution table like that below.

Number of Boys	Probability
0	
1	
2	
3	
4	

2. Now consider the following reasoning a student at Ellet High School in Akron, Ohio, used in completing the table in Activity 1.

To compute the probability of getting three boys and one girl she calculated
$(0.51)(0.51)(0.51)(0.49) \approx 0.065$.

To compute the probability of getting two boys and two girls she calculated
$(0.51)(0.51)(0.49)(0.49) \approx 0.062$.

To compute the probability of getting one boy and three girls she calculated
$(0.51)(0.49)(0.49)(0.49) \approx 0.060$.

a. How can you tell that the probabilities the student computed are not all correct?

b. What is wrong with her reasoning?

3. Careful counting of the possible sequences of births is essential to complete the table in Activity 1 correctly.

a. List all of the sequences of births that would result in a family with three boys and one girl.

- For each of the possible birth sequences, compute the probability that it will occur. What do you notice?

- Find the probability that a family of four children will have three boys and one girl. What probability rule did you use and why? Place your result in the appropriate place in the probability distribution table.

b. List all of the birth sequences that would result in a family with two boys and two girls.

■ For each of the birth sequences, compute the probability it will occur. What do you notice?

■ What is the probability that a family of four children will have two boys and two girls? Place your result in the table.

c. What is the probability that a family of four children will have one boy and three girls? Place your result in the table.

d. Check to be sure the probabilities add up to 1 (subject to round-off error).

4. In Activity 3, you listed all the possible birth sequences for particular events as an aid to counting them.

a. How could you use the idea of combinations to compute the probability that a family of four children will have three boys and one girl?

b. How could you use combinations to compute the probability that a family of four children will have two boys and two girls?

c. How could you use your result in Part a and combinatorial reasoning to determine the probability that a family of four children will have one boy and three girls?

5. Suppose a softball player has a batting average of .400. In the next game, she expects to be at-bat five times. One model that statisticians have investigated is whether a player's at-bats are independent. Independence would mean that the player has a 0.4 chance of making a hit each time she comes up to bat, no matter what has happened in previous at-bats. In this activity, assume that at-bats are independent; that is, she is perfectly consistent and doesn't tend to have streaks or slumps that require an explanation other than chance.

a. How many different sequences of "hits/outs" are there for five "at-bats"?

b. Determine the number of possible "hits/outs" sequences that correspond to:

■ no hits and five outs

■ one hit and four outs

■ two hits and three outs

■ three hits and two outs

■ four hits and one out

■ five hits and no outs

c. For each of the six types of sequences, compute the probability of getting one particular sequence.

d. Complete a copy of the table below and look for possible patterns.

Number of Hits	Number of Possible Sequences	Probability of One Particular Sequence	Probability
0			
1			
2			
3			
4	5	$(0.4)^4(0.6)$	$5(0.4)^4(0.6) \approx 0.077$
5			

e. Check your results to be sure you have the right total number of possible sequences and that the probabilities add up to 1.

6. In Investigation 1, you explored the situation of 12 people randomly selected from a large jury pool with 30% college graduates.

   a. Complete a copy of the following table by sharing the work among members of your group. Compare your results to those of other groups. Resolve any differences.

Number of College Graduates	Number of Possible Sequences	Probability of Each Sequence	Probability
0			
1			
2			
3			
4			
5			
6			
7			
8			
9			
10			
11			
12			

b. What is the probability of getting at least 4 college graduates on the jury? Compare that probability to your estimate from Activity 1 Part e of Investigation 1. Explain any difference.

c. What is the probability of getting 9 or more college graduates on the jury?

d. What numbers of college graduates would be a rare event?

Checkpoint

Look back at your results in Activities 5 and 6 to find a general pattern for computing binomial probabilities. Then apply and generalize the pattern in the following tasks.

ⓐ The faces of a tetrahedral die are painted different colors—red, white, blue, and black. Suppose you toss the die three times. A success in a toss is the red face on the bottom. Write an expression involving $C(n, r)$ for computing each probability:

- Probability of three successes
- Probability of two successes
- Probability of one success
- Probability of no successes

ⓑ Suppose that in a binomial situation there are n trials and the probability of a success is p. Write a formula that gives the probability of getting exactly x successes.

Be prepared to explain your formula for computing binomial probabilities.

The formula you agreed on in the Checkpoint is called the **binomial probability formula.**

On Your Own

Use the binomial probability formula to compute each probability.

a. Find the probability of getting exactly 6 doubles if you roll a pair of dice 13 times.

b. Find the probability of getting exactly 23 heads if you toss a fair coin 36 times.

c. In a large city where 30% of the population are college graduates, what is the probability that a randomly selected grand jury of 24 people will have exactly 8 college graduates? Two or fewer college graduates?

Chicago, Illinois

7. The binomial probability formula gives the probability of a given *number* of successes in a binomial situation. In this activity, you will examine how to use the formula to compute the probability of a given *proportion* of successes.

   a. Find the probability of getting exactly 25% college graduates on a jury of 12 people selected randomly from a large pool with 30% college graduates.

   b. Find the probability of getting 30% heads if you flip a coin 50 times.

8. Suppose a couple plans to have five children. Recall that approximately 51% of all babies born in the United States are boys.

   a. Use the binomial probability formula to construct the probability distribution for the number of girls in the family.

   b. Make a graph of the distribution and describe its shape.

   c. Make a table showing the probability distribution for the proportion of girls in the family.

d. Make a graph of the distribution of the proportion of girls and describe its shape.

e. Compare your graphs for Parts b and d.

9. Some calculators have capabilities for computing binomial probabilities. Explore the binomial probability functions of your calculator as you answer the following questions. Your calculator may have different displays and different commands.

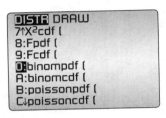
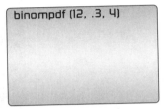

a. If 30% of people in a large city are college graduates and you pick 12 people at random, what is the probability exactly 4 are college graduates? What is the probability 4 or fewer are college graduates?

b. If 18% of students in a high school have their own car and you pick 20 students at random, what is the probability exactly 2 have their own car? What is the probability 3 or fewer have their own car? What is the probability 2 or more have their own car?

c. Use your calculator to evaluate **binomcdf(12,0.3,4)**.

■ Compare this answer to your answers in Part a.

■ Explain what the **binomcdf(** function does.

■ Use the **binomcdf(** function to answer the second and third questions in Part b above.

d. Find the probability of getting no more than 25% heads if you flip a coin 400 times. Why wouldn't you want to do this without the help of your calculator?

e. Suppose you roll a pair of dice 100 times. Find the probability that you will roll doubles on at least 20% of the rolls.

f. Describe how you can use your calculator to produce the probability distribution graph that you drew in Activity 8 Part b.

In this investigation, you discovered the binomial probability formula and learned to apply it to situations involving counts and proportions.

ⓐ Describe in words the formula for computing binomial probabilities and explain why it "works."

ⓑ Describe how the binomial probability formula can be used to find the probability of a given *proportion* of successes.

ⓒ Suppose that in a binomial situation there are n trials and the probability of success is p. Describe how you can use the binomial functions of your calculator to:

■ compute the probability of exactly x successes ($x \leq n$);

■ compute the probability of x or fewer successes ($x \leq n$); and

■ compute the probability of x or more successes ($x \leq n$).

Be prepared to share your descriptions with the entire class.

On Your Own

Complete each of the following tasks using the binomial probability formula. Then check your answer using the binomial functions on your calculator.

a. Suppose that 51% of the students in your school saw a particular movie. You take a random sample of 10 students.

■ Find the probability that exactly 30% of the 10 saw the movie.

■ Find the probability that fewer than 30% of the 10 saw the movie.

b. Construct a graph of the probability distribution for the situation of rolling a die 9 times and counting the number of sixes. What is the probability of getting 2 or more sixes?

Modeling • Organizing • Reflecting • Extending

Modeling

1. A softball player bats .400. Assume that every time she comes up to bat, the chance she will get a hit is 0.4. In an upcoming series, she expects to bat 10 times.

   a. Describe how to simulate this situation.

   b. Perform your simulation twice and add your results to a copy of the following frequency table, making a total of 1,000 trials.

Number of Hits	Frequency
0	6
1	47
2	126
3	215
4	258
5	170
6	118
7	46
8	11
9	1
10	0

   c. What numbers of hits would be considered rare events for this situation?

   d. Suppose the player gets only two hits in the upcoming series of games. Can this reasonably be attributed to chance or should she and her coach look for some other explanation?

   e. Some people don't believe the assumption of independence is reasonable with ball players. What do they mean?

2. Suppose that 30% of the eligible jurors in a large city are college graduates. Twenty-four jurors are selected for a grand jury.

   a. Describe how to simulate the selection of 24 grand jurors at random from a pool where 30% of the people are college graduates.

   b. Use your method to select 24 grand jurors. How many were college graduates? Add your result to a copy of the following frequency table and adjust column entries as necessary. The table shows the results from 499 simulations.

Number of College Graduates	Proportion of College Graduates	Frequency
0	0	0
1	0.04	1
2	0.08	5
3	0.125	21
4	0.17	34
5	0.21	53
6	0.25	86
7	0.29	79
8	0.33	78
9	0.375	62
10	0.42	39
11	0.46	24
12	0.5	9
13	0.54	5
14	0.58	3
15	0.625	0

c. Make a frequency histogram of the proportion of college graduates. How do the mean and spread of this distribution of the proportion of college graduates on a grand jury compare to those for the proportion of college graduates on a jury of 12 people from Activity 3 of Investigation 1?

d. Estimate the probability that a randomly selected grand jury will contain between 20% and 40% college graduates. Use your table from Activity 3 of Investigation 1 to estimate the probability that a jury of 12 people will contain between 20% and 40% college graduates.

e. What proportion of college graduates on a randomly selected grand jury qualifies as a rare event? On a jury of 12?

f. Suppose a newly selected grand jury ends up with one college graduate. Can this event reasonably be attributed to chance or should another explanation be considered? Explain your reasoning.

3. In the game of Yahtzee®, each player rolls five dice at once. Suppose you are at the end of a game and you need to get sixes.

a. What is the probability that none of the five dice will show a six?

b. What is the probability that exactly 2 of the dice will show sixes?

c. Construct the probability distribution table and graph for the number of sixes.

d. By looking at the graph, estimate the mean and standard deviation of the distribution.

4. In 1968, during the Vietnam War, Dr. Benjamin Spock (1903–1998) was on trial in Boston for conspiracy to violate the Military Service Act. He was accused of counseling young men on methods of avoiding the draft. It was thought that women would be more sympathetic to Dr. Spock since a larger percentage of women were opposed to the Vietnam War and since many women had used his book about child care. After a jury selection process of several stages, Dr. Spock ended up with a jury of twelve men, even though women made up more than half of the eligible jurors.

Dr. Benjamin Spock

a. Assume that women make up 50% of the eligible jurors and that jurors are selected at random from those eligible. Construct the probability distribution for the number of women on a Boston jury consisting of 12 members.

b. What numbers of women would constitute a rare event?

c. What is the probability of getting no women on the jury just by chance?

5. Cystic Fibrosis (CF) is a serious genetic disease. Approximately one in 31 Americans is an unknowing symptomless carrier of the defective gene. (Source: http://www.cff.org/facts.htm) A person can inherit CF only if both parents are carriers of the defective gene. In such cases, the child has a 25% chance of being born with CF, a 50% chance of being a symptomless carrier of the defective gene, and a 25% chance of not carrying the defective gene. Suppose one couple where both people are symptomless carriers of the disease plans to have 5 children.

a. What is the probability that none of the children will have CF?

b. What is the probability that exactly two of the children will have CF?

c. What is the probability that at least one of the children will not carry the defective CF gene?

Organizing

1. The device shown at the beginning of this unit and on the next page is called a *hexstat*. Small balls begin in the reservoir at the top, drop through the channels, and collect in the nine columns at the bottom. As a ball passes from the

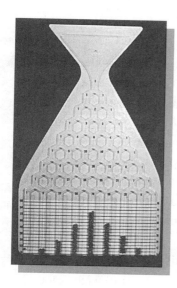

reservoir to a point where a channel branches, the ball is equally likely to go right or left.

   Imagine an experiment in which 256 balls are released from the reservoir of a hexstat and the columns into which the balls collect are noted.

a. Can the hexstat be considered a binomial situation? Explain.

b. Is the distribution of balls in the columns of the hexstat shown to the left typical?

c. What do the number labels on the channels represent? Is this pattern of numbers familiar?

d. Suppose the columns at the bottom are numbered 0, 1, 2, . . ., 8 from left to right.

■ How many different routes could a ball take to Column 0? What is the probability of a ball falling into Column 0?

■ How many different routes could a ball take to Column 5? What is the probability of a ball falling into Column 5?

2. In a large city, 1,465,241 of the 2,000,000 households recycle soft drink cans. If 12 households are selected at random, what is the probability that all recycle:

a. If you assume no replacement?

b. If you assume replacement?

c. Does it make much difference in your answers whether you assume no replacement or replacement?

3. Suppose that there are N people in a jury pool and k of them have some characteristic of interest.

a. If twelve jurors are selected at random without replacement, what is the probability that the first two jurors both have the characteristic? All twelve jurors have the characteristic?

b. How would your answers to Part a change if replacement were possible?

4. In a binomial situation, p is the probability of a success, $q = 1 - p$ is the probability of failure, and n is the number of trials.

a. Write out the expansion of $(p + q)^5$.

b. What is the numerical value of $p + q$?

c. What is the numerical value of $(p + q)^5$?

d. What have you just proved?

5. Suppose you flip a coin 8 times and count the number of heads. Show algebraically that the sum of the nine probabilities in the probability distribution table is 1. That is, show that

$$\sum_{x=0}^{8} C(8, x) \cdot (0.5)^x(1 - 0.5)^{8-x} = 1$$

(Recall that the $x = 0$ below the summation sign $\sum$ and the 8 above it tell you that the values of x start at 0 and go up to 8.)

Reflecting

1. The following situations are *not* binomial. For each situation, list which of the four characteristics of a binomial situation do not hold.

   a. Roll a die 35 times and on each roll note the number that appears on top.

   b. Select five students from your classroom and note whether each is male or female. The method of selection is to write the name of each student in your classroom on a slip of paper. Select a slip at random. Do not replace that slip. Select another slip at random. Don't replace that slip either. Select another slip at random. Continue until you have five names.

   c. Monitor the four tires of a car and count the number that go flat during a long trip.

   d. Flip a coin and count the number of trials until you get a head.

   e. Select 25 cars at random and count the number of cars of each color.

2. In Activity 6 of Investigation 2, you used combinations to count the number of possible sequences of 12 jurors with, for example, 4 college graduates. Since order matters, why did you use combinations rather than permutations?

3. In 1996, about 26% of residents of the United States were under the age of 18. (Source: 1990 U.S. Census as reported in *The World Almanac and Book of Facts 1997*. Mahwah, N.J.: World Almanac Books, 1996, page 379.)

   a. Write a numerical expression that gives the probability of selecting 1,000 United States residents at random and getting exactly 500 who are under the age of 18.

   b. Use your calculator to compute this probability. What happened?

4. Suppose that you flip a fair coin ten times.

   a. List a sequence of five heads and five tails that you could get. What is the probability of this particular sequence?

   b. List a sequence of nine heads and one tail that you could get. What is the probability of this particular sequence?

   c. If you flip a fair coin ten times, are you more likely to get five heads and five tails or nine heads and one tail? How does this reconcile with your answers from Parts a and b?

Extending

1. In Course 3, Unit 2, "Modeling Public Opinion", you used simulation to construct a chart of 90% box plots like that below.

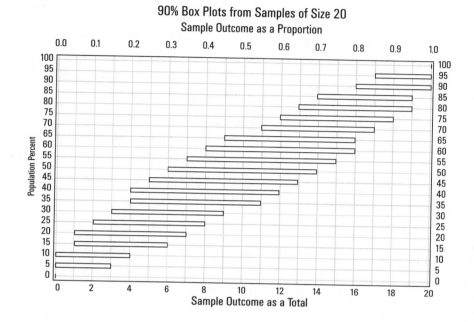

90% Box Plots from Samples of Size 20

   a. Describe what the box plot for a population with 30% successes represents.

   b. Use the binomial probability formula to construct the exact probability distribution for the number of successes in a binomial situation with $n = 20$ and $p = 0.3$.

   c. Make a 90% box plot for the number of successes in the binomial distribution from Part b.

   d. Compare your box plot with that in the chart. Is there any difference?

2. A population of ten items has four "successes" and six "failures."

$$S\ S\ F\ S\ F\ F\ F\ S\ F\ F$$

   a. What is the proportion of successes?

   b. You can code this binomial population by renaming each success as a 1 and each failure as a 0:

$$1\ 1\ 0\ 1\ 0\ 0\ 0\ 1\ 0\ 0$$

   Find the mean $\mu = \dfrac{\sum x \cdot f}{n}$ and standard deviation $\sigma = \sqrt{\dfrac{\sum (x - \mu)^2 \cdot f}{n}}$ of these ten numbers.

c. Suppose that you have a population that contains 16 successes and 4 failures.

■ When this population is coded as above, how many 1s will there be? How many 0s?

■ Find the mean and the standard deviation of the coded population.

d. Develop formulas for the mean and standard deviation of a coded population of size N with k 1s and $(N - k)$ 0s. Write your formulas in a simpler form using the proportion of successes.

e. Check the accuracy of your formula for the standard deviation in Part d by using it to recompute the standard deviation for the population in Part b and the population in Part c.

3. For a binomial situation, suppose that a population of size N contains S successes and F failures. Suppose you take a random sample of size n.

a. If the sampling is done *with replacement,* explain why the probability of getting exactly s successes and f failures is given by the following formula:

$$C(n, s)\left(\frac{S}{N}\right)^{s}\left(\frac{F}{N}\right)^{f}$$

b. If the sampling is done *without replacement,* explain why the probability of getting exactly s successes and f failures is given by the **hypergeometric** formula:

$$\frac{C(S, s) \cdot C(F, f)}{C(N, n)}$$

c. Suppose a group of 25 students has 15 students who play a musical instrument. If the sampling is done with replacement, find the probability that if you select 8 students at random, exactly 6 play a musical instrument. Then find the probability if the sampling is done without replacement.

4. Examine the following tree diagram. Here, p is the probability of a success and $q = 1 - p$ is the probability of a failure in a binomial situation.

a. What is the next row?

b. Explain what this tree diagram shows.

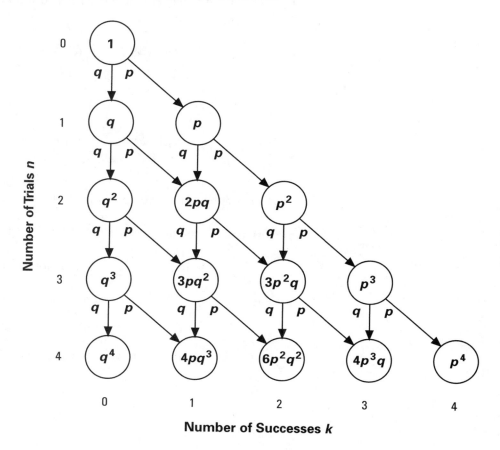

1. The price of a jacket is $35 during a 20% off sale. How much did the jacket originally cost?

   (a) $42.00   (b) $43.75   (c) $20.00   (d) $55.00   (e) $26.25

2. $\left(\dfrac{14}{125x^5}\right)\left(\dfrac{5x^2}{56y}\right)(10y^4) =$

   (a) $\dfrac{1}{1,000x^3y^5}$ (b) $\dfrac{10y^3}{x^3}$ (c) $\dfrac{3x^3y^3}{100}$ (d) $\dfrac{10x^3}{y^3}$ (e) $\dfrac{y^3}{10x^3}$

3. The graphs of the two equations $2x + y = 7$ and $3x - 6y = 9$ are

   (a) two perpendicular lines   (b) two distinct parallel lines

   (c) the same line   (d) not straight lines

   (e) two intersecting lines that are not perpendicular

4. If $f(x) = \dfrac{7}{x-2}$, for what value of x does $f(x) = 3$?

   (a) 7   (b) $\dfrac{13}{3}$ (c) 3   (d) $\dfrac{1}{3}$ (e) 2

5. The function $f(x) = x^2 - 10x + 25$ has how many different zeroes?

   (a) 2   (b) 0   (c) 3   (d) none   (e) 1

6. If $3|x - 5| = 6$, then $x =$

   (a) 7 or −3   (b) 7 or −7   (c) 7 or 3   (d) 3 or −3   (e) 8 or 2

7. Which of the following could be a portion of the graph of $y = \frac{2}{x^2}$?

(a) 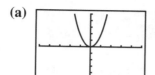   (b) 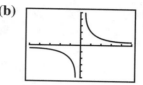   (c)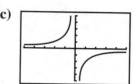

(d) 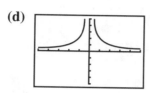   (e)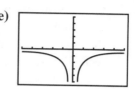

8. In the figure shown, tan $A =$

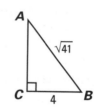

   (a) $\frac{5}{4}$ (b) $\frac{\sqrt{41}}{5}$ (c) $\frac{4}{5}$ (d) $\frac{4}{\sqrt{41}}\pi$ (e) $\frac{5}{\sqrt{41}}$

9. Solve for x: $\log 2x + \log 5 = 3$

   (a) -1 (b) $\frac{3}{10}$ (c) $\frac{1,000}{7}$ (d) $\frac{995}{2}$ (e) 100

10. Rewrite $\sqrt{\frac{9x^4}{y^3}}$ using exponential notation, where $x > 0$ and $y > 0$.

   (a) $3x^2\sqrt{y^3}$ (b) $3\left(\frac{x}{y}\right)^{\frac{4}{3}}$ (c) $3x^{\frac{4}{3}}y^{\frac{4}{3}}$ (d) $3x^2y^{-\frac{3}{2}}$ (e) $3x^2y^2\sqrt{y}$

Characteristics of Binomial Distributions

In the last lesson, you constructed several binomial distributions, observed their shapes, and estimated their means and standard deviations. In Investigation 1 of this lesson, you will learn how to visualize the shape of a binomial distribution if you know n and p. In Investigation 2, you will discover simple formulas for the mean and the standard deviation of a binomial distribution. But first, consider the following situation.

According to an annual nationwide survey of college freshmen, two-thirds of both male and female freshmen planned to earn a graduate degree (master's or doctorate) or an advanced professional degree (such as law or medicine). (Source: Higher Education Research Institute, Annual Freshman Survey UCLA, 1997.) Suppose you have a random sample of 200 college freshmen and count the number who say they plan to get an advanced degree. The graph of the binomial distribution of the number of freshmen who plan to get an advanced degree is shown below.

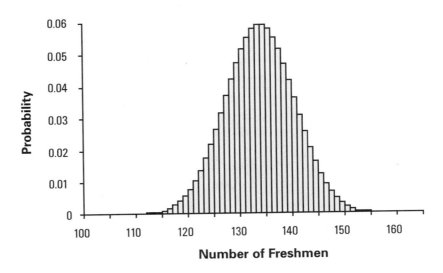

Examine the binomial distribution on the previous page.

ⓐ What is the approximate shape of the graph? Explain what the bar between 140 and 141 means.

ⓑ How many freshmen would you expect to say that they plan to earn advanced degrees?

ⓒ How can you find the standard deviation of this probability distribution? What information does the standard deviation give you?

ⓓ How do you think the shape, center, and spread would change if the sample size was much smaller? Much larger?

ⓔ How do you think the shape, center, and spread would change if you graphed the proportion of successes rather than the number of successes?

INVESTIGATION 1 ▸ The Shapes of Binomial Distributions

The graph of the binomial distribution for the number of freshmen who plan to get advanced degrees looks approximately normal. In this investigation, you will see that not all binomial distributions are approximately normal in shape. However, you will be able to predict when they will be if you know the probability of a success *p* and the sample size *n*.

1. According to the United States Bureau of the Census, 20% of the population of the United States are children; that is, age 13 or younger. (Source: *The World Almanac and Book of Facts 1997.* Mahwah, N.J.: World Almanac Books, page 387.) Suppose you take a random sample of people from the United States. The following graphs show the binomial distributions for the number of children in random samples varying in size from 5 to 100.

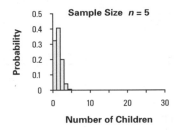
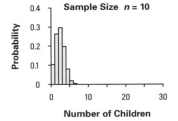
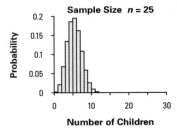

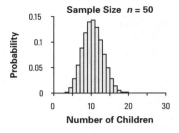

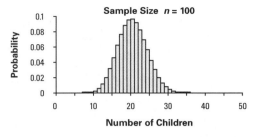

a. Determine the exact height of the tallest bar on the graph for a sample size of 10.

b. Why are there more bars as the sample size increases? How many bars should there be for a sample size of *n?* Why are there only 7 bars for a sample size of 10?

c. What happens to the shape of the distribution as the sample size increases?

d. What happens to the mean of the number of successes as the sample size increases?

e. What happens to the standard deviation of the number of successes as the sample size increases?

2. Examine the following graphs. They show binomial distributions for the number of heads when a fair coin is tossed various numbers of times.

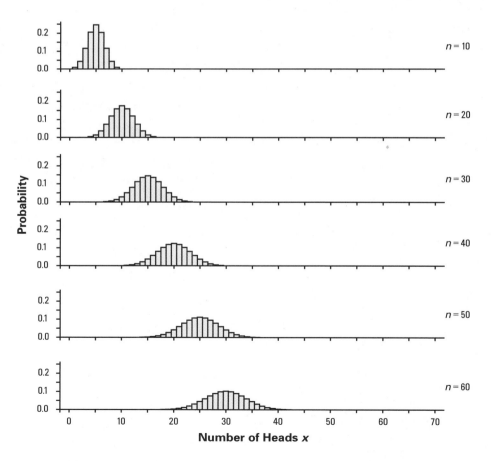

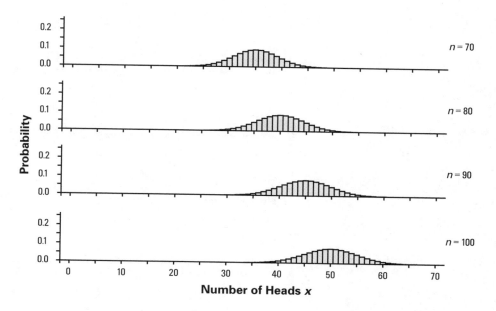

a. What happens to the shape of these distributions as the sample size n increases?

b. What happens to the mean of the probability distribution as n increases?

c. What happens to the standard deviation as n increases?

3. Now consider what happens when the sample size is fixed and the probability of success varies. The set of graphs below show the binomial distributions for a sample size of 40 and probabilities of success varying from 0.10 to 0.90.

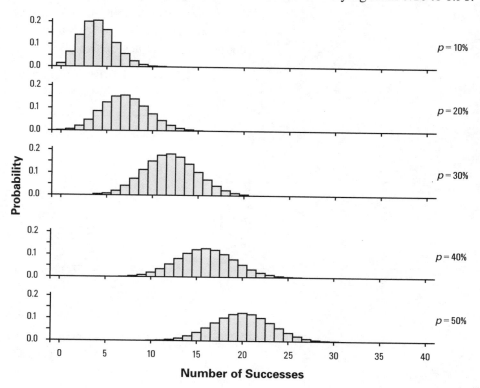

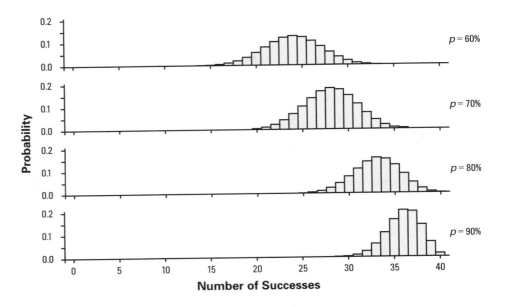

a. Which of these distributions are a bit skewed? What happens to the shape of the distributions as the probability of success *p* increases? Which of these distributions has a shape that is closest to normal?

b. What happens to the mean of the number of successes as the probability of success *p* increases?

c. What happens to the standard deviation as *p* increases?

d. What symmetries do you see in this set of graphs?

e. How is this set of graphs similar to the box plot charts from fixed sample sizes you made in Course 3, Unit 2, "Modeling Public Opinion"? The box plot chart for samples of size 40 is shown below.

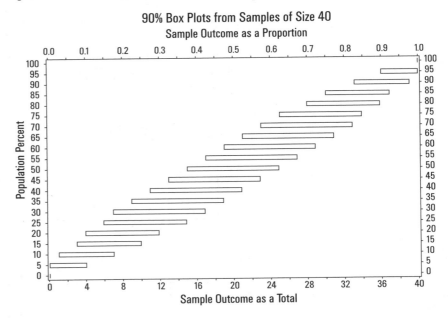

4. Based on your work in Activities 1 through 3, draw conclusions about the effect of sample size or value of p on the shape of the graph of a binomial distribution.

   a. Complete each sentence using the word "more" or "less."

   ▪ With a fixed sample size, the farther p is away from 0.50, the _____ skewed the binomial distribution.

   ▪ Usually, with a fixed value of p, the larger the sample size, the _____ skewed the binomial distribution.

   b. What are the exceptions to the statement in the second item of Part a?

5. To predict whether the graph of a binomial distribution will look approximately normal, compute both np and $n(1 - p)$ and check to see if both are at least 10.

   a. The value np can be interpreted as the expected number of successes. How can you interpret $n(1 - p)$?

   b. Which of the distributions in Activity 1 can be considered approximately normal using the above guideline? Does this agree with your visual impression?

   c. Which of the distributions in Activity 2 can be considered approximately normal using this guideline? Does this agree with your visual impression?

   d. Which of the distributions in Activity 3 can be considered approximately normal using this guideline? Does this agree with your visual impression?

6. Imagine the binomial distribution with $n = 35$ and $p = 0.2$.

   a. Is this distribution skewed left, skewed right, or symmetric?

   b. Where is it centered? Estimate its standard deviation.

   c. Check your answers to Parts a and b using the binomial function capabilities of your calculator to make a graph of this distribution.

Checkpoint

Think about a binomial distribution with probability of a success p and sample size n.

a As n increases, but the probability of a success p remains the same, what happens to the shape, center, and spread of the binomial distribution for the number of successes?

b As p increases from 0.01 to 0.99, but n remains the same (for example, $n = 50$) what happens to the shape, center, and spread of the binomial distribution for the number of successes?

Be prepared to discuss your descriptions of changes in the binomial distributions.

On Your Own

Think about patterns of change in binomial distributions as the sample size or probability of success varies.

a. How does the binomial distribution for the number of successes in a sample of size 25 and probability of success 0.3 differ from a binomial distribution with sample size 50 and probability of success 0.3?

b. How does the binomial distribution for the number of successes in a sample of size 25 and probability of success 0.3 compare to the binomial distribution with sample size 25 and probability of success 0.7?

In the first part of this investigation, you examined the shape, center, and spread of binomial distributions of the *number* of successes in a random sample. Now examine these same characteristics of distributions of the *proportion* $\hat{p}$ of successes.

7. How do you convert the number of successes in a binomial situation to the proportion of successes?

8. Shown below are the graphs from Activity 1 with the scale on the *x*-axes changed to one that gives the proportion $\hat{p}$ of children in the sample.

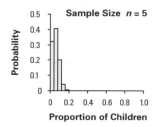

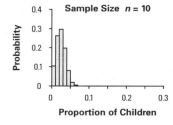

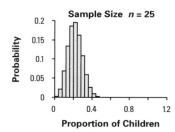

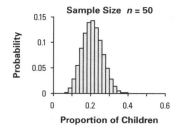

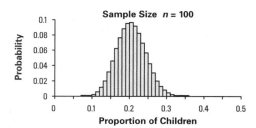

a. What happens to the mean of the sample proportions as the sample size increases?

b. What happens to the standard deviation of the sample proportions as the sample size increases? Why does this make sense?

9. On a copy of each of the graphs from Activity 2, change the scale on the *x*-axis to one that gives the sample proportion of heads, $\hat{p}$.

   a. What happens to the mean of the proportion of heads as the sample size increases?

   b. What happens to the standard deviation of the proportion of heads as the sample size increases?

Checkpoint

Consider a binomial situation with probability of success *p* and sample size *n*.

  ⓐ If *n* increases but *p* remains the same, what happens to the shape, center, and spread of the distribution of the sample proportions?

  ⓑ Compare the graphs of the distributions of $\hat{p}$ and of $1 - \hat{p}$ for a fixed sample size *n*.

  ⓒ Summarize the differences between the binomial distribution for the number of successes and the distribution for the corresponding sample proportions.

   Be prepared to discuss the variations in the distributions.

▶On Your Own

Think about patterns of change in distributions for the sample proportion $\hat{p}$ as the sample size, or probability of success varies.

a. How does the distribution of the sample proportion $\hat{p}$ from a sample of size 25 and probability of success 0.3 differ from the distribution with sample size 50 and probability of success 0.3?

b. How does the distribution of the sample proportion $\hat{p}$ from a sample size of 25 and probability of success 0.3 compare to the distribution with sample size 25 and probability of success 0.7?

c. Compare your answers for Parts a and b with your corresponding answers to Parts a and b of the "On Your Own" on page 306.

INVESTIGATION 2 ▶ Simple Formulas for the Mean and the Standard Deviation

Recall that the formula for the mean of a probability distribution is

$$\mu = \sum x \cdot p(x)$$

Similarly, the formula for the standard deviation of a probability distribution is

$$\sigma = \sqrt{\sum (x - \mu)^2 \cdot p(x)}$$

In this investigation, you will see that these formulas can be simplified in the case of binomial distributions.

1. According to the United States Bureau of the Census, 20% of the population of the United States are children (aged 13 or younger). Suppose you take a random sample of four people living in the United States and count the number of children.

   a. Complete this probability distribution table for the number of children in your sample of size 4.

Number of Children x	Probability $p(x)$
0	0.4096
1	0.4096
2	0.1536
3	
4	0.0016

   b. Use the formulas above to compute the mean and standard deviation of the probability distribution in Part a.

   c. In computing the mean of the above distribution, you could also simply reason that if 20% of the population are children, the mean number of children in a random sample of four people should be 20% of 4 or 0.8. Compare this value with the mean value you computed in Part b.

2. Part c of Activity 1 illustrates a general formula for computing the mean of a binomial distribution. The mean number of successes in n trials with probability of success p is

$$\mu = np$$

There is also a much simpler formula for the standard deviation of a binomial distribution:

$$\sigma = \sqrt{np(1 - p)}$$

   a. Verify that this formula for the standard deviation gives the same result as that in Activity 1 Part b.

b. Now refer back to the graphs in Activity 1 of Investigation 1 of this lesson. Complete the following table for those graphs. In each case, $p = 0.2$.

Sample Size n	Mean μ	Standard Deviation σ
5		
10		
25		
50		
100		

c. If you double the sample size, what happens to the mean? To the standard deviation?

d. How does the mean vary with the sample size? How does the standard deviation vary with the sample size?

3. Consider this table for binomial distributions with $n = 9$ and various values of p. The **variance** σ^2 is the square of the standard deviation.

Probability of a Success p	Mean $\mu = np$	Variance σ^2
0.1	0.9	0.81
0.2	1.8	1.44
0.3	2.7	1.89
0.4	3.6	2.16
0.5	4.5	2.25
0.6		
0.7		
0.8		
0.9		

a. Complete the table.

b. What patterns do you see in the table?

c. Plot the points (p, σ^2). What type of function model would match the pattern of change shown in the graph?

d. Describe at least three possible methods for finding an equation showing the relationship between the probability of success and the variance.

e. Use two of these methods to find an equation.

4. Examine the formula for the standard deviation of a binomial distribution.

a. Explain how the formula supports your generalization about the standard deviation in Activity 2 Parts d and e.

b. If you quadruple the sample size, what happens to the variance? To the standard deviation?

5. You can use the formulas for the mean and standard deviation of the *number* of successes to derive corresponding formulas for the *proportion* of successes.

  a. If the mean number of successes is $\mu = np$, what computation would you do to get the mean *proportion* of successes? Write the formula for the mean proportion of successes.

  b. Why does the result in Part a make sense intuitively?

  c. If the standard deviation of the number of successes is $\sigma = \sqrt{np(1-p)}$, what computation would you do to get the standard deviation of the *proportion* of successes? Write the formula in the simplest form possible.

  d. By examining your formula from Part c, what can you determine about the standard deviation for the proportion of successes as the sample size increases?

  e. Why does the result in Part d make sense intuitively?

Checkpoint

When studying a binomial situation, it is often helpful to know the mean and standard deviation of the number of successes or the proportion of successes.

 ⓐ Compare the formulas for the mean and standard deviation of the number of successes in a binomial distribution to the corresponding formulas for the proportion of successes.

 ⓑ Describe how the formulas for the mean and standard deviation can be used to explain the differences in the probability distributions for the number of successes and the proportion of successes as the sample size increases, but the probability of a success remains the same.

Be prepared to share your comparison and explanation with the class.

On Your Own

Consider a binomial distribution with $n = 3$ and $p = 0.45$.

a. Make a probability distribution table giving the number of successes.

b. Find the mean of the number of successes using the formula $\mu = np$ and then using the formula $\mu = \sum x \cdot p(x)$.

c. Find the standard deviation of the number of successes using the formula $\sigma = \sqrt{np(1-p)}$ and then by using the formula $\sigma = \sqrt{\sum (x - \mu)^2 \cdot p(x)}$.

d. Find the mean and standard deviation of the distribution of the sample proportion $\hat{p}$.

Modeling • Organizing • Reflecting • Extending

Modeling

1. Ten percent of the population of the United States is between the ages of 18 and 24. Suppose you have a random sample of 1,500 residents of the United States.

   a. Will the binomial distribution for the number of people between ages 18 and 24 in your sample be approximately normal? Explain your reasoning.

   b. Find the mean and standard deviation of the binomial distribution for the number of people between ages 18 and 24.

   c. Make a sketch of the distribution, including a scale on the *x*-axis that shows the mean and one, two, and three standard deviations from the mean.

   d. Would it be a rare event to get 130 people between ages 18 and 24?

2. Twenty percent of the residents of the United States are children (aged 13 and younger). Suppose you take a random sample of 200 people living in the United States.

   a. Will the binomial distribution of the number of children in your sample be approximately normal? Why or why not?

   b. Find the mean and the standard deviation of the binomial distribution for the number of children.

   c. Make a sketch of the distribution, including a scale on the *x*-axis that shows the mean and one, two, and three standard deviations from the mean.

   d. How many children would it take for the number in the sample to be two standard deviations above average?

   e. How many children would it take for the number in the sample to be two standard deviations below average?

   f. What is the probability that the number of children in a sample will be more than two standard deviations above or below the mean? More than one standard deviation above or below the mean?

   g. What numbers of children in the sample constitute a rare event?

h. Suppose someone claims they have taken a random sample of 200 people from the United States and they got 45 children. They were a bit upset because they knew they should expect 40 children. What would you say to them?

3. In 1998, 82.5% of people aged 25 years and above in the United States had graduated from high school. (Source: www.census.gov/population/www/socdemo/educ-attn.html) Suppose in one random sample of 500 people over age 25 in the United States, there were 420 people who reported graduating from high school. Would this be considered a rare event?

4. About 49% of people aged 15–24 in the United States are female. During the 1997–1998 academic year, about 59% of the 27,086 students enrolled at California State University, Northridge were women. (Source: *Cal State Northridge Factbook 1997/98.*) Can the extra 10% reasonably be attributed to chance or should the university look for some other explanation?

Organizing

1. Match each of the descriptions of a binomial distribution below with its corresponding graph.

   a. $p = 0.1$, $n = 40$

   b. $p = 0.2$, $n = 20$

   c. $p = 0.4$, $n = 10$

   d. $p = 0.8$, $n = 5$

Check your answers by producing the graphs of the distributions on your calculator.

i.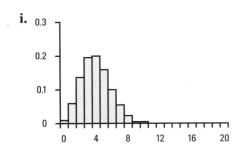

ii.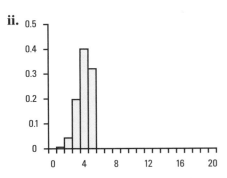

iii.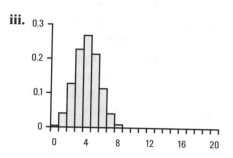

iv.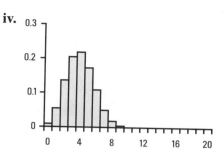

2. If you look closely at the graphs in Activity 3 of Investigation 1, you will note that the graphs for *p* and 1 − *p* are reflection images of each other. Explain why the symmetry exists by analyzing the binomial probability formula.

3. Find the probability that if you roll two dice 32 times you get doubles exactly 25% of the time.

4. In Activity 3 of Investigation 2, you may have discovered that for a fixed sample size, there is a quadratic relationship between the probability of success *p* and the variance σ^2.

   a. Make a plot of the data (*n*, μ) from Activity 2 of Investigation 2.
   - What does the pattern indicate about the relationship between *n* and μ?
   - Write an equation that expresses this relationship.
   - How could you have deduced this equation without making the scatterplot?

   b. Make a plot of the data (*n*, σ) from Activity 2 of Investigation 2.
   - What does the pattern indicate about the relationship between *n* and σ?
   - How is this pattern suggested by the formula for the standard deviation?

Reflecting

1. Have you *proved* the simplified formula for the mean of a binomial distribution $\mu = np$? Have you *proved* the simplified formula for the standard deviation? If so, explain how you did it. If not, explain why not.

2. Under what conditions are the mean and standard deviation of a binomial distribution equal?

3. Consider a binomial distribution with *n* = 100 and *p* = 0.4.

   a. Suppose you didn't know the simplified formula for the mean of a binomial distribution. Make an estimate of the number of additions and subtractions, and the number of multiplications and divisions it would take to compute the mean of the distribution using the standard formula for the mean of a probability distribution if you already have the complete probability distribution table.

b. Suppose you didn't know the simplified formula for the standard deviation of a binomial distribution. Make an estimate of the number of additions and subtractions, and the number of multiplications and divisions it would take to compute the standard deviation of the binomial distribution using the standard formula for the standard deviation of a probability distribution. Assume you already have the complete probability distribution table and you do not use the list feature of your calculator.

4. In this lesson, you have seen that a binomial distribution often can be considered "approximately normal." Why is the word "approximately" always attached to the description? Can a binomial distribution ever be exactly normal? Explain.

Extending

1. Suppose your drive to school takes either 4 minutes, 9 minutes, or 17 minutes, each with equal probability. Your drive home from school takes either 4 minutes, 6 minutes, or 11 minutes, each with equal probability. Assume that morning and afternoon drive times are independent.

a. Make a table of the probability distribution for the number of minutes it takes you to get to school. Find the mean and variance of this distribution.

b. Make a table of the probability distribution for the number of

A student is looking for a space in the school parking lot.

minutes it takes you to get home from school. Find the mean and variance of this distribution.

c. Construct the probability distribution for the total number of minutes you spend traveling to and from school. Find the mean and variance of the total time.

d. How could you have found the mean and variance of the total time from knowing the mean and variance of the morning and of the afternoon times?

e. Can you find the standard deviation of the total time from knowing the standard deviations of the morning and afternoon times?

Now suppose that the drives aren't independent and that long morning drives always are paired with long afternoon drives, short morning drives always are paired with short afternoon drives, and middle-length morning drives always are paired with middle-length afternoon drives.

f. Construct the probability distribution for the total number of minutes you spend traveling to and from school. Find the mean and variance of the total time.

g. Can you find the mean and variance of the total time from knowing the mean and variance of the morning and afternoon times?

2. Recall that the mean and standard deviation of a probability distribution are given by:

$$\mu = \sum x \cdot p(x)$$
$$\sigma = \sqrt{\sum (x - \mu)^2 \cdot p(x)}$$

To prove, in the case of a binomial distribution with probability of success p and sample size n, that these formulas can be simplified to

$$\mu = np$$
$$\sigma = \sqrt{np(1 - p)}$$

requires a theorem from mathematical statistics. The theorem says that if you select two values x_1 and x_2 at random with replacement from a finite population with mean μ and variance σ^2, then the mean of all possible values of $x_1 + x_2$ is $\mu + \mu$. Also, if x_1 and x_2 are selected independently, then the variance of all possible values of $x_1 + x_2$ is $\sigma^2 + \sigma^2$.

a. Find the mean and variance of this probability distribution.

b. Explain why this probability distribution represents the possible results of one trial from a binomial situation.

x	$p(x)$
0	$1 - p$
1	p

c. Let x_1 be the result from one trial and x_2 be the result of a second trial. What does $x_1 + x_2$ represent? Use the probability distribution theorem to find the mean and variance of this sum.

d. Suppose you do n independent trials from this distribution and add up the results. Find the mean and the variance of the probability distribution of the sum.

e. What did you show in Part d?

3. In Investigation 2, you examined a simple formula for the standard deviation of a binomial distribution of the number of successes with n trials and probability of success p. In this task, you will further analyze the formula to make sure it gives the values you would expect.

a. What do you think should be the standard deviation of the binomial distribution when $p = 1$? Does the formula give this value?

b. What do you think should be the standard deviation of the binomial distribution when $p = 0$? Does the formula give this value?

c. You observed that there was symmetry in the binomial distributions for p and $1 - p$. If you know the standard deviation of the binomial distribution with n trials and probability of success p, what is the standard deviation of the binomial distribution with n trials and probability of success $1 - p$? Does the formula give this value?

d. For a fixed number of trials n, for which value of p should the standard deviation be largest? How does the formula reflect this fact?

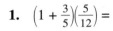
1. $\left(1 + \frac{3}{5}\right)\left(\frac{5}{12}\right) =$

   (a) $\frac{9}{17}$ (b) $\frac{1}{3}$ (c) $\frac{2}{3}$ (d) $\frac{1}{4}$ (e) $\frac{13}{17}$

2. How many hours does it take a person to travel 360 miles at an average speed of 40 miles per hour?

   (a) 90   (b) 320   (c) 400   (d) 9   (e) 14,400

3. Which of the following lines is parallel to the line whose equation is $y = -5x + 7$?

   (a) $y = 5x + 7$ (b) $y = -5x - 7$ (c) $y = 5x - 7$

   (d) $y = 2x$ (e) $y - 5x = 2$

4. If $f(x) = 2x + 9$ and $g(x) = -3x + 7$, then $f(x) - g(x)$ is

   (a) $5x - 2$ (b) $-x + 2$ (c) $5x + 2$ (d) $-5x - 2$ (e) $x + 2$

5. What is the vertex of the parabola whose equation is $y = 3(x - 6)^2 + 9$?

   (a) $(6, 9)$ (b) $(9, 6)$ (c) $(-6, 9)$ (d) $(9, -6)$ (e) $(3, 3)$

6. Solve $|2x - 1| < 7$ for x.

    (a) $x < 4$ (b) $-4 < x < 4$ (c) $-6 < x < 8$ (d) $x < 3$ (e) $-3 < x < 4$

7. Which of the following is a polynomial function whose zeroes are 3, 6, and –2?

    (a) $f(x) = x^3 + 7x^2 - 36$ (b) $f(x) = x^3 - 11x^2 + 36x - 36$

    (c) $f(x) = x^3 - 36$ (d) $f(x) = x^3 - 7x^2 + 36$

    (e) $f(x) = x^3 - 7x^2 - 36x - 36$

8. The length of a rectangle is 5 units more than its width. If its width is x, then its perimeter is

    (a) $2x + 5$ (b) $x^2 + 5$ (c) $x^2 + 5x$ (d) $x^4 + 10$ (e) $4x + 10$

9. If $5^x \cdot 5^{x+2} = 5^3$, then $x =$

    (a) 0.5 (b) 1 (c) 1 or -3 (d) 61.5 (e) 3

10. Simplify $\sqrt{75} + \sqrt{98} - 3\sqrt{12}$.

    (a) $7\sqrt{2} - \sqrt{3}$ (b) $7\sqrt{2} + 11\sqrt{3}$ (c) $6\sqrt{6}$

    (d) $-2\sqrt{161}$ (e) $7\sqrt{2} + \sqrt{3}$

Lesson 3

Chance Variation in a Binomial Situation

In binomial situations with a large number of trials, you can draw on your observations from Lesson 2 in order to estimate probabilities. In that lesson, you saw that a binomial distribution with probability of success p and sample size n is approximately normal for large values of n. In this lesson, you will examine how this fact can be used to determine whether a particular outcome is a rare event or one that is reasonably likely to occur.

Think About This Situation

Suppose you would like to determine if spinning a penny is fair. To spin a penny, you hold it edgewise against a hard flat surface with one finger. With the index finger of the opposite hand, you flick the penny so that it spins around vertically on the surface until it lands flat. You spin a penny 900 times and count the number of heads.

a Do you think this process will give about the same number of heads as tails?

b If this process tends to give the same number of heads as tails, what would the distribution of all possible outcomes look like?

c How many heads or how few heads would you have to get before you would reject the hypothesis that the probability of getting a head when you spin a penny is 0.5?

d Think back to your work with the normal distribution in Course 3. How did the table of standardized values assist you in answering questions about normal distributions?

INVESTIGATION 1 ▶ Using the Normal Distribution to Approximate Binomial Probabilities

In Lesson 2, you saw that to compute the probability of getting a given number of successes x in a binomial situation with n trials and probability of success p, you could use the binomial probability formula:

$$P(x \text{ successes}) = C(n, x)(p)^x(1 - p)^{n - x}$$

or the binomial probability function capability of your calculator:

$$\text{binompdf(n,p,x)}$$

In general, if both np and $n(1 - p)$ are 10 or greater, you also can use the properties of a normal distribution to approximate binomial probabilities. Methods for doing this will be developed in the following activities.

1. Suppose you spin a penny 900 times and count the number of heads. Think about the distribution of all possible outcomes under the assumption that spinning the coin is fair.

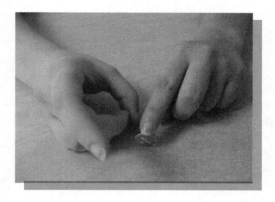

   a. Is this a binomial distribution?

   b. What is the mean number of heads in the distribution of all possible outcomes? What is the standard deviation of the number of heads?

   c. What is the shape of the distribution?

   d. Still assuming that spinning the coin is fair, what is the probability of getting exactly 415 heads?

   e. Find the probability of getting 415 or fewer heads. Describe how you could use your calculator to compute this probability.

   f. Try to use your calculator to find the probability that you get 4,450 or fewer heads if you spin the penny 9,000 times. What is the largest value of n your calculator will accept?

Computing exact binomial probabilities is a great deal of work, even for a calculator. However, using the statistical theory you have already learned, you can approximate probabilities such as that in Activity 1 Part f very closely.

2. In Course 3, Unit 5, "Patterns in Variation," you learned how to find the probability of events that had a normal distribution. First, you computed a standard score, or z-score, $z = \frac{x - \mu}{\sigma}$, and then you found the probability using the following table. Recall that a standard score gives the number of standard deviations from the mean.

z	Proportion Below	z	Proportion Below	z	Proportion Below
−3.5	0.0002	−1.1	0.1357	1.3	0.9032
−3.4	0.0003	−1.0	0.1587	1.4	0.9192
−3.3	0.0005	−0.9	0.1841	1.5	0.9332
−3.2	0.0007	−0.8	0.2119	1.6	0.9452
−3.1	0.0010	−0.7	0.2420	1.7	0.9554
−3.0	0.0013	−0.6	0.2743	1.8	0.9641
−2.9	0.0019	−0.5	0.3085	1.9	0.9713
−2.8	0.0026	−0.4	0.3446	2.0	0.9772
−2.7	0.0035	−0.3	0.3821	2.1	0.9821
−2.6	0.0047	−0.2	0.4207	2.2	0.9861
−2.5	0.0062	−0.1	0.4602	2.3	0.9893
−2.4	0.0082	0.0	0.5000	2.4	0.9918
−2.3	0.0107	0.1	0.5398	2.5	0.9938
−2.2	0.0139	0.2	0.5793	2.6	0.9953
−2.1	0.0179	0.3	0.6179	2.7	0.9965
−2.0	0.0228	0.4	0.6554	2.8	0.9974
−1.9	0.0287	0.5	0.6915	2.9	0.9981
−1.8	0.0359	0.6	0.7257	3.0	0.9987
−1.7	0.0446	0.7	0.7580	3.1	0.9990
−1.6	0.0548	0.8	0.7881	3.2	0.9993
−1.5	0.0668	0.9	0.8159	3.3	0.9995
−1.4	0.0808	1.0	0.8413	3.4	0.9997
−1.3	0.0968	1.1	0.8643	3.5	0.9998
−1.2	0.1151	1.2	0.8849		

If you wish, you can get the values in the table by using the normal probability function capability of your calculator.

```
DIST DRAW
 1: normalpdf(
 2: normalcdf(
 3: invNorm(
 4: tpdf(
 5: tcdf(
 6: x²pdf(
 7↓ x²cdf(
```

a. Suppose the weights of alley cats are normally distributed with a mean of 12 pounds and a standard deviation of 2 pounds.

- Use the table on the previous page to find the probability that a randomly selected alley cat weighs less than 11.5 pounds. Compare your answer to that found using the normal distribution function on your calculator: `normalcdf(−999999,11.5,12,2)`.

- Find the probability that a randomly selected alley cat weighs more than 15 pounds.

b. Suppose a distribution is normal with a mean of 450 and standard deviation of 15. What is the probability a randomly selected value from this distribution is greater than 463?

c. Suppose a distribution is normal with a mean of 50 and standard deviation of 5. What is the probability a value randomly selected from this distribution is between 39.5 and 60.5?

3. Think back to the coin spinning situation in Activity 1.

   a. How can you use the idea of standard scores and the normal distribution to approximate the probability of getting 415 heads or fewer out of 900 spins if spinning a coin is a fair process?

   b. Compare your answer with that in Activity 1 Part e. Should the two probabilities be equal?

   c. Estimate the probability that you get 4,450 or fewer heads if you flip a fair coin 9,000 times.

4. About 20% of the population of the United States are children (aged 13 or younger). Suppose you select 250 residents of the U.S. at random. Use standard scores and the normal distribution to approximate the requested probabilities.

   a. What is the mean of the distribution of the number of children in all possible samples? The standard deviation?

   b. What is the probability of getting 40 or more children?

   c. What numbers of children would constitute a rare event?

   d. What is the mean of the distribution of the sample proportion $\hat{p}$? The standard deviation of the distribution of the sample proportion?

   e. What is the probability that 15% or fewer in your sample will be children?

   f. What proportions of children in the sample would constitute a rare event?

   g. How are the answers for Parts c and f related?

5. The procedure you used in Activities 3 and 4 is called the **normal approximation to the binomial distribution.**

   a. Explain why using the normal distribution in Activities 3 and 4 is an approximation to the exact probability. Draw a sketch to illustrate your explanation.

   b. Use the binomial probability formula to find the probability of getting 3 or fewer heads when flipping a fair coin ten times.

   c. Use the normal approximation to find the probability of getting 3 or fewer heads when flipping a fair coin ten times.

   d. Compare your results in Parts b and c. Is the approximation very close? Explain why it should be or shouldn't be.

On Your Own

Check your understanding of the normal approximation to the binomial distribution. Suppose you roll a pair of dice 600 times and count the number of times you get doubles.

a. What is the mean, standard deviation, and shape of the distribution of all possible outcomes?

b. What is the probability that you get doubles 95 or fewer times?

c. What numbers of doubles would constitute a rare event?

d. What is the mean, standard deviation, and shape of the distribution of the *proportion* of times you get doubles?

e. What is the probability you will get doubles less than 20% of the time?

INVESTIGATION 2 A Test of Significance

In the last investigation, you considered the question of whether spinning a penny is a fair process. To test this, suppose you spin a penny 900 times and get 415 heads. With a fair coin, you should get around 450 heads, but probably not exactly 450 heads. Can getting only 415 heads reasonably be attributed to the variation that occurs just by chance in random samples? (The variation that occurs from one random sample to another is called **chance variation**.)

1. Think through the logic of how to determine whether getting 415 heads on 900 spins of a penny can be attributed to chance variation.

   a. If spinning a penny is fair, what proportion of the time will heads occur?

   b. Suppose spinning a penny *is* fair. Describe the distribution of the number of heads in samples of size 900.

   c. How many heads occurred in the actual sample of size 900?

   d. Still supposing that spinning a penny is fair, what is the probability of getting 415 or fewer heads in a random sample from this population?

   e. Is the result from the sample likely to occur with a fair process? Can you reasonably attribute the proportion from the sample to chance variation, or do you now doubt the fairness of the process of spinning a penny?

2. The sequence of logic outlined in Activity 1 is called a **z-test for a proportion**. You established that getting 415 heads out of 900 is a **statistically significant** result; that is, it is not the kind of result you would expect if the process of spinning a coin is fair. The z-test for a proportion consists of the following five steps. Read each step and connect it back to the appropriate part of Activity 1.

   I. Write a statement about the proportion of successes hypothesized to be in the population. This statement is called a **null hypothesis**.

   II. Assume that the null hypothesis is true. Sketch the distribution of the number (or proportion) of successes that would result from all possible random samples of a given size. The distribution shows you the variation that you would expect just by chance *if the null hypothesis is true*.

   III. Take an actual random sample from the population and find the number (or proportion) of successes in that sample.

   IV. Still assuming that the null hypothesis is true, determine if the result from the sample is a rare event.

   V. If the result from the sample isn't a rare event, you can reasonably attribute the result to chance variation. You have insufficient reason to doubt that the null hypothesis is true and so you **do not reject the null hypothesis**. If the result from the sample is a rare event, this casts doubt on the null hypothesis and you **reject the null hypothesis** and call the result statistically significant.

3. Suppose you wish to set up a *z*-test for each of the following situations. What would the null hypothesis be in each case?

   a. You want to determine if spinning a nickel is fair.

   b. You want to determine if a boy has the same chance to be elected senior class president as a girl in the high schools in the United States.

   c. You want to find out if people under the age of 18 are just as likely to attend action movies as people of other ages. You know that 26% of the population of the United States are under the age of 18.

   d. You suspect that a pair of dice isn't fair so you test it to find the proportion of the time it gives a sum of 7 or a sum of 3.

4. Suppose that 30% of the eligible jurors in a large judicial district are college graduates. You examine a sample of 1,200 jurors in this district and find that only 300 of the 1,200 jurors were college graduates. You want to determine if this number can reasonably be attributed to chance variation or whether you should look for some other explanation. Perform a *z*-test for a proportion, going through the five steps in Activity 2.

5. Suppose you want to determine if flipping a penny is fair. You flip a penny 800 times and get 417 heads. Do you have any evidence that flipping this penny is an unfair process? Answer this question by performing a *z*-test for a proportion.

6. Dr. Dorthe Hansen and her colleagues at the John F. Kennedy Institute in Glostrup, Denmark identified 3,072 women who had suffered a traumatic event, such as a death or serious illness in her immediate family, right around conception. They found that 49% of the 3,072 births were boys, compared with 51.2% of births in the population at large. Is this sufficient evidence to reject the hypothesis that women who suffer a traumatic event around the time of conception have the same proportion of babies that are boys as in the population at large? Answer this question by going through the five steps of a *z*-test. (Source: *Los Angeles Times,* August 30, 1999, page S1.)

7. The diagram below shows the four cases that can result from a jury trial.

| | | Defendant is actually | |
		Innocent	Guilty
Decision of the jury	Innocent		
	Guilty		

   a. Two cases are correct decisions. Which are they?

   b. Which case is considered the worst error in the American judicial system?

   The diagram on the next page shows the four cases that can result from a significance test.

		Null hypothesis is actually	
		True	False
Decision based on the sample	Do not reject null hypothesis	_____	_____
	Reject null hypothesis	_____	_____

c. Two cases are correct decisions. Which are they? Rejecting a null hypothesis that is actually true is called a **Type I error**. Not rejecting a null hypothesis that is actually false is called a **Type II error**. Which two cases are these?

d. What would cause you to reject a null hypothesis that is actually true?

Checkpoint

Significance testing is one of the most common types of statistical reasoning.

a Describe the steps in a z-test for a proportion.

b Why do we assume the null hypothesis is true if we are trying to disprove it?

Be prepared to explain your description and thinking to the entire class.

On Your Own

Suppose you hear a report that 45% of students wear a shirt or jacket that has a logo or other advertisement on it. You believe that this percentage is wrong. You take a random sample of 750 students and find that 359 are wearing a shirt or jacket with a logo or other advertisement on it.

a. Suppose that the original claim is correct. Describe the distribution of the number of students wearing logos or other advertisements from all possible samples of size 750.

b. Can you reasonably attribute the number of students wearing a logo in the sample to chance variation, or do you have evidence that the original claim is false? Answer this question by going through the five steps of a z-test. Could you be making a Type I error, a Type II error, both, or neither?

Modeling

1. According to the 1990 U.S. Census, approximately 10% of the population of the United States were between the ages of 18 and 24 at that time.

   a. Describe the distribution of the number of people this age in all possible random samples of size 1,000 from the population of the United States.

   b. Suppose you do not believe that this is the correct proportion for your city. You take a random sample of 1,000 residents of your city and find that 117 are between the ages of 18 and 24. Do you have evidence to support your belief? Answer this question by going through the five steps of a z-test.

   c. What numbers of people between 18 and 24 would be rare events if your null hypothesis is true?

2. Sixty-eight percent of the children in the United States live with both parents. (Source: "Report Card on State of U.S. Youth Shows Mixed Results." *Los Angeles Times,* July 3, 1997.)

   a. Describe the distribution of the proportion of children who live with both parents in all possible random samples of size 500 from the population of children in the United States.

   b. Suppose you believe that this is not the correct proportion for your city. You take a random sample of 500 children and find that 214 live with both parents. Do you have evidence to support your belief? Answer this question by going through the five steps of a z-test.

   c. What proportions of children living with both parents would be rare events if your null hypothesis is true?

3. Suppose that in a poll of a random sample of 1,200 voters, 73% of the sample said they approved of the job that the President was doing. The night before the poll, the President's Press Secretary had claimed that 75% of the voters approve of the job the President is doing. Should the Press Secretary retract the statement? Answer this question by performing a z-test for a proportion. Could you be making a Type I error, a Type II error, both, or neither?

4. In 1996, 20.7% of babies born in the United States were delivered by cesarean section (surgical delivery). (Source: *Monthly Vital Statistics Report:* vol. 46, no 11, supp. NCHS 1998.) Carla believed that the proportion in 1998 might not be 20.7%. Suppose she randomly selected a sample of 1,200 births in the United States during 1998 and found that 231 of the births were by cesarean section. Does she have evidence to support her belief? Answer this question by going through the five steps of a *z*-test. Could you be making a Type I error, a Type II error, both, or neither?

Organizing

1. What two different approximating normal distributions could you use in a *z*-test where the sample size is 200 trials and the null hypothesis is that the probability of a success on each trial is 0.25?

2. Using the normal approximation, write a symbolic rule for finding the outer 5% of a binomial distribution with sample size *n* and probability of success *p*.

3. In Course 3, Unit 5, "Patterns in Variation," you learned to make control charts for a measurement in an industrial process. The desired mean was in the center of the chart and zones were marked off by drawing horizontal lines at 1, 2, and 3 standard deviations from the mean. Control charts can also be made to track the proportion of defects in a process. Suppose that your company manufactures potato chips, placing 150 in each can. A certain amount of breakage is unavoidable, but your company is committed to holding the overall breakage rate to no more than 8%. Periodically you sample a can of 150 chips and count the number of broken chips.

   a. Make a control chart showing the zones for this process.

   b. Suppose you are using the test that the process is out of control if the proportion of broken chips in a single sample is more than three standard deviations from the mean. How many broken chips in a can would it take before you stopped the process?

4. The normal distribution is a **continuous distribution.** An outcome from a continuous distribution can be any real number between the largest and smallest possible values. The binomial distribution is a **discrete distribution.** The possible outcomes from a discrete distribution can be listed (although the list may be infinitely long). In the case of the binomial distribution, the values must be whole numbers between 0 and *n*. What other contexts have you studied that have continuous distributions? What other situations have you examined that have discrete distributions?

Reflecting

1. Is the normal approximation to the binomial distribution equally good in all situations? If not, in what situations is it better? Explain.

2. Why is "null hypothesis" a good choice of words?

3. After performing a *z*-test, there are two possible conclusions:
   - Reject the null hypothesis.
   - Do not reject the null hypothesis.

   Instead of the latter statement, is it the same thing to say that you "accept the null hypothesis?" Explain your reasoning.

4. Suppose a student asks you this question: "I flipped a coin 100 times and got only 35 heads. That is a rare event for sure with a fair coin. But it *can* happen with a fair coin. So why do I reject the hypothesis that the coin is fair?" How would you answer?

Extending

1. Some calculators will do all of the computations for a *z*-test for you. For example, on a TI-83, to test whether getting 415 heads on 900 spins of a penny can be attributed to chance variation, you can enter the $\boxed{\text{STAT}}$ TESTS menu and select 1-PropZTest. The symbol p_0 stands for the proportion hypothesized in the null hypothesis, so for this problem you would have:

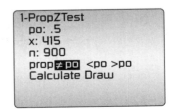

Pressing [ENTER] when **Calculate** is highlighted gives the following screen:

```
1-PropZTest
 prop ≠.5
 z= -2.333333333
 p= .0196306137
 p̂= .4611111111
 n= 900
```

a. Explain what each entry in the final screen means.

b. Someone claims that 8% of people are left-handed. A random sample of 1,500 people finds 158 are left handed. Is this sufficient evidence to reject the claim? Use **1-PropZTest** to solve this problem.

2. The equation for a normal curve is

$$y = \frac{1}{\sigma\sqrt{2\pi}}\, e^{-\frac{1}{2}\left(\frac{x-\mu}{\sigma}\right)^2}$$

where μ is the mean and σ is the standard deviation. Graph the normal curve that approximates the binomial distribution of the number of successes with 100 trials and probability of success 0.4. Explain how you decided on an approximate viewing window. How does your choice of window relate to the binomial distribution?

3. A company buys rubber bands for use inside of a wind-up toy that it manufactures. The rubber bands aren't supposed to break when stretched 6 inches.

However, some always do, so the company tests each shipment that comes in. The company is willing to accept a shipment of rubber bands if 10% or fewer in a sample of 200 break when stretched 6 inches. If more than 10% break, the entire shipment is rejected. (Each shipment consists of tens of thousands of rubber bands.) The procedure the company uses is called **acceptance sampling.**

a. Suppose that a shipment actually contains 15% of rubber bands that will break when stretched 6 inches. What is the probability that the company will reject the shipment?

b. What is the probability the company will reject the shipment if it actually contains 8% rubber bands that break when stretched 6 inches?

1. The cost of a television set was $880.00. During a sale, the price decreased to $704.00. What was the percent of the discount off the original price?

    (a) 20%   (b) 0.2%   (c) 25%   (d) 0.25%   (e) 15%

2. Simplify $\dfrac{12a^2 + 6a}{6a}$.

    (a) $12a^2$ (b) $2a$ (c) $13a$ (d) $2a + 1$ (e) $12a^2 + 1$

3. Find the distance between $P(-3, -5)$ and $Q(5, 2)$.

    (a) $\sqrt{113}$ (b) $\sqrt{13}$ (c) $\sqrt{56}$ (d) 15   (e) $\sqrt{15}$

4. Given the following graph of $y = f(x)$, which of the graphs below could be a portion of the graph of $y = f(x + 5)$?

    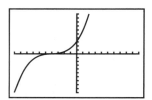

    (a) 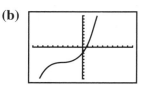   (b)   (c)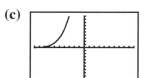

    (d) 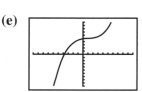   (e)

5. Solve for x: $(x - 5)(x + 2) = -6$.

    (a) $x = 5$ or $x = -2$ (b) $x = -5$ or $x = 2$ (c) $x = 5$ or $x = 2$

    (d) $x = -4$ or $x = 1$ (e) $x = 4$ or $x = -1$

6. If $(x + 2)(x - 7) \leq 0$, then

(a) $x \leq -2$ or $x \geq 7$ (b) $x \leq -7$ or $x \geq 2$ (c) $-2 \leq x \leq 7$

(d) $-7 \leq x \leq 2$ (e) $x \leq -2$ and $x \geq 7$

7. The sketch below shows the graph of a polynomial function $f(x)$ and the graph of $f(x) + b$. If the scale on both axes is 1, find the value of b.

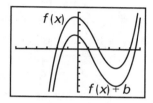

(a) 4   (b) 5   (c) 2   (d) -6 (e) -3

8. Find the height h in $\triangle ABC$.

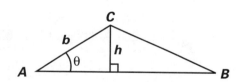

(a) $\frac{\cos \theta}{b}$ (b) $\frac{\sin \theta}{b}$ (c) $\tan \theta$ (d) $b \sin \theta$ (e) $b \cos \theta$

9. If $27^{x + 1} = 9^{2x}$, then $x =$

(a) 1   (b) 3   (c) $\frac{3}{2}$ (d) $\frac{2}{3}$ (e) 2

10. Solve $\sqrt[3]{x} + 5 = -3$.

(a) -2 (b) 8   (c) -512 (d) 512   (e) -8

Lesson 4

Experiments: Proving Cause and Effect

Many medical experiments are designed to determine which of two treatments gives better results. Is aspirin better than acetaminophen for headaches? Does a sprain heal faster if the part receives exercise or if it is rested? Do people have fewer heart attacks if they exercise than if they don't? Although medical experiments are the ones you hear about

the most often, experiments are done in many other fields. For example, which fertilizer causes plants to grow higher? Which detergent makes clothes whitest? Which engine oil makes an engine run longer?

In this lesson, you will learn how to design a good experiment and how to use a significance test to determine whether one treatment is more effective than another.

Think About This Situation

Joseph Lister (1827–1912), surgeon at the Glasgow Royal Infirmary, was one of the first to believe in the theory of Louis Pasteur (1822–1895) that germs cause infection. In an early medical experiment, Lister disinfected the operating room with carbolic acid before 40 operations. He did not disinfect the operating room before another 35 operations. Of the 40 operations in which carbolic acid was used, 34 patients lived. Of the 35 operations in which carbolic acid was not used, 19 patients lived.

a Why did Joseph Lister need to have one group of patients for whom he didn't disinfect the operating room?

b Does the study above provide convincing evidence that disinfecting operating rooms with carbolic acid results in fewer deaths than not disinfecting? Explain your thinking.

c How is the Lister experiment similar to, and different from, experiments you have conducted in your science classes?

INVESTIGATION 1 Characteristics of Experiments

Most experiments are designed to prove cause and effect. Lister wanted to prove that disinfecting operating rooms with carbolic acid results in fewer deaths (presumably through the mechanism of killing bacteria that might infect the person). Only through an experiment like Lister's can you come to such a conclusion.

1. A common science experiment attempts to determine if mung bean seeds that are given a gentle zap in a microwave oven are more likely to sprout than mung bean seeds that aren't given a zap.

Mung beans that were zapped in a microwave oven.

   a. In such an experiment, what is the cause and what is the effect?

   b. For his experiment, Carlos zapped 10 mung bean seeds and 8 sprouted. Explain why Carlos shouldn't conclude that mung beans zapped in a microwave are more likely to sprout than if they hadn't been zapped.

   c. For her experiment, Mia took 20 mung bean seeds, picked out the nicest looking 10 and zapped them. Of the 10 that were zapped, 8 sprouted; of the 10 that were not zapped, 5 sprouted. Explain why Mia shouldn't conclude that mung beans zapped in a microwave are more likely to sprout than if they hadn't been zapped.

   d. For her experiment, Joann took two mung beans, flipped a coin to decide which got zapped, and zapped that one only. The mung bean that got zapped sprouted and the one that didn't get zapped did not sprout. Explain why Joann shouldn't conclude that mung beans zapped in a microwave are more likely to sprout than if they hadn't been zapped.

   e. Design an experiment to determine if mung beans are more likely to sprout if they are zapped in a microwave.

Experiments are one method used to compare two proportions. Surveys and observational studies provide two other methods. The results must be interpreted differently, however, depending on which type of study is used to collect the data.

In a **sample survey**, random samples are taken from two populations and the percentages of successes compared. The purpose of a sample survey, as you saw in Course 3 of *Contemporary Mathematics in Context,* is to generalize from the samples to the populations from which they were drawn.

In a typical **experiment**, one or more **treatments** (conditions you want to compare) are randomly assigned to an available group of people (or objects), called **subjects**. The purpose of an experiment is to establish cause and effect—

does one treatment cause a different effect than the other treatment? A true experiment must have three characteristics:

- **Random assignment** Treatments are assigned randomly to subjects.
- **Replication** Each treatment involves more than one subject.
- **Comparison group or control group** Either the group that gets the treatment is compared to a group that gets no treatment (the control group) or two groups that get different treatments are compared.

In an **observational study,** random selection isn't involved in the data collection. An observational study sometimes can establish that two variables are associated—more of one tends to be associated with more (or less) of the other—but an observational study cannot establish cause and effect. Generalization to a larger population is often difficult for observational studies as well. Both observational studies and experiments should be repeated a number of times on different populations before results become generally accepted.

2. Which characteristic(s) of a true experiment was (were) missing in Activity 1 in the mung bean seed study of:

   a. Carlos?

   b. Mia?

   c. Joann?

3. Describe whether each study below is an experiment, a sample survey, or an observational study. If you need more information in order to tell for sure, describe what information you need.

   a. Lister's carbolic acid study described in the "Think About This Situation" on page 332.

   b. In a study in Berlin of 239 people who had lung cancer, 98 (41%) kept a pet bird. Of 429 similar people who did not have lung cancer, 101 (23.5%) kept a pet bird. (Source: Kohlmeier, L, et al. "Pet birds as an independent risk factor for lung cancer: case-control study," *British Medical Journal,* 305 (1992) pages 986–989. Copyright CRC Press, Boca Raton, Florida. Summarized in D. J. Hand et al., London: *A Handbook of Small Data Sets,* Chapman & Hall, 1994, page 92.)

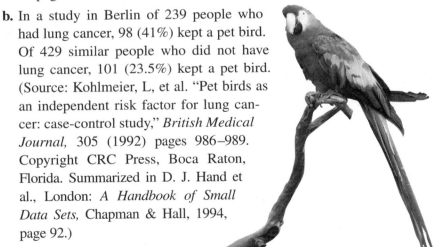

c. In a Gallup Poll conducted March 24–26, 1997, one quarter of men say they go to church every week, while one third of women say this. This poll was based on a randomly selected national sample of 1,009 adults. (Source: "Religious Faith Widespread but Many Skip Church," Gallup Poll Archives: http://www.gallup.com)

In 1954, the largest medical experiment to date was carried out to test whether the newly developed Salk vaccine was effective in preventing polio. Almost 750,000 children participated in the portion of the study described below. This study incorporated all three characteristics of an experiment: use of a control group of children who received a *placebo* injection (an injection that looked—and felt!—like a regular immunization but contained only salt water); random assignment to children of the placebo injection or Salk vaccine injection; and assignment of each treatment to several hundred thousand children. (Source: Paul Meier, "The biggest public health experiment ever" in *Statistics: A Guide to the Unknown,* 3rd ed. (Edited by Judith Tanur, et al.) Pacific Grove, Calif.: Wadsworth and Brooks/Cole Advanced Books and Software, 1989 pages 3–14.)

Jonas Salk, a year after the vaccine trial began.

4. Many difficulties in testing the Salk vaccine had been anticipated. Explain how you think the three characteristics of an experiment—control group, replication on a large number of children, random assignment—helped overcome each difficulty described below.

  a. The incidence of polio was very low, even without immunization.

  b. The vaccine wasn't expected to be 100% effective.

  c. One possible approach would have been to immunize all children in the study and compare the incidence of polio to that of children the same age the previous year. However, the incidence of polio varied widely from year to year.

  d. One possible experimental design would have been to let parents decide whether their child was vaccinated and compare the rates of polio of the vaccinated and unvaccinated children. In the United States, polio was primarily a disease of children from middle and upper income families and so those children's parents were especially anxious to get them vaccinated.

5. In a **subject-blind** experiment, the person receiving the treatment does not know which treatment he or she is getting. In an **evaluator-blind** experiment, the person who decides how well the treatment works doesn't know which treatment the person received. If an experiment is both subject blind and evaluator blind, it is called a **double-blind** experiment.

  a. The Salk experiment was double blind. One reason this was necessary was because the diagnosis of polio isn't clear-cut. Paralytic cases are obvious, but they are the exception. Sometimes polio looks like a bad cold and so professional judgment is needed. How might a doctor's knowledge of whether or not a child had been immunized affect his or her diagnosis? How might this invalidate the experiment?

b. Is it possible that the Lister carbolic acid experiment was subject blind? Evaluator blind? Double blind? Explain.

6. Many studies have shown that people tend to do better when they are given special attention or when they believe they are getting competent medical care. This is called the **placebo effect**. Even people with post-surgical pain report less discomfort if they are given a pill that is actually a placebo (a pill containing no medicine) but which they believe contains a painkiller.

   a. Describe how the design of the Salk experiment controlled for the placebo effect.

   b. Was the placebo effect a consideration in the Lister experiment? Explain.

7. A **lurking variable** helps to explain the association between two other variables, but is not the explanation that the study was designed to test. Treatments are assigned randomly to subjects to eliminate lurking variables as much as possible. Consider each of the following studies.

   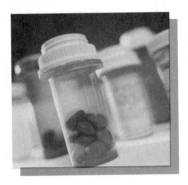

   a. The following statement appeared in the article "Boost Your Brain" in *USA Weekend* on March 3–5, 2000, page 7:

   "Older people taking vitamin supplements, notably B vitamins, had 'higher cognitive performance' than non-supplement takers and 'scored as well as or better than younger adults on verbal memory' according to University of New Mexico researchers."

   The article doesn't say if this conclusion is from an experiment or from an observational study. Assuming this is an observational study, name a lurking variable and describe how it might account for this association. How could you determine if vitamin B supplements do cause higher cognitive performance?

   b. On July 2, 1999, *USA Today* ran a special report, "Death by the gallon," by James R. Healey, that said that 18% of all vehicles on the road are small cars, yet they account for 37% of vehicle deaths in 1997. Defenders of small cars say it's not the size of the car that accounts for these figures, but a lurking variable. What could that variable be? (Source: Copyright 1999, *USA Today*. Reprinted by permission.)

c. The "Women Really Can Do It All" article in the *Family Care Health Monitor* Vol. 4, January/ February 1999, page 2 published in a study in the *Journal of Health and Social Behavior*: "A new study suggests that being Supermom has its perks. A 10-year study of 3,331 women showed that generally their health benefited when juggling a career and family responsibilities, compared with their less-busy counterparts. Women fill their days with house work, office work, and they often care for young children and/or aging parents. There was some concern that all this activity would wreak havoc on their health. But according to the new findings, this doesn't seem to be the case. ... The health benefits from employment and marriage were thought to come from the extra income and social support." What lurking variable(s) does the journal say may be responsible for the association between working mothers and good health? What is another possible explanation?

Checkpoint

In this investigation, you examined characteristics of a well-designed experiment.

a Explain why all three characteristics of an experiment are necessary.

b Why are subject blinding and evaluator blinding desirable in an experiment?

c How does random assignment help reduce the effect of lurking variables?

Be prepared to share your explanations with the entire class.

On Your Own

To find out if students do better on exams where the easier problems come first, a teacher wrote two versions of an exam, one with the more difficult problems first and a second containing the same problems only with the easier ones first. She gave the first version to her first period class and the second version to her second period class. She will compare the

percentage of students who pass with the first version to the percentage of students who pass with the second version.

a. Is this study an experiment, a survey, or an observational study? Is this study subject blind? Is it evaluator blind? Name at least one lurking variable for this study.

b. Describe how the teacher could improve the design of her study.

INVESTIGATION 2 Do Two Treatments Give Different Results?

Unlike a sample survey, in an experiment you usually don't have random samples from some larger population. Typically, the subjects used are those who happen to be available and give informed consent. The randomness comes from assigning the treatments to your subjects. By randomizing, you trust that any initial differences among the subjects, such as severity of illness, get spread out evenly between the two treatments. Consequently, you feel justified in concluding that any difference in results between the two groups is due to the effect of the treatments.

The null hypothesis for a test of the difference of two proportions in an experiment should be of the following form:

Any difference between the two groups at the end of the experiment is due to chance variation, not to any effect from the treatments.

1. In this activity, you will investigate the kind of results that Lister could have expected if carbolic acid had no effect at all in preventing deaths. Although it is not known whether Joseph Lister randomly assigned the carbolic acid treatment or the non-carbolic acid treatment to his patients, assume for the purposes of the following activities that he did.

   a. Suppose that the null hypothesis is true: carbolic acid had no effect at all. How many of the 75 people operated on would have lived if Lister had used carbolic acid in every operation? If he hadn't used it in any of the 75 operations?

b. Simulate this situation using 53 red beads (or counters) to represent the 53 people who lived and 22 blue beads (or counters) to represent the 22 people who died. Place them all in a bag and mix them well. Draw 40 beads out at random to represent the people who had operations where carbolic acid was used. Let $\hat{p}_c$ be the proportion of people in this sample who lived. The 35 beads remaining in the bag represent the people who had operations where carbolic acid was not used. Let $\hat{p}_n$ be the proportion of people in this sample who lived. Compute $\hat{p}_c - \hat{p}_n$.

c. By dividing the work up among groups, repeat the procedure in Part b until your class has 20 values of $\hat{p}_c - \hat{p}_n$. Add your 20 values of $\hat{p}_c - \hat{p}_n$ to a copy of the distribution below. This distribution already displays 180 values of $\hat{p}_c - \hat{p}_n$.

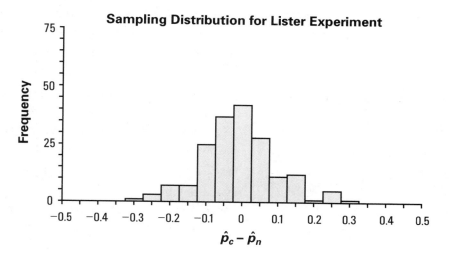

d. Compute $\hat{p}_c - \hat{p}_n$ for the actual results from Lister's experiment.

e. If carbolic acid made no difference, would Lister's actual result be reasonably likely to happen or would it be a rare event? What can you conclude?

f. Could you be making a Type I error, a Type II error, both, or neither? Explain.

The significance test you performed in Activity 1 is called a **randomization test**. It is due to R.A. Fisher (1890–1962), perhaps the greatest statistician of all time. Although the randomization test is conceptually straightforward, constructing the distribution of $\hat{p}_c - \hat{p}_n$ requires quite a bit of work.

2. In this activity, you will learn how to find a theoretical approximation to the distribution of $\hat{p}_c - \hat{p}_n$ for Lister's experiment. Examine the sampling distribution prepared by the class in Activity 1, Part c.

   a. What is the shape of the distribution?

   b. Approximately, what is its mean? Theoretically, what should the mean be? Why?

   c. The standard deviation of this distribution can be approximated by the following formula:

   $$\sqrt{p(1-p)\left(\frac{1}{n_1} + \frac{1}{n_2}\right)}$$

   In this formula, p stands for the proportion of all people in the experiment who lived and n_1 and n_2 are the numbers of people in the two treatment groups (carbolic acid and no carbolic acid). Use this formula to approximate the standard deviation of the sampling distribution.

   d. Using your results in Parts a, b, and c, identify the values of $\hat{p}_c - \hat{p}_n$ that would be rare events if carbolic acid had no effect.

   e. Can the difference between the percentage of patients who survived when the operating room was disinfected and the percentage of patients who survived when it wasn't reasonably be attributed to chance variation, or should you look for some other explanation? Explain your reasoning.

3. One thing you can't assume about Lister's experiment is that his patients were anything like a random sample from all possible people who needed operations. The only randomization was in assigning treatments to patients. In light of this, which of the following is the best conclusion to draw from Lister's experiment?

   ■ If Lister were to disinfect the operating rooms of all patients, the death rate would be lower than if he didn't disinfect the operating room.

   ■ The most reasonable explanation for the difference between the death rates of Lister's two groups of patients is whether carbolic acid was used or not.

The procedure you used in Activity 2 is called a *z-test for the difference of two proportions*. The procedure is outlined in the chart on the next page.

z-Test for the Difference of Two Proportions

To conduct a z-test for the difference of two proportions:

1. Write a *null hypothesis* that states that any difference found in the experiment is due to the fact that in the random assignment of treatments to subjects, one treatment group happened to get more subjects who would do better anyway and not to the fact that one treatment is any better than the other.

2. Perform the experiment and find the proportion of successes in each treatment group. Find the difference between these proportions, $\hat{p}_1 - \hat{p}_2$. If the null hypothesis is true, the distribution of all possible values of $\hat{p}_1 - \hat{p}_2$ has the following characteristics:

   - a shape that is approximately normal;
   - mean 0;
   - standard deviation

   $$\sqrt{p(1-p)\left(\frac{1}{n_1} + \frac{1}{n_2}\right)},$$

   where p is the total number of successes in both treatments divided by the total number of subjects in both treatments, n_1 is the number of subjects given the first treatment, and n_2 is the number of subjects given the second treatment.

   This distribution shows the variation that you would expect just by chance if the null hypothesis is true.

3. Still assuming that the null hypothesis is true, determine if the actual difference $\hat{p}_1 - \hat{p}_2$ between the two treatments is reasonably likely to occur or is a rare event. You can do this by computing the z-score for $\hat{p}_1 - \hat{p}_2$.

4. If the difference between the two samples $\hat{p}_1 - \hat{p}_2$ is reasonably likely to occur under the condition that the null hypothesis is true, you can attribute the difference from the experiment to chance variation and have no reason to doubt that the null hypothesis is true. You *do not reject the null hypothesis*. If a difference as large as that from the experiment is a rare event under the condition that the null hypothesis is true, this casts doubt on the null hypothesis. You *reject the null hypothesis*.

You can only use this z-test if the number of successes and the number of failures in each treatment group is 5 or more. This restriction guarantees that the distribution of all possible values of $\hat{p}_1 - \hat{p}_2$ is approximately normal.

4. Fish oil contains omega-3 fatty acids, which are thought to have various health benefits. In a study at Harvard University, 15 patients with manic depression were given 14 capsules of fish oil per day and 20 patients with manic depression received a placebo of 14 capsules of olive oil. After four months, 2 of the 15 patients taking fish oil had a relapse, while 11 of the 20 taking olive oil had a relapse. Treatments were randomly assigned to patients. (Source: *The Los Angeles Times,* May 3, 1999, page S3.)

a. What is the null hypothesis for this study?

b. Can you use a z-test for the difference of two proportions to determine if the results of this study are statistically significant? Explain your reasoning.

c. Describe how to conduct a randomization test to test your null hypothesis.

d. Conduct one trial of a randomization test and add it to the 499 results below, which show the proportion who got fish oil who relapse minus the proportion who got olive oil who relapse. What is your conclusion?

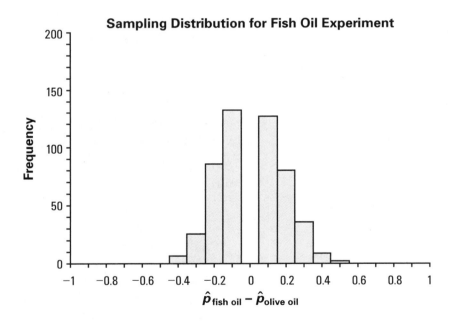

e. Explain why there is no bar above 0.

5. Suppose you find that of 250 people who eat blueberries, 156 have stained teeth. Of 250 people who don't eat blueberries, 130 have stained teeth. Determine if the difference between the two percentages is statistically significant; that is, can the difference in the percentages with stained teeth reasonably be attributed to chance or should you look for some other explanation?

6. Each of the descriptions below suggests how the data in Activity 5 might have been obtained. Decide whether a sample survey, an experiment, or an observational study is described. Then write the conclusion that can be drawn from each study.

   a. A list of people who eat blueberries and a list of people who don't eat blueberries were somehow obtained and 250 were randomly selected from each group. Then their teeth were examined by dentists and classified as "stained" or "not stained."

   b. A group of 500 people who agreed to participate in the experiment were randomly divided into two groups—those who would eat blueberries and those who would not. After two months, their teeth were examined by dentists and classified as "stained" or "not stained."

   c. A dentist keeps track of her patients, asking each if they eat blueberries or not, and classifies their teeth as "stained" or "not stained." She asks until she gets 250 who eat blueberries and 250 who don't.

Checkpoint

In this investigation, you examined two methods—randomization test and z-test—for determining whether the difference in the proportions from an experiment is statistically significant.

a Explain how to use a randomization test to determine if the difference is statistically significant.

b Explain how to use a z-test to determine if the difference is statistically significant.

c What does it mean if the results of an experiment are called "statistically significant"?

Be prepared to share your explanations with the entire class.

On Your Own

In the Salk experiment, 82 of the 200,745 children who received the Salk vaccine were diagnosed with polio. Of the 201,229 children who received the placebo, 162 were diagnosed with polio.

a. Perform a *z*-test for the difference of two proportions to determine if the difference is statistically significant.

b. Could you be making a Type I error, a Type II error, both, or neither? Explain.

MORE

Modeling • Organizing • Reflecting • Extending

Modeling

1. In an experiment to determine if it is better to cut plum root cuttings so that they are long or short, the following results were obtained for cuttings that were to be planted at once. (Source: M. S. Bartlett, "Contingency table interactions," *Journal of the Royal Statistical Society Supplement,* Vol. 2, 1935, pages 248–252. Copyright CRC Press, Boca Raton, FL. Summarized in D. J. Hand et al., *A Handbook of Small Data Sets.* London: Chapman & Hall, 1994, page 15.)

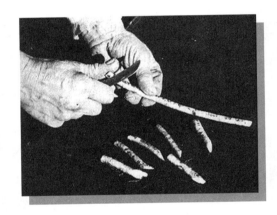

Length	Cutting Died	Cutting Survived	Total
Long	84	156	240
Short	133	107	240
Total	217	263	480

a. This study was a true experiment. Describe how it might have been designed.

b. Describe how to use a randomization test to determine if the difference in the proportions of cuttings that survived is statistically significant.

c. Use a z-test to determine if the difference in the proportions of cuttings that survived is statistically significant. Write a conclusion that can be drawn from this experiment.

d. It's silly to think about making this experiment subject blind. Could it have been evaluator blind? Explain.

2. The following table gives the results from a study where a researcher dropped a handful of pencils in an elevator, making it appear to be an accident. After many trials, the researcher compared the proportions of males and females in the elevator who helped pick up the pencils. (Source: Jessica M. Utts, *Seeing through Statistics,* 2nd Ed., Pacific Grove, CA.: Duxbury Press, 1999, pp. 222–223. Original source: B. Latane and J.M. Dabbs, Jr., "Sex, group size, and helping in three cities." *Sociometry* 38 (1975), pp. 180–184.)

	Helped	Didn't Help	Total
Men	370	950	1,320
Women	300	1,003	1,303
Total	670	1,953	2,623

a. Does this appear to be a sample survey, an experiment, or an observational study? Explain your reasoning.

b. Can the difference between the percentage of men and the percentage of women who helped pick up the pencils reasonably be attributed to chance variation?

c. Name a lurking variable that might help explain the conclusion that men are more helpful than women.

d. Write a conclusion about what can be learned from this study.

3. The number of children in the Salk experiment may seem excessive, but it was necessary. In the 1950s, before the Salk vaccine, the rate of polio in the U.S. was about 50 per 100,000 children. Suppose the experiment had "only" 40,000 children in the placebo injection group and 40,000 children in the Salk vaccine group. Also, suppose the vaccine is 50% effective; that is, it eliminates half of the cases of polio.

a. How many children in the placebo group would you expect to get polio? How many children in the Salk vaccine group would you expect to get polio?

b. Perform a z-test using the numbers in Part a to see if the researchers would have had sufficient evidence to reject the hypothesis that the Salk vaccine and the placebo are equally effective.

c. Is the null hypothesis actually true or false? Did you make a Type I error, a Type II error, both, or neither?

Now suppose that there were 100,000 children in each group.

d. How many children in the placebo group would you expect to get polio? How many children in the Salk vaccine group would you expect to get polio?

e. Perform a z-test using the numbers in Part d to see if the researchers would have had sufficient evidence to reject the hypothesis that the Salk vaccine and the placebo are equally effective.

f. Is the null hypothesis actually true or false? In this case, did you make a Type I error, a Type II error, both, or neither?

g. Apparently sample size matters in significance testing. Why should this be the case?

4. Data such as the following appear in the information sheets for prescription medications. The term **clinical trial** means a medical experiment in a real-life situation.

Adverse Experiences Reported in Placebo-Controlled Clinical Trials

Adverse Experience	Prescription Medication ($n = 679$)	Placebo ($n = 671$)
Headache	2.5%	1.5%
Nausea	1.6%	1.5%
Dizziness	1.5%	0.3%
Drowsiness	1.3%	0.9%
Indigestion	1.3%	0.6%

a. Which of the "adverse experiences" meet the criteria for performing a z-test of the difference of two proportions?

b. Can the difference in the percentage of patients who got a headache be reasonably attributed to chance variation, or should the difference be attributed to the different treatments?

Organizing

1. Examine the formula for the standard deviation of the distribution of $\hat{p}_1 - \hat{p}_2$:

$$\sqrt{p(1-p)\left(\frac{1}{n_1} + \frac{1}{n_2}\right)}$$

a. What happens to the standard deviation when p remains the same but the number of subjects in each treatment is quadrupled? Prove your answer algebraically.

b. What happens to the standard deviation when the number of subjects remains the same, but p moves away from 0.5? Prove your answer algebraically.

2. If the two samples are the same size, n, simplify the formula for the standard deviation of the distribution of $\hat{p}_1 - \hat{p}_2$:

$$\sqrt{p(1-p)\left(\tfrac{1}{n_1} + \tfrac{1}{n_2}\right)}$$

3. Suppose a null hypothesis is false. Are you more likely to reject it with small sample sizes or large sample sizes? Use algebraic reasoning to explain your answer.

4. Recall that the variance is the square of the standard deviation.

a. Suppose you take a sample of size n_1 from a population with proportion p of successes and find the proportion $\hat{p}_1$ of successes in the sample. What is the variance of the distribution of all possible values of $\hat{p}_1$?

b. Suppose you take a sample of size n_2 from a population with proportion of successes p and find the proportion of successes in the sample $\hat{p}_2$. What is the variance of the distribution of all possible values of $\hat{p}_2$?

c. Recall from your previous work that variances add when the two variables X and Y are independent. That is, the variance of the distribution of $X + Y$ is variance of X plus variance of Y. This fact is also true for the variance of $X - Y$. That is, the variance of the distribution of $X - Y$ is variance of X plus the variance of Y. Use this fact and your results from Parts a and b to show that the standard deviation of the distribution of $\hat{p}_1 - \hat{p}_2$ is

$$\sqrt{p(1-p)\left(\tfrac{1}{n_1} + \tfrac{1}{n_2}\right)}$$

Reflecting

1. Suppose that the manufacturer of a cold medicine conducts a randomized, double-blind placebo study and concludes that taking the medicine results in a 38% reduction in the duration of cold symptoms.

a. Describe exactly how this experiment could have been conducted.

b. If you had all the results of the study, could you use the techniques you have learned to determine if the results could reasonably be attributed to chance or whether the cold medicine actually works? Why or why not?

2. An experiment and a sample survey both require randomization.

a. Describe the randomization required in each type of study.

b. What conclusions can be drawn as a result?

3. Experiments with crash test dummies have shown that airbags reduce serious injuries in the event of an automobile crash.

   a. Why haven't experiments been performed on humans?

   b. Describe what such an experiment with humans would involve.

4. Suppose there is a statistically significant difference between the proportion of successes in one group and the proportion of successes in another group. Which of the following is the conclusion that can be drawn if this study was a sample survey? An experiment? An observational study?

   a. There appears to be a difference between the two groups studied that cannot reasonably be attributed to the random assignment of treatments to subjects, and the experimenters can attribute that difference to the different ways the two groups were treated after the assignment.

   b. There appears to be a difference between the two groups studied that cannot reasonably be attributed to chance, but the experimenters cannot determine the cause for sure.

   c. If the experimenters were to examine all possible subjects in the two populations from which the groups were taken, the proportion of successes in those two populations would be different.

Extending

1. A second part of the Salk study used the following design: In the schools in the study, all second graders were vaccinated if their parents gave permission. The rate of polio for these vaccinated children could then be compared to the rate for the second grade children who were not vaccinated because their parents did not give permission.

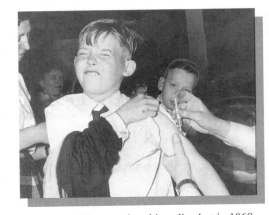

A ten-year-old boy receives his polio shot in 1960.

   a. In this portion of the study, 221,998 second graders were vaccinated. Of these, 76 were diagnosed with polio. There were 123,605 second graders not vaccinated and 66 of them were diagnosed with polio. Test the null hypothesis that the vaccine is not effective.

b. It appears from Part a that the vaccine didn't work all that well. However, the unvaccinated children in the second grade should not have been used as the control group. Explain why not and how it affected the results.

c. The Salk study did not, in fact, use the unvaccinated children in second grade as the control group. All first- and third-grade children in the schools in the study were left unvaccinated and these children served as the controls. Was it possible for this part of the Salk study to be subject blind? Evaluator blind?

d. In the schools where the parents of second grade children decided whether they would be vaccinated or not, there were 66 cases of polio among the 123,605 second grade children whose parents did not give permission for them to receive the Salk vaccine. In the schools where children were selected at random to be vaccinated or not from among those children whose parents gave permission for them to be in the experiment, there were 162 cases of polio among the 210,229 children who received the placebo. Is this a statistically significant difference? How do you explain this result?

2. In this task, you will learn how to conduct Fisher's *exact test*, which is based on the same idea as the randomization test, but doesn't use simulation. In a psychology experiment, a group of 17 people were told that they would be subjected to some painful electric shocks and a group of 13 people were told they would be subjected to some painless electric shocks. (Source: A. Schachter. *The Psychology of Affiliation*, Stanford, CA: Stanford University Press, 1959, pages 44–45.) The subjects were given the choice of waiting with others or alone. (In fact, no one received any shocks.) Here are the results:

Type of Shock	Wait Together	Don't Care or Wait Alone	Total
Painful	12	5	17
Painless	4	9	13

a. Explain why you shouldn't use the *z*-test in this situation.

b. Describe how to use a randomization test to see if the difference in the proportions who choose to wait together is statistically significant.

c. Suppose that what people were told, in fact, had no effect on whether they preferred to wait together or alone. Using techniques you learned in Unit 4, "Counting Models," compute the probability that if 16 people out of the 30 in the study chose to wait together that exactly 4 of them would, just by chance, be among the 13 who were told they would get painless shocks.

d. Continue to suppose that what people were told made no difference in their decision. Find the probability that, if 16 people out of the 30 in the study chose to wait together just by chance, 4 or fewer of them would be among the 13 who were told they would get painless shocks.

e. What can you conclude about whether the difference in the proportions who choose to wait together is statistically significant?

3. In a psychology experiment, 23 first grade children were shown 40 black-and-white slides of various pictures. They were told to look carefully as they would be asked about them. Later the same day, the children were shown 40 pairs of slides side by side. One of each pair was one of the 40 slides the children had seen earlier in the day. The children were asked to specify which it was. (Source: Doris R. Entwisle and W. H. Huggins, "Children's recall of pictorial information." *Statistics: A Guide to the Unknown,* 3rd ed. (Edited by Judith Tanur et al.) Pacific Grove, CA: Duxbury Press, 1989, pages 126–131.)

a. If a child was just guessing, how many slides would it be reasonably likely for him or her to identify correctly just by chance?

The point of the experiment was to see if children remembered black-and-white or color slides better. Thus, the experiment was repeated with a different class of 30 first graders, only this time the slides were in color. The results are shown below. A child who identified 26 slides or more correctly was said to be scoring above chance level and a child who identified 14 slides or fewer was said to be scoring below chance level.

Slide Type	Number of Children Scoring Above Chance Level	Number Scoring Below Chance Level	Total Number of Children
Black/white	21	2	23
Color	29	1	30

b. Suppose whether the slides were colored or not made no difference. Compute the probability that if 3 children out of the 53 in the study scored below chance level that, just by chance, exactly 1 of them would be in the color slide group.

c. Continue to suppose that the type of slide made no difference. Compute the probability that if 3 children out of the 53 in the study scored below chance level that, just by chance, 1 or fewer of them would be in the color slide group.

d. What can you conclude about whether the difference in the proportions who scored below chance level is statistically significant?

e. Technically, it is not appropriate to use either the randomization test or Fisher's exact test with these data. Why not?

4. Some children have asthma that is induced by exercise. A study of 71 children with a prior history of mild, moderate, or severe asthma found that after exercise, 32 children had an immediate 15% or more fall in FEV1 (a measure of lung capacity). Nine of these 32 children still had a fall several hours later. The other 23 of these 32 children had an immediate response only, with no significant changes in FEV1 within an 8-hour follow-up. (Source: F. Sano, D. Sole, and C. K. Naspitz, "Prevalence and characteristics of exercise-induced asthma in children," *Pediatric Allergy Immunology,* November 1998, pages 181–185.)

a. Is this a survey, an observational study, or an experiment? Explain your choice.

b. Is it appropriate to use the techniques of this lesson to provide evidence that there is a difference between the proportion who had an immediate fall in FEV1 only and the proportion who had a fall that lasted longer?

5. Some calculators will perform the *z*-test for the difference between two proportions. Determine whether your calculator will do such a test. If so, use it to perform a *z*-test to determine if the difference in the proportion of plants grown with Fastgro fertilizer that live two or more seasons and the proportion of plants grown with Longlife fertilizer that live two or more seasons is statistically significant. Use the data from the following table.

Number of Seasons	Fastgro	Longlife
Less Than 2	72	67
2 or More	178	183

1. Last week, Pat drove an average of 32.2 miles per day. How many miles total did Pat drive last week?

    (a) 4.6   (b) 46   (c) 225.4   (d) 2,254   (e) 460

2. $\dfrac{2}{x} - \dfrac{1}{3y} =$

    (a) $\dfrac{2y-x}{3xy}$ (b) $\dfrac{1}{x-3y}$ (c) $\dfrac{2y-x}{xy}$ (d) 1   (e) $\dfrac{6y-x}{3xy}$

3. Solve $ax - a = x + b$ for x.

    (a) $\dfrac{2a+b}{1}$ (b) $\dfrac{a+b+1}{a}$ (c) $\dfrac{a+b}{a-1}$ (d) $\dfrac{b-a}{a-1}$ (e) $\dfrac{a+b}{a+1}$

4. Which of the following equations is not an equation of a function?

    (a) $y^2 + x^2 = 4$ (b) $x^2 + y = 4$ (c) $x + y = 4$

    (d) $\dfrac{x}{y} = 4$ (e) $xy = 4$

5. The smaller solution of $x(x + 4) = 21$ is

    (a) -4 (b) -7 (c) -3 (d) 7   (e) 0

6. $|4 - x| < 3$ is equivalent to

   (a) $-1 < x < 1$ **(b)** $-7 < x < -1$ **(c)** $1 < x < 7$

   (d) $-7 < x < 7$ **(e)** $x < 7$

7. Which of the following is not a zero of the polynomial
   $y = (x^2 + 1)(x^2 - 9)(x^2 + 5x - 6)$?

   (a) 1 **(b)** -1 **(c)** 3 **(d)** -3 **(e)** -6

8. The minimum value attained by $y = 3 \sin(2x - 1)$ is

   (a) -1 **(b)** $\dfrac{1}{2}$ **(c)** -3 **(d)** -2 **(e)** -4

9. If $\log_3 x = 5$, then $x =$

   (a) 243 **(b)** 15 **(c)** 125 **(d)** $\dfrac{5}{3}$ **(e)** 1.5

10. $\sqrt[3]{x}\,\sqrt[4]{x} =$

   (a) $\sqrt[7]{x}$ **(b)** $\sqrt[12]{x}$ **(c)** $x\sqrt[7]{x^5}$ **(d)** $\sqrt[12]{x^7}$ **(e)** $\sqrt[7]{x^{12}}$

Looking Back

Binomial situations come up often in surveys and experiments. In this unit, you have developed and studied statistical methods for making sense of binomial situations, including: identifying binomial situations, using the binomial probability formula and technology to construct binomial distributions and compute binomial probabilities, sketching the graph of a binomial distribution, computing the mean and standard deviation of a binomial distribution, using the normal approximation to estimate binomial probabilities, and performing a significance test for a proportion. In the last lesson, you learned the characteristics of a well-designed experiment and how to perform a significance test to see if the difference between two treatments can reasonably be attributed to chance. The tasks in this final lesson will help you review and synthesize these important ideas.

1. Suppose that 6.5% of working people in Houston, Texas regularly take public transportation to work. Suppose that you randomly survey 80 working adults in Houston and ask if they take public transportation to work.

   a. Explain why this can be treated as a binomial situation.

   b. Determine the probability that 10 of the people that you survey take public transportation to work.

      ■ Use the binomial probability formula.

      ■ Use a binomial probability function on your calculator.

   c. Determine the probability that no more than 2 of the people you survey take public transportation to work.

      ■ Use the binomial probability formula.

      ■ Use a binomial probability function on your calculator.

   d. Would it be a rare event to have only one of the people that you survey take public transportation to work? Explain your reasoning.

2. About two-thirds of college freshmen in the United States say they plan to get an advanced degree. (Source: Higher Education Research Institute, Annual Freshman Survey, UCLA, 1997.) Suppose you have a random sample of 200 college freshmen and count the number who say they plan to get an advanced degree. The graph of the distribution of all such samples is shown below.

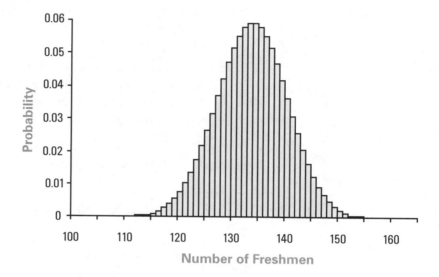

a. What is the expected number of freshmen who plan to earn advanced degrees? The standard deviation of the number of freshmen who plan to earn advanced degrees?

b. On a copy of the above graph, change the scale on the *x*-axis so that it gives the proportion of students in the sample who

plan to earn advanced degrees. What is the mean of the proportion of freshmen who plan to earn advanced degrees? The standard deviation?

c. How does the mean of the number of students who plan to get advanced degrees change as the sample size increases? How does the standard deviation change?

d. How does the mean of the distribution of the sample proportion change as the sample size increases? How does the standard deviation change?

3. Suppose that a company makes candies with a colored coating. Some of the candies have chocolate inside, while others have caramel. Suppose that 30% of the chocolate candies have a brown coating.

   a. If you take a random sample of 185 chocolate-filled candies, what is the probability of getting 40 or fewer that are brown?

   b. To test the hypothesis that 30% of the caramel candies also are brown, the students in a class counted the number of brown candies in a large bag of caramel candies. Out of 185 caramel candies, 40 were brown. What should the students conclude?

4. Examine the following article which appeared in the *Los Angeles Times* on February 15, 1999 (Section S, page 3).

Rest Not Necessarily Best for Sciatica

Bed rest is the most commonly prescribed treatment for sciatica, which is characterized by shooting pains down the leg caused by a compressed nerve in the spine. A new study in Thursday's New England Journal of Medicine, however, suggests bed rest is not particularly effective.

Dutch researchers sent half of 183 sciatica sufferers to bed for two weeks and gave the other half painkillers and encouraged them to get on with their lives. They found that, after two weeks, 70% of those in the bed rest group felt better, compared with 65% in the group not sent to bed. After 12 weeks, 87% of patients in both groups reported improvement.

---

   a. Does this reported study appear to be a survey, an experiment, or an observational study? What additional information would you have to know in order to decide for sure?

   b. Could this study have been double blind? Explain.

   c. Perform a z-test to determine if the difference between the percentage of those patients with bed rest who felt better after two weeks and the percentage of those patients without bed rest who felt better after two weeks can reasonably be attributed to chance variation.

   d. The information given in the article suggests a possible lurking variable in this study of bed rest versus no bed rest. What is it?

Many situations for which probabilistic questions are asked are binomial situations.

ⓐ What are the characteristics of a binomial situation?

ⓑ Describe the reasoning behind the binomial probability formula.

ⓒ Describe how to determine the shape, mean, and standard deviation for the binomial distribution of the number of successes; of the proportion of successes.

ⓓ Describe how to compute the probability of getting x or fewer successes in a binomial situation with n trials and probability of success p using:

- the binomial probability formula;
- a binomial probability function on your calculator; and
- the normal approximation.

ⓔ What is a null hypothesis? What does it mean if you "reject the null hypothesis"?

ⓕ What is the difference between a survey, an experiment, and an observational study? What inferences can be drawn from each?

ⓖ Describe how to conduct a randomization test of the hypothesis such that the difference in the proportion of "successes" between two treatments in an experiment can reasonably be attributed to chance variation.

Be prepared to share your descriptions and thinking with the entire class.

On Your Own

Write, in outline form, a summary of the important mathematical concepts and methods developed in this unit. Organize your summary so that it can be used as a quick reference in future units and courses.

Index of Mathematical Topics

A

Acceleration, 5, 6, 17, 18
Acceptance sampling, 329
Accumulated change, estimating from a graph, 53–54
Accumulation at variable rates, 52–73
Addition of vectors, 88, 102
Algebraic reasoning, using to deduce derivative rules, 47
Angular velocity, 123
Arcs, 119–122
Area
  surface, 181
  using to evaluate definite integrals, 61–62
Arrows, 82
Average rate of change, 8
  $f(x)$ rule, 27

B

Bernoulli, Jacob, 267
Bernoulli inequality, 267
Binomial distributions
  approximately normal, 305
  characteristics of, 300–317
  constructing using simulation, 277–282
  graphs of, 301–307
  mean, formula, 307–310
  mean of, as sample size increases, 303, 306
  normal approximation, 322
  shape of, as sample size increases, 303
  standard deviation, formula for, 307–310, 346
  standard deviation of, as sample size increases, 303, 306
Binomial expansions, 293
  and combinations, 247
  and Pascal's Triangle, 246
Binomial expressions, 245
Binomial population code, 295
Binomial probabilities
  counting methods to compute, 282
  using normal distribution to approximate, 319–322
Binomial probability
  formula, 282–289, 319
  functions on calculator, 288
  mean formula, 307–310

standard deviation formula, 307–310
Binomial situations, 276–299
  chance variation, 318–331
  compared to waiting-time situations, 281
  comparing probabilities for, 319
Binomial Theorem, 245–249, 248
Box plot charts, 304

C

Cause and effect, proving, 332–353
Chance variation, 318–331
Change, rate of
  average, 8
  average versus instantaneous, 11
  estimating at a point, 3–11
  estimating at a point and finding the slope of a linear function, 29–31
  estimating from a table, 4, 11
  for familiar functions, 22–51
  instantaneous, 2–21
  of linear functions, 23–24
Chu Shih-Chieh, 246
Circles, 119–122
  area of a, 151
Circular motion, 119–122, 123
Combinations, 222–231, 245–249
  $C(n, k)$, 229, 255
  and coefficients of binomial expansions, 247
  counting formulas for, 228
  features on a calculator, 229
  notation for, 234
  and Pascal's Triangle, 247
  and permutations, 229
  properties of, 248
Combinatorics, 217, 235
Commutative property of vector addition, 88, 102
Comparison group, 333
Component analysis, 92, 93
Components of a vector, 90
Composition of functions, 153, 154
  $g(f(x))$, 153
  noncommutativity of, 154

Computer graphing software, 109, 124
Conditional probability, 252
Constant of proportionality, 206
Continuous distribution, 327
Control charts, 327
Control group, 333
Coordinates and vectors, 94–98, 102, 103
Correlation coefficient
  interpreting, 192
  r, 205, 206
Cosine, 89
  Law of, 92
Counterexample, 259
Counting
  argument, 217
  in mathematics, 240–257
  methods of, 216–239, 282
  Multiplication Principle of, 219, 242
  using organized lists, 218
  using tree diagrams, 218
  when repetitions are allowed, 237
Curve, normal
  equation for, 329

D

Data
  linearizing, 180–209
  transforming, 183
Deceleration, 5
Decibels, 169
Decibel scale, 169
Definite integrals, 60–64
  of $f(x)$ from a to b, 61
  using area to estimate, 61–62
  using a calculator or computer routine to evaluate, 62
  using rectangles to estimate, 60–61
Degrees, 121
Derivative
  decreasing, 38
  estimating by the slope of the graph, 39
  estimation rule, 34
  exponential function, 36
  function f', 33
  functions, 32–35
  graph, 37–40
  increasing, 38
  linear function, 34
  notation, 47
  periodic function, 36

positive, 38
power function, 36
quadratic function, 34
rules, 47
sums of functions, 49
using a function rule to estimate at a point, 33
zero, 38
Difference, 168
Difference function, 34
Differentiation, 46, 69
Directed line segments, 83
Direction (heading), 83, 95, 104
Discrete distribution, 327
Distributive property of scalar multiplication over vector addition, 88, 102
Dot product, 105
Double-blind experiment, 335
dy/dx, 47

E

Edge coloring, 253
Elliptical orbits, 125, 133
Elliptical paths
  parametric equations for, 125, 133
Empty set, 230
Erdos, Paul, 240
Errors, 186
Evaluator-blind experiment, 335
Experiments, characteristics of, 333–338
Exponential equations, using logarithms to solve, 166
Exponential functions, 25
  derivative of, 36
  estimating instantaneous rates of change of, 25
  fitting, 186–189
  inverses for, 159–164
  linearizing, 182
  using log transformations, 186–189
Exponential regression equations and technology, 187
Exponential rules, 25
Exponents, properties of, 164

F

Factorial, 226
Fisher, R.A., 339
Fisher's exact test, 349
Fractals, 151
Fractal tree, 151–152

Frequency distributions
  histogram of, 278
  for the number of successes compared to proportion of successes, 281
Frequency table, 277
  using to estimate probability, 278
Function(s)
  composition, 145, 153, 154
  difference, 34
  estimating the derivative of a, at a point, 175
  exponential, 25, 36, 159, 182, 186–189
  finding equation of inverse of a, 148
  interpreting the derivative of a, 45
  inverse cosine, 155
  inverses, 142–157
  inverse sine, 155
  linear, 23–24, 34
  logarithmic, 158–179
  one-to-one, 144
  periodic, 36
  piecewise-defined, 155
  power, 36, 149
  quadratic, 24–25
  straightening, 181–185
  square root, 183
  sums of, 49
  undifferentiable, 46
$f(x)$, 27
  properties of $f'(x)$ and the graph of, 43
$f(x)$ rule, 27
  average rate of change, 27
  instantaneous rate of change, 27
  overall pattern of change, 27
  using to approximate slope of the graph at a particular point, 43
  using to approximate slope of the graph between two points, 43
$f'(x)$, 32, 47
  algebraic rule for, 33
  graph of $f(x)$ and properties of, 43

G

Geometric series, 266, 274
Geometric transformations, inverses of, 154
General Multiplication Rule, 242
Graph
  binomial distributions, 301–317
  complete, 253, 261
  of a curve, 32
  cycle, 253
  derivative, 37–40
  distance, 31
  estimating rate of change, 11
  function inverse, 147–150
  rate of change, 59

Graphing calculator, 30–31, 35, 46, 109, 116, 124, 187, 288

H

Heading, 82, 94, 95, 104
Histogram
  estimating mean and standard deviation, 278
  of frequency distribution, 278
Horizontal line test, 152
Hypergeometric formula, 296

I

Independent events,
  Multiplication Rule for, 242
Infinity, 259–264
Inner product, 105
Instantaneous rates of change, 2–21
  $f(x)$ rule, 27
Integers
  positive, 237
  sum of the first n odd positive, 263
Integration, 69
Inverse functions, 142–157
  evaluating from tables, 145
  function composition, 145
  graphs, 147–150
  parametric equations and, 154
  relationship between f and f^{-1}, 144
  relationship between range of f and domain of f^{-1}, 146
Inverse cosine function, 155
Inverse sine function, 155

K

Kline, Morris, 131
Koblitz, Neal, 138

L

Law of Cosines, 92
Law of Sines, 105
Least squares, method of, 195
Least squares regression line, 186
  equation, 186
Leibniz, Gottfried, 46, 47
Linear form, 206
Linear functions, 23–24
  derivative of, 34
  derivative of inverse of, 155
  finding slope of, and estimating rate of change at a point, 29–31

Linearizing data, 180–209
  exponential functions, 182
  power models, 199
  square root functions, 183
  translated power functions, 207
  $y = ax^2$, 182
  $y = x^2$, 193
Linear motion
  modeling, 80–107
  parametric models for, 109–115
  simulating, 108–135
Linear scale, 159
Local linearity, 29–32
Logarithmic equations, solving, 162
Logarithmic expressions, evaluating, 162
Logarithmic functions, 158–179
Logarithmic scale, 158, 168–172
  construction, 171
Logarithms, common, 159–164
  Power Property, 166, 266
  Product Property, 165
  Quotient Property, 165
  reexpression and equation solving with, 164
  using to solve exponential equations, 166
  $y = \log x$, 161
Log-log transformations, 198–201, 207
Log transformations, 186–189
Lurking variable, 336

M

Mathematical induction, 258–269
  principle of, 261
  proof by, 260
Midpoint Connector Theorem, 104
Modeling linear motion, 80–107, 109–115
Motion
  linear, 80–107, 108–135
  nonlinear, 108–135
Multiplication Principle of Counting, 219, 242
Multiplication Rule
  General, 242
  for independent events, 242
  for probability, 234, 241–244

N

Nautical mile, 82
Net change, 60–64
  and velocity, 56–60
Newton, Isaac, 46
90% box plots, 295
Nonlinear motion
  parametric models for, 115–119
  simulating, 108–135

Normal approximation to the binomial distribution, 322
Normal distribution, 321
Null hypothesis, 323

O

Observational study, 334
One-to-one function, 144
Orbits
  elliptical, 125
  simulating, 123–126
Order, 223
Overall pattern of change
  $f(x)$ rule, 27

P

Parameter, 111
Parametric equations, 109, 111, 112
  for circular motion, 120, 123
  combining, 131
  for elliptical orbits, 125, 133
  interpreting graphs, 132
  and inverse functions, 154
  for lines versus circles, 122
Parametric function of calculator or computer graphing software, 109
Parametric models
  for linear motion, 109–115
  for nonlinear motion, 115–119
Pascal, Blaise, 246
Pascal's Triangle, 245–249, 251, 255, 293
  and binomial expansions, 246
  and combinations, 247
Periodic function
  derivative of a, 36
Permutations, 222–231
  counting formulas for, 226–227
  and combinations, 229
  features on a calculator, 229
  $P(n, k)$, 229
Phi, 102
Piecewise-defined function, 155
Placebo effect, 336
Poincaré, Henri, 267
Power function
  derivative of a, 36
  inverses of, 149
  translated, linearizing, 207
Power models, linearizing, 199
Power Property of logarithms, 166, 266
Prime number, 176
Probability, 241
  Addition Rule for, 242
  conditional, 252
  distribution, 277

Index of Contexts

Photo Credits

2, Mark Gibson/Visuals Unlimited; 7, Bill Hogan/*Chicago Tribune;* 9, Herald American; 11, Chris Berman/*Chicago Tribune;* 12, Anne Cusack/*Chicago Tribune;* 13, James Mayo/*Chicago Tribune;* 14, James Mayo/*Chicago Tribune;* 17 (right top), AP Photo; 17 (right bottom), Fran Brown; 24 (right top), Walter Kale/*Chicago Tribune;* 24 (left center), Randy Wells/Stone; 25, R. Calentine/Visuals Unlimited; 26 (left center), Carolyn Galati/Visuals Unlimited; 26 (right center), Carolyn Galati/Visuals Unlimited; 31, National Aeronautics and Space Administration; 35, Table Mesa Productions LTD/West Stock; 37, Akron Public Schools; 41 (right bottom), Mike Fisher/*Chicago Tribune;* 42 (right bottom), With permission from General Motors Company Truck and Coach Public Relations; 43, David M. Phillips/Visuals Unlimited; 46 (left bottom), Hulton Getty Images; 46 (right bottom), Hulton Getty Images; 48, Joeff Davis/*Chicago Tribune;* 53, Mark Gibson/Visuals Unlimited; 56 (right bottom), Courtesy Texas Instruments Incorporated; 65, J.F. Causse/Stone; 66, The Studios of Potente, Inc., Kenosha, Wisconsin; 69, Jerry Kobalenko/Stone; 74, Pat Rogers/UPI; 75, Courtesy Texas Instruments Incorporated; 76, AP/NASA; 77, W.S. Ormerod Jr./Visuals Unlimited; 79, National Aeronautics and Space Administration; Unit Opener, 79, National Aeronautics and Space Administration; 80, Jacques M. Chenet/CORBIS; 93, Bob Langer/*Chicago Tribune;* 96, Mark Gibson/Visuals Unlimited; 100, Walter Kale/*Chicago Tribune;* 105, Arthur R. Hill/Visuals Unlimited; 113 (left bottom), National Oceanic and Atmospheric Administration NOAA Historical Photo Collection NOAA Photo Library; 114 (left bottom), (center bottom), (right bottom), National Aeronautics and Space Administration; 116, Tim Boyle/*Chicago Tribune;* 117 (center), Jim Prisching/*Chicago Tribune;* 117 (right bottom), AP Photo/1991; 124, A.J. Copley/Visuals Unlimited; 125, Ken Anderson/West Stock; 127 (left top), Dennis O'Clair/Stone; 127 (center), John Kringas/*Chicago Tribune;* 128, *Chicago Tribune;* 132 (right top), José Moré/*Chicago Tribune;* 136, Mark Gibson; 137 (right top), AP Photo/1993; 137 (right bottom), AP Photo/1991; Unit Opener, 141, Gareth Jones/Stone; 145, National Motorcoach Network, Inc.; 150 (right center), *Chicago Tribune;* 151 (right top), National Aeronautics and Space Administration; 151 (left bottom), Richard Johnson/Visuals Unlimited; 154, Bob Clay/Visuals Unlimited; 158, José Moré/*Chicago Tribune;* 161, Courtesy Texas Instruments Incorporated; 167, Steve McCutchen/Visuals Unlimited; 170 (left bottom), AP Photo; 172, *Chicago Tribune;* 174, Carl Hugare/*Chicago Tribune;* 177 (right center), Leonard Lee Rue/Visuals Unlimited; 180, John Irvine/*Chicago Tribune;* 190, Courtesy of US Postal Service/AP Photo; 198, National Aeronautics and Space Administration; 205, Mark Gibson/Visuals Unlimited; 210, Kathy Richland/Photography; Unit Opener, 215, Nick Dolding/Stone; 217, José Moré/*Chicago Tribune;* 222, Michael Kustermann; 223, Frank Hanes/*Chicago Tribune;* 225, Kelly MacLean; 227, Chuck Berman/*Chicago Tribune;* 229, John Irvine/*Chicago Tribune;* 231, UPI Telephoto; 233 (right top), Photo credit Comstock, Inc.; 234, Walter Kale/*Chicago Tribune;* 235 (right center), Jack Demuth; 235 (bottom), W.W. Norton and Company, Inc.; 236, Leonard Lessin, Science Source/Photo Researchers; 240, Math Horizons Magazine; 241, Eduardo Contreras/*Chicago Tribune;* 243, *Chicago Tribune;* 246, © Bettmann/CORBIS; 251 (right top), Charles Cherney/*Chicago Tribune;* 251 (left center), Al Francekevich/The Stock Market; 253, Courtesy of The Needham Research Institute, Cambridge; 254, Cathe Centorbe/San Francisco; 267, © Hulton-Deutsch Collection/CORBIS; 271 (right bottom), Website for Tamar Schlick; 273 (left top), UPI Photo; Unit Opener, 275, Photo from MATHEMATICS: AN INTEGRATED SERIES TESTING PROGRAM, copyright © 1967 by Harcourt, Inc., reproduced by permission of the publisher; 276, Churchill & Klehr/Stone; 279, Billy E. Barnes/PhotoEdit; 280, Michael Newman/PhotoEdit; 283, Myrleen Cate/PhotoEdit; 284, Gerald West/*Chicago Tribune;* 287 (right bottom), Patricia Lopez; 288, Fran Brown; 290, Gerald West/*Chicago Tribune;* 291, YAHTZEE® GAME is a trademark of Hasbro, Inc. ©2000 Hasbro, Inc. All rights reserved. Used with permission.; 292, AP Photo; 293, Photo from MATHEMATICS: AN INTEGRATED SERIES TESTING PROGRAM, copyright © 1967 by Harcourt, Inc., reproduced by permission of the publisher; 294, Al Francekevich/The Stock Market; 296, The Daily Northwestern; 300, Cynthia Black; 311, The Daily Northwestern; 312, The Daily Northwestern; 314, AP Photo; 321 (left top), Bill Hogan/*Chicago Tribune;* 321 (right bottom), Don Casper/*Chicago Tribune;* 326, Will Hart/PhotoEdit; 329, Phil Martin Photographer; 333, Jakarta International School; 335, UPI; 337, The Daily Northwestern; 344, Garland Publishing, Inc.; 347, Deneve Feigh Bunde/Visuals Unlimited; 348 (right top), Insurance Institute for Highway Safety/AP Photo; 348 (right bottom), *Chicago Tribune File Photo;* 350, SIU/Visuals Unlimited; 351, Matt Marton/*Chicago Tribune;* 354, Nancy Stone/*Chicago Tribune;* 355, Charles Osgood/*Chicago Tribune*

Unlisted photographs are property of Everyday Learning Corporation